SCIENCE AND DESIGN OF

PROBLEM SOLVING SYSTEMS

JANOS KORN

(THE PURPOSE OF CHANGE IS PROBLEM SOLVING)

AUGUST 2021

We cannot solve our problems with the same thinking we used when we created them'. [A quotation from A. Einstein]

'The *philosophers* have only interpreted the world in various ways. The *point* however is to change it'. [On Marx's tombstone in Highgate Cemetery, Levene, 2010]
Modification by author: 'The *scientists* have only interpreted the world in various ways. It is the job of *systems/structures* to change it'.

'The purpose of change is problem solving'. [Janos Korn]

'Viewing parts of the world in terms of their structure is systems thinking'. [Janos Korn]

'Systems are created for solving problems through accomplishment of change of state or disequilibrium'. [Janos Korn]

'Ideas can be wonderful or evil but to turn them into action they have to be expressed in precise terms. Hence, the aim is to turn speculative and fragmented thinking in the field of systems thinking into more basic and exact reasoning structures'. [Janos Korn]

'The 'symbolic language' of conventional science is 'mathematical modelling',
'The 'symbolic language' of systems science is 'linguistic modelling'. [Janos korn]

Acknowledgement

The author would like to express his gratitude once again to his former colleagues, Dr Frank Huss and Mr John Cumbers and to keep their memory alive, and to Mr Andras Takats, for all their contribution to the early development of linguistic modelling which took place in the 1980s. My sincere thanks are extended to the Open University where I had been exposed to ideas of human activity scenarios and spent an inspiring time of my life. I am very grateful to the country of the United Kingdom which accepted me as a citizen and gave me the opportunity of higher education and subsequent career.

PREAMBLE

Summary: Perhaps the most *general* notion abstracted from the existence and operation of natural and artificial, inanimate and living things, is the 'concept of equilibrium and its 'change''. Living things, apart from being subject to change due to accidents by chance, are engaged in 'changes' called *problem solving* in accordance with *purpose*, both are *innate*, universal in the living sphere and are a particular form of change. No change takes place by itself, the *general* notion of agent which induces the change is called 'system or structure', innate or artificial. Accordingly, the two concepts, 'problem solving' and 'systems or structures' are connected but currently discussed by and large separately and inadequately. The aim of the proposed symbolic structure of 'systems theory' is to discuss the two concepts as an *integrated whole* resulting in *product* and *systems design thinking*. [End of Summary]

Human beings are constantly engaged in creating thoughts deliberately or instinctively based on processing the results of output of perception by the sense organs or using their imagination. They may express the thoughts into symbolic structures such as natural language [most frequently used], gestures, road signs, works of art, mathematics and a variety of others any of which when cast in a 'medium', is called a 'model'. Conventional science of physics accepts only models which can be tested against observation, experiment or application for their truth value. The envisaged 'systems science' based on 'systems theory' operates along similar principle but with systemic content i.e. viewing aspects of parts of the world from the point of view of their 'structure'. Design thinking is concerned with models called prototypes which have been created methodically or by instinct or ingenuity to specifications to correspond to requirements to fit or to match a material or mental object. Problem solving is about finding the means capable of converting an unsatisfactory or inadequate state of affairs into one that is judged to be acceptable. The objective of this book is to introduce a *systems theory* which is a symbolic structure with systemic content integrated with the idea of problem solving which prompts thinking of 'systems and product design' and fosters creativity, inspiration, intuition.

People have no difficulty in recognising 'structures or systems' in static or dynamic state when they perceive entities described as concrete [motor car [just off the assembly line in static state], motor car and driver [in motion, in dynamic state], symbolic [the statue of the king], abstract [quality such as a cloth with smooth feel and bright colour] or imaginary [centaur]. In fact, the terms 'system or structure' have been in use for a long time like the Ptolemaic or Copernic system, 'A system of logic' of Mills, the philosopher, and now in every day life. Normally the term 'system' is referred to an entity which, when perceived, appears 'complex' or a 'set of things considered as a connected whole [Anon., 1993] and which would be difficult to elaborate in detail [much easier to think of it as a whole and using the 'vague term system'] and/ or appears to be engaged in some kind of potential or actual activity.

Using the term 'structure' is clear, no problem, especially when it is applied to concrete things which obviously consist of discernible parts like 'the tall crane on a building site', 'the writing desk in the office' or 'an algebraic equation' and so on. All in static state. Using the term 'system' should not be a problem either but people usually apply the term to something not so straightforward as a 'structure'. Perhaps the difference between the application of the terms 'structure' and 'system' is that the former is understood to be something 'static' like a 'bridge' whereas the latter appears to be 'dynamic' like a 'frog'. For example, we have 'a natural system [volcano erupting, solar system]', 'an artificial system [a transport system such as a high speed train in motion or the railway network in a district]', a 'living system [digestive system or a part of it like the pancreas]'. People also say 'the system broke down [when the computer in the office stopped working]' or 'the central heating system warming the house' or 'the belief system which is in action when affecting the mental state of believers'. All in dynamic state.

However, whether we speak of 'structure' or 'system' we speak of the same 'concept seen to consist of *related parts* each with a function to perform contributing to the functioning of the whole, the idea of holon [Koestler, 1967], which is the agent destined to resolve 'problematic issues" [The author's idea]. The translation of this idea into a particular kind of symbolic structure is the **central question** and to attempt an answer is the **central task** of the current research.

The production of symbolic structures in the mind which when implemented in a medium, is called a model is an 'intellectual exercise' requiring great mental effort and ingenuity exerted over time. This kind of exercise is usually exerted by individuals driven by self interest which may have turned out to be of interest to a group of people or a society as a whole and is called 'human need'. Models are the product of practically limitless 'imagination' which resides in the brain/mind apparatus. In many cases models are based on thoughts or concepts derived from the results of perception of aspects of parts of the world which are *empirical models*. The 'systemic or structural view' of parts of the world is an empirical view.

There are a number of recognised, well organised models or 'intellectual products' for the 'change of mental state' as part of resolving 'problematic issues' which have been developed by individuals over the millennia. They have been invented and developed by people usually with intense 'interest, curiosity, emotions' because it was felt that they could contribute to satisfying *human need* and are shown in Table P1.

In Table P1. the 'intellectual products' or models are the result of well defined and recognised 'intellectual activities' for attempting to satisfy physical and mental 'human needs'. We anticipate that there is a 'systems science' also a well defined activity with its

INTELLECTUAL ACTIVITIES	MODELS	HUMAN NEED
A. Conventional science of physics	Testable models	Reliable knowledge
B. Fine/performing arts	Imaginative models	Emotional states
C. Social sciences including medicine	Mostly untestable models of living activities	Mostly speculative approaches to social problems
D. Conventional engineering	Designed prototypes	Certainty of performance of products
E. Religions	Habits, rituals, devotion	Peace of mind

INTELLECTUAL ACTIVITIES	MODELS	HUMAN NEED
F. Ideas of social order	Idealistic views, beliefs	Benefits/otherwise to human groups
G. *Systems science*	*Structural models*	*Universal 'problem solving'*

Table P1. Summary of intellectual products

'structural model' to accomplish 'problem solving' as a universal activity and need of living things. This is the reason for its existence and operation for generating models. In fact, there
is no such thing at the moment. However, there is a need to supplement the ever present *'innateness'* of ability of living things 'to solve problems' so as to facilitate understanding the mechanism of this mental activity, its fundamentals, to appreciate the design of its means of resolution and to fit it into the background of recognised intellectual activities. The basic aim of current work is to create this kind of 'systems science' for peer review and, if passes scrutiny, to develop it for application in organisations and in teaching.

Remarks &&&

Entries A., B., C., D., E. and F. in Table P1. are well accepted disciplines in the fields of intellectual activities which exert their appropriate and significant contribution to social, intellectual, mental and material lives of human beings and on technology to serve their survival, convenience, productivity, well being of mind and body, striving for higher performance and so on. Although anticipated to have similar features, entry G. does not seem to make appreciable contribution to advancement of society and technology. Perhaps this state of affairs exists because the current, confused and confusing field of 'systems activity' is dominated by speculative but inspiring thinking, ideas under the banner of 'systems science' or 'systems thinking' or just generated at random without purpose. There is 'systems thinking' allegedly applied in running organisations, also there are inadequate, vague methods created about 50 – 40 years ago which make the general 'structural or systemic view' of parts of the world fragmented including the pioneering idea of General Systems Theory.

These methods have inadequate knowledge content to make them generally teachable at school and higher level much like aspects of conventional science such as physics. Notions from conventional science such as entropy, energy, open and closed systems and so on, are borrowed. It appears that no critical discussion is admitted by systems thinkers, preservation of the status que prevails. Current work by the author is set against this climate and its aim is to offer and alternative path fit into Table P1. [Lewin, 1981].

End of **Remarks &&&**

Matador
Unit E2 Airfield Business Park,
Harrison Road, Market Harborough,
Leicestershire. LE16 7UL
Tel: 0116 2792299
Email: books@troubador.co.uk
Web: www.troubador.co.uk/matador
Twitter: @matadorbooks

ISBN 978 1803135 014

British Library Cataloguing in Publication Data.
A catalogue record for this book is available from the British Library.

Typeset in 11pt Minion Pro by Troubador Publishing Ltd, Leicester, UK

Matador is an imprint of Troubador Publishing Ltd

CONTENTS

I. INTRODUCTION

---The aim of INTRODUCTION: We describe briefly what is understood here by 'problem solving' i.e. identification and statement of an unsatisfactory 'state of affairs' followed by an attempt to turn it into a satisfactory one. This requires the design of the means for the accomplishment of the 'change of state' or to bring about a resolution of the problematic issue or the unsatisfactory state of affairs. The task of a dynamic structure or system is to act as the means to attempt to resolve the problem. The objective of this book is to describe how these two aspects, the creative part i.e. the identification and suggested resolution of the problem and the analytical part i.e. the design of system, the means of resolution, can be integrated into a 'systems theory'. This approach is the basic idea behind the current work by the author or how to integrate 'systems thinking' and 'problem solving'. ---

I.1. Description of the aim of the book

Here the term 'problem' or 'problematic situation' refers to a state of affairs which can confronts a living thing and is found unsatisfactory. The number and variety of 'problematic situations' are immense and growing all the time as circumstances change or human imagination conjures up new ones and diminishing as problems are resolved. For example, 'the crossword puzzle is to be filled in by a person', 'the shoelace is to be tied up by a boy', 'productivity of workers is to be increased by the management', 'a portrait of the landlord is to be painted by the artist', 'the unceasing quarrel between the two nations is to resolved by the peacekeepers', 'the overgrown grass is to be grazed by the cows', 'a timid mouse is to be caught by the snake', 'the face of the sunflower is to be turned towards the sun', 'the speed of the rotating shaft is to be increased by the control system driving it' etc.

The sentences in the last paragraph are of the 'subject-predicate form' using the passive voice of the verb and make 'complete sense' [Burton, 1984]. They are symbolic models written on paper using the symbolism of natural language and exhibit a 'structure' of sentence elements so as to make complete sense.

Changing the structure or the order of words, loses or changes the meaning, for example, 'to be a timid mouse is caught by the snake' or the word 'bran' changed into 'barn' changes the meaning or designation. We can make the following remarks regarding this kind of structure:

1. We can infer that there is a problem because the verbs indicate that 'currently something is missing or not yet done or to be done'. We add this missing elements to the sentences =
    'An *unfilled* crossword puzzle is to be filled in...',
    'An *untied* shoelace is to be tied...',
    'The *untouched* grass is to be grazed...' and so on.
    The sentences consist of subjects qualified by the past participle of the verb functioning as adjectival phrases which locate the state or action, and predicates.

Accordingly, we assert that usually we can tell there is a problematic situation from the description or 'story' in natural language which implicitly can imply a prevailing problem in a scenario.

2. There is a future state of affairs implied by the infinitive phrase which appears to be the 'resolution' of the problematic issue once the action is completed subject to the prevailing conditions such as uncertainties arising from the circumstances, environments, promises by unreliable people involved, state of the weather and so on, thus, =
    'to be filled in' leads to 'filled in', 'to be painted' leads to 'painted' and others which designate completed action,
3. We note that the sentences or statements also contain a 'living or artificial agent' the function of which is to accomplish the 'change of state of affairs' =
    'person', 'the artist' or 'control system' and so on.

However, the statements *do not show*:
1. The 'means used by the agents' to accomplish the change or 'product',
2. The living things which are supposed to benefit from the 'changed state of affairs' or 'resolution of the problem', if there is any that has been achieved. For example, 'the untied shoelace is to be tied by 'the hands of the boy [means]' to his satisfaction [beneficiary]'.

3. The living thing or part of it like the brain/mind who coordinates the activities implied by the story of the scenario.

All these mental and physical activities are directed towards solving problems if achievement of an acceptable solution is possible [Rittel, Webber, 1973].

There is a similar line of thinking in [Checkland, Scholes, 1995] which suggests a schema of 'do X by Y to achieve Z'. For example, this can be translated into a particular case in natural language by 'tie [imperative mood of the verb] the untied shoelace [problematic issue] using the boy's hands [means] so as to arrive at the tied shoelace [resolution]'. In this schema we have the:

'The problem or the problematic situation or issue is indicated implicitly by X', The 'future state or the resolution or the achievement' which is the interpretation of Z, and The 'means of accomplishment of the change' which may be seen as Y.

The agent who is supposed to do the 'tying' is not explicitly mentioned but it is implied as the 'boy'. However, there is no indication of any further development of the schema which, using the imperative mood, can lead to application in algorithms in computer programmes'.

Perhaps based on background knowledge, we can say that we have been discussing the constituents of an as yet implied 'problem solving scheme'. Using the discussion above, the suggested scheme consists of two parts:

I. First, change of a 'problematic situation' or a problem to a new, envisaged situation which needs to be such as to satisfy the *expectation* of a living thing. The recognition of the problem and the intellectual accomplishment or conjecture of an envisaged change is the result of the mental effort of creativity, inspiration and/or ingenuity produced by imagination. However, the 'initial' and 'final' states each of which is described by 'physical or mental properties' such as 'from white to blue' or 'from ignorant to knowledgeable' must be such as to be possible to be accomplished by a single agent in a single action. For example, 'an unfilled crossword puzzle' cannot be turned into 'a blue crossword puzzle' by such an agent or 'an unheated room' can be changed into a 'heated or warm room' but not into a 'yellow room' by a single agent.

We note that as far as change of state is concerned the object carrying the change is treated to remain 'invariant', its 'property' has changed.

II. Second, the 'organised, *production structure* referred to as system' and the means or '*product structure* or system' produced or used by the former and required for carrying out the change of state by being constructed so as to be capable of developing an 'interaction or an influence'. For example,
An 'electric motor [product structure] is constructed to produce mechanical power [interaction] not a waterfall', or
A 'piece of music [product structure] is constructed to produce the emotion of elation [influence]', or
An 'advertisement [product structure] is constructed to produce first of all information to induce temptation in people to buy an artifact [influence], or
A 'bed [product structure] is constructed to provide people with comfortable means for rest [influence]'.

Products are produced by 'production structures' called 'manufacturing systems' according to specifications derived from use by 'utilising systems' such as a 'car factory' or a 'taxi ride by the manager from the station to the office', respectively. [Korn, 2020a,b].

We can say that structures or systems are created or manufactured for the accomplishment of changes of state, a generalisation of Newton's 1st law of motion. Or the 'purpose of change is problem solving when problem solving is understood in terms of 'change of equilibrium' [Korn, 2016].

At this stage we can say that the **intention of this book** is to show how a 'systems theory inclusive of a problem solving scheme' is constructed which, thus, combines the two parts, the 'problem solving thinking' and the 'systemic, structural view' into an integrated whole. Construction of the symbolic models for both parts is an *empirical exercise*. The first part is the *creative, innovative part*. It is shown how this part generates the 'systems and products design thinking' towards producing the second or analytical part.

Problem solving in the sphere of living things is **innate** and is applied instinctively but it is as 'general as the action of gravity in the material sphere'. People have no difficulty with recognising a 'system' or a 'complex structure' of related things [in static state] or interacting things [in dynamic state], the means of changing state when faced by specific parts of the world. For example, people may say 'I have a "sports complex' near where I live' or the "tramway system' in our town operates day and night'. More concretely, an instant of complex structure in static state is described by the complex sentence 'The cork floats on a pond of water which is connected to a lake located in the park belonging to the council' and that of a complex structure in dynamic state or a 'scenario' is given by the 'story' or 'narrative' 'The unruly boy kicked the heavy ball which hit the window of the nearby house. The broken window angered the owner who set about chasing the boy'. Static states are signalled by 'stative verbs [float]' and dynamic states or events are described by 'dynamic verbs [kick]' [Korn, 2009].

The proposed 'systems theory' has the following characteristics:

1. It consists of a number of 'principles' and 'linguistic modelling' which is based on a 'story' or 'narrative' of 'complex structures' in static states and 'scenarios or events' expressed in natural language, the 'primary model' accessible to all [Korn, 2018],

2. Being an *empirical theory*, obliges it to use abstract or 'model terms' being theoretical terms to be widely applicable must be 'general' but can be related to those used in 'story terms' i.e. it can be expressed in *operational terms* if there is a need,

3. At its basis lie:

   A. The view that the 'structural or systemic view' of parts of the world is general, indivisible and hierarchical (nested) and there is no alternative [Korn, 2018],

   B. The notion of 'change' or 'disequilibrium' is connected to 'problem solving' and caused by dynamic systems. The proposed 'systems theory' intends to present a unified approach to change of equilibrium states or problems and resolutions and systems which makes it generally applicable to modelling inanimate, animate and artificial structures or systems,

4. The contents of this book present novel features but basically they are reproduced with modifications from presentations in conferences, published papers and previously written books. Acknowledgements and thanks to publishers are given here.

The following description is intended as a brief personal background showing how the author came to believe that there appeared to be a need for a new approach to modelling the 'structural or systemic view' of parts of the world. A similar description is given in [Korn, 2009].

The author attended a higher education course in the early 1950's in the then Soviet Union, currently Russia, which was attempted to give students a multidisciplinary knowledge. It succeeded only teaching some economics and other related topics like production in a descriptive manner added to less in depth engineering knowledge in parallel. At that time nobody had any idea about development of 'systems knowledge' or trying to integrate branches of existing knowledge. However, it was a pioneering attempt. The author had not completed the course because he was compelled to return to Hungary then under Soviet domination and was allowed to enter the Technical University of Budapest doing a mechanical engineering undergraduate course. This institution was engaged in imparting knowledge of physics and chemistry etc followed by highly in depth knowledge of 'mechanical components' predominantly from the point of view of their construction with students having had to do large amounts of engineering drawing to perfection paying little attention to the function, modelling and performance of components as 'systems elements'. This institution maintained high levels of tradition in teaching carried out by professors of very high reputation, dignity and discipline but having no awareness of 'systems thinking'. Shortly after the author came to the UK in 1956 he entered a mechanical engineering course in London University thanks to the generosity of the British people and government. As far as teaching content was concerned this course was not much different from that in the Hungarian one except that it was considerably simplified due its being a three year course not a five year one.

Subsequently the author became a lecturer in mechanical engineering teaching 'control systems' in particular which was about using block diagrams and transfer function analysis as its symbolic model. This kind of modelling caused much disturbance in engineering courses because it did not fit into their curricula. The author realised that this was because the modelling was about structures or systems and was 'signal based' which was contrary to the 'power based' and component biased engineering courses except electronics engineering. Students in electronics engineering had little difficulty in coping with signals and feedback [Finniston, 1983, Nise, 2008, with much detail in Korn, 2009].

Perhaps biased by his educational experience and having noticed this problematic situation, the author set about further developing the already upcoming multidisciplinary approach to engineering systems analysis which was based on the 'classification of variables' [Sanford, 1965, MacFarlane, 1970, Korn, 2017]. This development consisted of extending the approach to control systems and embracing thermal effects or non isothermal operations. This led to including temperature and entropy flow as the thermal variables into a classification of energy converters of which heat transfer was a part. Inclusion of thermal networks into multidisciplinary network analysis of transient phenomena became possible with exhibiting the 2nd law of thermodynamics as part of an engineering system with further representations of highly non linear systems (I consider this a major achievement of my career. I shall always remember the instant when I set up the two non linear differential equations representing an electrical resistance not as a resistor but as an 'electrothermal energy converter' on the analogue computer and observed the graphs as a function time of current and temperature decreasing and increasing respectively. This showed the decreasing electrical and increasing thermal power [Korn, 2012]. The author had taught this approach solving engineering problems already but there was no further interest.

During these turbulent times in engineering education with control systems entering, the question of how 'design' could be taught, with official enquiries trying to resolve the problems, the author became a part time tutor at the Open University in the 'systems department'. Here he was exposed to pioneering and inspiring attempts to model human activity scenarios as part of a course in 'systems behaviour'. These attempts by and large were descriptive, varied from one scenario to another because there was no 'systems theory' to apply and difficult to understand by students and lecturers alike. Then in the late 1970's the 'Checkland methodology' now known as Soft Systems Methodology, came along which was a pioneering and comprehensive initiative at problem solving in human activity scenarios. Although not easy to follow, this was a new and general method still in sporadic use despite its shortcomings which are perhaps not seen and certainly not admitted by its proponents [Feilden, 1963, Beishon, Peters (ed), 1976, Checkland, 1982]. An expanded version of this story is given in [Korn, 2009].

Nowadays we are witnessing a huge expansion of 'systemic activities' through societies, publications, meetings, conferences, postgraduate work and teaching in universities. All this feverish activity is based on the highly speculative initiative of von Bertalanffy and colleagues of the 'systems phenomenon' being general leading to desultory attempts at symbolic modelling [Bertalanffy, 1950, Beer, 1979]. Other directions of distorted, mostly highly speculative thinking like 'cybernetics', 'systems engineering' and 'problem solving' lately seeking an elusive 'PSM' or problem structuring method, have emerged. A methodical problem solving as an aid to guide in handling problematic situations in modern society with large financial, technical and human risks involved, is highly desirable. These strands of intellectual efforts have been unable to produce this kind of initiative although this has been their implicitly implied aim. Conventional science of physics and its many derivatives in mathematical modelling, for example, management science and operational research, have been very successful in providing such an aid. It might be an idea to suggest a new initiative to explore whether it is possible to propel 'systems thinking' in a direction which would bring it closer to modelling along more concrete lines in accordance with the empirical nature of the 'structural or systemic view' while fostering the speculative, creative thinking by the fertile, impossible to supress human imagination.

The author perhaps due to his exposure to varied engineering education, has been critical of all past and current activity in the systems field. The result has been the intuitive and conscious intellectual effort that has been going on for a long time, to recognise that the 'function of dynamic structures or systems is change things so as to solve problems' and to produce the model which can exhibit this idea in a symbolic form. This book is intended to be a summary of this work.

CHAPTER 1

CHARACTERISTICS OF SYMBOLIC STRUCTURES

The aim of CHAPTER 1

Living things are open to their natural [forest], artificial [aeroplane] and social [relations, friends and neighbours] environments including their own bodies, through their sense organs which receive the appropriate sense input for vision, hearing, taste, touch, smell and 'physical and mental feelings [pain, love]'. Instances of this input are then transmitted to the 'brain/mind' apparatus which converts them into thoughts which can also be generated by imagination [spontaneously or by reasoning]. Thoughts can then be expressed in symbolisms such as natural language to be, or not, encoded in material medium. Material medium is necessary so as impinge on the sense organs of agents including self. For example, 'a book can be read by its readers and its writer'. We set out to discuss the features of the various of symbolisms which living things use to navigate in their environment in the course of survival, achievement of ambitions and maintenance of more or less constant temperature for their operation.

In particular, the intention of this chapter is to examine characteristics of natural language which make it, as it stands, an unsuitable symbolism to function as a 'reasoning structure' and to consider briefly the reasoning structures other than natural language but are based on natural language. The characteristics which a particular symbolism needs to have to function as a reasoning structure for representing an *empirical view* of aspects of parts of the world, are put forward.

1.1 Features of natural language as a symbolism

In general, we do not know much about living things such as plants, animals and microscopic creatures like a virus but we know by experience that human beings can generate 'thoughts' using their 'brain/mind' organ by means of

1

'imagination' and the variety of inputs from 'sense organs' leading to opinions, judgements etc and possible action. Thoughts may be viewed as the large scale 'emergent property' resulting from the molecular activities of neurons or 'elementary constituents' just like 'density' of material can be seen as the result of state or activities at atomic level [Nagel, 1968, Searle, 1984].

Thoughts can be expressed in terms of 'symbols' which are, thus, representations of thoughts and can be manipulated to memorise and to express different or more complex thoughts. For example, I think (as a result of observation or sense input): 'I am sitting here typing and there is nice sunshine outside' and (I conclude) 'Instead I should be sitting outside' which can be followed by action: 'I get up and go outside' or no action: 'I ignore the sunshine'. However, we are aware that the same mental and physical action can take place without any thought just by 'perceiving the sunshine and walking out instinctively'. In fact it is likely that plants, animals and human infants act mostly without generating any thoughts let alone expressing them in symbols except in case of animals at a higher level of intelligence like chimpanzees. They operate 'instinctively' perhaps using their brain/mind. Plants and microorganisms have no facility like brain/mind as far as we know.

Symbols are the means of expressing thoughts to affect self and others. For example, 'A thought: 'I want to go to he cinema' followed by symbol address to my son: 'I am going to the cinema, you want to come with me ?" Here we have used the 'symbolism' or 'organised collection of symbols', of 'natural language'. Natural language is the most widely used symbolism open to anyone. Its syntax or structure is common to all spoken languages evolved so as to enable the linguistic element of 'sentence' to carry 'complete meaning' and is perhaps an inheritable trait. For example, the sentence 'The table is around the corner in the next room' has complete meaning, we can imagine it i.e. we can turn it into thought with meaning but 'The table is' has not.

Natural language is the most expressive symbolism, rich in linguistic complexities, innuendoes etc, representing long and complex stories of imaginary and actual scenarios and open to ways of manipulations such as formal logic and informal arguments.

Formal logic and arguments are 'reasoning structures'. The well known arguments are those understood to be 'explanations and predictions of states of affairs thought to be real or imaginary' using the form of 'logical conditional'.

For example, the following is a representation or description of an event by means of the 'statement' carried by a sentence: 'Moisture formed on the outside of the glass when it was filled with ice water' which can be expressed as a logical conditional 'If the glass is filled with ice water then moisture forms on the outside of the glass'. The logical conditional exposes a statement of fact to 'doubts' because the antecedent, the part between 'if' and 'then' functions as a 'hypothesis' i.e. it is no longer a statement of fact and the consequent, the part after 'then' functions as the means for testing the conditional for its 'truth value [Copi, 1978]. For if the consequent turns out to be false and the antecedent is true then the conditional fails. In other words, 'filling the glass with ice water' has not caused 'moisture to form on the outside of the glass'.

XYZ. --- Accordingly, there is a need to search for a new hypothesis as the original hypothesis has been 'falsified'. [Popper, 1972]. This kind of reasoning is the basis of conventional science of physics which was a major innovation in the Renaissance although Archimedes had already used it perhaps without realising it. His proving that the crown of King Hiero II of Syracuse consisted of part silver was an instance of using a hypothesis for testing if it is true. This daring intellectual achievement is described in detail in [Korn, 2013]. ---

The conditional can be turned into an 'explanation' if we say that 'Moisture is formed on the outside of the glass 'because' the glass was filled with ice water'. The connective 'because' that connects the two sentences, signals an 'explanation'. We note that if a description of an observed or imaginary phenomenon is given, here 'Moisture....', then the sentence(s) followed by 'because' is offered as an 'explanation'. However, when we use the logical conditional and assume that a description of a real or imaginary phenomenon is given, here '**If** 'A glass is filled with ice water' followed by the consequent **then** 'Moisture is formed on the outside of the glass', we have the formalism of 'prediction'. [Hempel, Oppenheim, 1948, Chomsky, 1957, Burton, 1984, Copi, 1978, Hospers, 1978, Korn, 2009].

Apart from 'representation of real and imaginary appearances', a symbol or a symbolism can be used for 'communication' of thoughts involving a 'generator or sender and a receiver of thoughts'. Since the receiver, a living thing, is able to sense or to observe phenomena only by means of h/her sense organs which are sensitive to physical effects, a symbol must be converted into a material thing or 'object'. This material object or 'medium' is called here 'model' and as such can provoke an appropriate reaction from a receiver having sensed and processed the 'message' by the brain/mind. A 'signal' is a symbol carried through a 'medium'. For example, a 'story [using the symbols of natural language] on pages of paper [medium, reflecting light into the eyes]' or a 'set of differential equations [using the symbols of mathematics] dictated to students by the lecturer [medium, air pressure waves impinging on the eardrum]' or 'a message that the ship has arrived [using the symbols of natural language] encoded in smoke signals [medium, still air and perceived by eyes]' or the 'expression of motherly love [using the symbol of feeling of emotion] realised by Michelangelo through his stone sculpture of 'Pieta' [medium, light waves hitting the eyes]'.

These are examples of 'symbols encoded in medium' ready to be impinged on one of the sense organs of a receiver, a response may not be provoked. Symbolic models as just described, can be used for carrying out the scheme of 'falsification' as indicated by the logical conditional and discussed in more detail in section 1.3.

'Symbols encoded in medium' ready to be communicated is a 'message', here called 'information'. The term refers to specific thoughts intended 'to inform' or to impart specific knowledge about the occurrence of an event or awareness or recognition of the identity of states of affairs so as to achieve a change of state of mind. These thoughts are generated by a living thing called the 'sender' capable of provoking, or not, a mental or physical response from a 'receiver'. The 'receiver' can be the 'sender' at the same time, for example, when a 'person reads the notice of 'the match takes place tomorrow at 12.00 hours' to be circulated in the village'.

The function of 'information' is to reduce uncertainty of the 'occurrence' of an event or awareness or recognition of the 'identity' of a state of affairs described by sentences with complete sense or meaning with 'specific dynamic, main verbs'. We can usually imagine such a scenario described by such a sentence.

For example:

1. Uncertainty of occurrence of an event --- 'The stationmaster announced [specific verb] that the train is on its way [uncertain, vague information]' which is modified to

   'The stationmaster announced [specific verb] that the train coming from Bristol scheduled time of arrival here is 09.25 hours, is about 35 km away and will arrive on time [more certain information]'.

2. Awareness of identity of states of affairs --- For example, 'John noticed that there is an animal on the field [uncertain, vague information]' which is modified to

   'There is an animal with two short horns, four legs, brown colour, carrying an udder for milking [adjectival phrase] standing still [adverb] on the green field richly adorned with grass not far from the village [adjectival phrase]'.

Remarks

a. Information carried by 'context free sentences' is uncertain. Adjectival and adverbial qualifiers of sentence elements turn such sentences into 'context dependent sentences' which carry more certainty, especially if the qualifiers can be quantified. In general, qualification and quantification reduces uncertainty and imparts 'precision' to information and to representation [Korn, 2009, 2010].

b. The occurrence of events and recognition of identity of states of affairs described by context free sentences are more uncertain than those described by context dependent ones. Or the first type is 'more' likely to occur' or 'more probable to find in the world' but their

'Informatic content' is less, and
'Cognitive value' is 'less'.

The second kind are 'less' likely to occur or they are 'less' probable but carry 'more' information or more certainty. Accordingly, the amount of information is inversely proportional to the probability of

Occurrence of events or

Recognition of identity of states of affairs.

The less probable the occurrence of an event or recognition of identity of a state of affairs the more knowledge they carry and the better they enable a receiver to act accordingly or not.

c. However, 'probability' of the contents of sentences acting as 'information' could not be assessed without appreciating the 'meaning' of sentence elements and that of the complete sentence. More specifically:

- The 'informative content' of a sentence is measured by its 'probability': The less probable a sentence is the higher its informative content, and
- The 'cognitive value' of a sentence is associated with 'meaning': The more qualified the sentence elements are the more meaningful it is or the more knowledge it carries.
- In both cases assuming that the human agent is able to select and apply the appropriate concepts which are 'well formed' and 'meaningful' [Floridi, 2010].

The conclusion is that both these measures of usefulness of information are connected to the 'specificity of sentence elements themselves' and the 'specificity and number of qualifiers of sentence elements'. For example, the sentence element, a noun phrase,: 'stomach' is more specific than 'digestive system' and 'there is a rectangular, steel tray on the square table' is more recognisable than 'there is a tray on the table'. 'Specificity' is the opposite of 'generality' and an idea or concept may be called 'specific' when it can be executed in practice. 'Symbol grounding problem' is the background theory [Steels, 2007].

d. The concept of 'information' is closely connected to that of 'problem solving'. In the former we also have:

1. A person or agent carrying a 'problematic issue' = A receiver in an 'ignorant state of mind',
2. The 'product' the function of which is to change the state describing the 'problematic issue' into a state regarded as resolved 'problem' = 'Information',
3. The 'system or dynamic structure' the function of which is to generate the 'product' = 'Sender of information'.

Use of natural language

As a result of the preceding discussion, we conclude that natural language, apart from its major role in everyday discussion and communication and the variety of its use in social, organisational [government, law, companies etc] and philosophical communications, is used in:

1. Formulating expressions in formal logic, in particular, serving as the basis of 'scientific thinking',
2. Generating arguments such as explanations and predictions,
3. Formulating formal expressions for communication and information.

End of **Remark**

1.2 Introducing the aim of the current work

We introduce the following suggestions:

A. The unit of discourse in the symbolism of natural language is the symbol of 'sentence' or a 'number of words arranged so as to make *complete thought*' i.e. the 'subject – predicate form' which locates a part of the world, the object of interest [the subject], and the 'view or opinion about the subject'. The declaration of a sentence is called a 'statement'.

B. Theoretically we can make an 'infinite number' of statements about any part of the world all of which are 'hypothetical'. Thus, complete knowledge is impossible to attain. In practice we are satisfied with one or a few statements selected by a 'point of view' or interest of an observer or stakeholder which can be organised or structured or expressed as a system so as to constitute a 'model' when encoded in a 'medium'.

C. Human beings appear to have developed a need for expressing their thoughts by a large variety of symbols leading to models which are considered more efficient ways of communication and can appeal to the reason or emotion handling part of the brain/mind. There is, thus, a large variety of models like:

1. Mathematical models which are a major departure from communicating verbally the quantitative aspects of a part of the world. Its introduction

attributed to Galileo at the Renaissance following the ancients like Greeks, in particular Archimedes, initiated the development of 'conventional science of physics'.

2. Signs such as 'road signs' which are an efficient way of making statements conveying 'information', for instance, the sign of a 'circle with an arrow bent to the left' can be interpreted by a car driver as the instruction: 'turn right'.

3. Variety of forms of the fine and performing arts such as painting or dancing appeal to emotions, sculptures of kings and others stand for their dignity, recognition of their contribution to society and so on.

However, all models are open to 'interpretation' which is usually carried out in terms of natural language and is prone to mistakes, subject to prejudices, used as means of influencing people and so on.

D. The concept of 'property' or adjectival and adverbial qualifiers, is the fundamental unit of specifying aspects of an object or agent or of an event which themselves are described by noun phrases or 'stative' and 'dynamic' verbs [Burton, 1984]. The state of affairs of an object or a part of the world is signalled by a 'stative verb' such as in '[This large, piece] of wood floats [down the river]' or the 'student was [absent]'. An event is indicated by a 'dynamic verb' as in 'The chimpanzee [the hairy, mother monkey] jumped [from one branch of a tree to another in the forest]' where the qualifiers are in brackets, also indicating the 'cases of nouns' [Filmore, 1968, Korn, 2009, 2013, 2016].

It is the finding of the 'right kind of property in the sense of acting as a qualifier of itself and other sentence elements' and to act as the basic structural element which is the fundamental question in constructing symbolic structures. The main problem of current 'systems thinking' is that workers in the field have not been able or unwilling or unaware of the problem which is attempted to be resolved by the current work of the author.

The aim of the current work in 'systems thinking' including this book, is to develop a 'Systems theory' that integrates 'problem solving thinking' and the 'systemic or structural view' of parts of the world'. We are engaged in 'systems thinking' when we think about parts of the world in terms of the 'systemic or structural view' of these parts.

ABC. --- 'The 'systemic or structural view' is described as pervasive, empirical, indivisible and hierarchical in the sense of nested which operates so as to solve problems', the **1ˢᵗ principle of systems**' [Korn, 2018]. ---

Perhaps the most well known example of the systemic view is the 'atomic view of matter' which is representative of any piece of material, observable, universal and its higher levels of complexity are molecules, compounds, mixtures. *'Nested'* means that each level of complexity contains constituents at the lower level, for instance, 'molecules consist of atoms'.

The proposed 'systems theory' is intended to act as the symbolism for representing and communicating the structural aspects of parts of the world in their generality as implied by **ABC.**

1. Kinds of parts of the world: 'concrete (animate, inanimate), symbolic, abstract or imaginary' description of any of which constitutes the *semantics*.

2. A 'structure' by definition i.e. 'an arrangement of parts' or a 'complex functional entity' is comprised of 'constituents'. Accordingly, we stipulate that any part of the world at whatever level of complexity and of whatever kind consists of the appropriate kinds of 'elementary constituents' or the *syntax*. There is no alternative.

3. The symbolism that can represent or model and communicate aspects of this generality of the 'empirical' world must be equally, or nearly so, general. Such a criterion can only be fulfilled by 'natural language'. However, natural language as used by people in their every day activities, is rich in expressive power of observed facts, emotions, products of imagination and so on. People have also evolved linguistic complexities for the expression of complicated linguistic elements to extend the representation capability of language like 'subordinate clauses' such as '[that he was fired] is no surprise to me' in which the subordinate clause enclosed in square brackets, stands for a noun phrase. Also, there are 'complex sentences' which have a 'main clause' and other clauses which qualify the main clause. For example, '[As soon as I arrived in New York], I telephoned home' [Burton, 1984, Korn, Huss, Cumbers, 1988, Korn, 2009].

4. Natural language is widely applicable as a representation of parts of the world or a 'story' or 'narrative' and is capable of being formalised as we have seen in section 1.1. However, perhaps *people's imagination and innovative urge* dictated to find different ways and means of saying the same thing about parts of the world i.e. representation. For example, in the arts the styles change, we can compare the painting of Madonna by a medieval artist with that of Rembrandt. Also, ancient builders had been using measurements of geometrical shapes in constructing the pyramids, for instance, however, it was Galileo who not only measured the times taken by stones to fall from the top of the tower of Pisa but gave rise to creation of the symbolic model as a mathematical function connecting speed, position and time. Apart from the fine and performing arts, range of different ways of expressions have been practiced by humanity such as gestures by hands, changes in features of the face, smoke signals by Indians, flags by sailors, road signs and so on.

For reasons in points 3. and 4. natural language has proved unsuitable for standing as a symbolism for representation or symbolic model of parts of the world, in particular, that of the 'systemic or structural view'. Workers in the systems field since the 1950's have not thought of using this symbolism as the basis for development of a 'comprehensive systems theory'. Mathematical modelling was too restrictive, it can take into account quantifiable properties only ignoring properties that can be highly influential such as 'emotions and social properties like being rich'. Natural language can take this kind of effect into account, it is very generally applicable. Instead workers set a different direction of inquiry into motion:

1. They embarked on speculative approaches which is still the fashion,
2. They recognised the generality of the 'systemic or structural view' and floated the idea of General Systems Theory which has never been turned into an acceptable reasoning scheme, 3. So workers had developed a number of inadequate symbolic models leading to fragmentation of the single subject matter of 'systems, structures [Bertalanffy, 1950, Boulding, 1956, Klir, 1969, Beer, 1979, Maturana, Varela, 1980, Checkland, 1982, Jackson, 2000, Yolles, 2004, and many others].

DEF. --- Natural language is the 'primary symbolism'. All other symbolic representations are its modifications and usually can be 'read' in terms of natural language subject to *interpretation*. For constructing the symbolic model representing the 'systemic or structural view' of parts of the world, we propose *not to develop* a new symbolism like a 'network model' but to modify the 'story' in natural language itself into *processed natural language* called 'linguistic modelling' as part of the envisaged 'systems theory'. The advantage of this approach is that a 'systems theory' can:

1. Model aspects of activities of living things, in particular, 'human activity scenarios' such as effects of emotive [anger, charitable] and social [rich, lonely] properties on development of how further actions may evolve,
2. Carry mathematical models of conventional science at the object level which may affect 'decision making', for example,
3. The quantitative aspects, if any, of a 'story' can be extracted and novel models can be constructed such as mathematical. ---

Linguistic modelling will be introduced in subsequent chapters. However, before this we introduce those features which a symbolism requires for acting as a representation of a part of the world.

1.3 Characteristics of symbolic structures

Natural language is a symbolic model that in generality matches the generality of the 'systemic or structural view'. To conform to the 1st principle of systems as stated in part 1.2., any symbolic model can be viewed as a 'structure' which is composed of 'structural elements'. To identify the 'basic, elementary constituent' of such a structure which can be regarded as indivisible at any level of complexity, is a 'problematic issue' resolution of which can take a long time.

For example, recognition of the 'atomic view of matter' which had been put forward by the ancient Greeks, has taken about 2000 years, conventional science of physics uses 'physical properties of matter' such as force, speed, current and voltage etc as 'elementary constituents' which was introduced during the 15th century Renaissance. This idea was extended to 'network analysis of engineering systems' preceded by 'block diagrams' in transfer function analysis of control systems, and list can go on [Brown, Campbell, 1948, Korn, 2012].

The 'subject-predicate' form of the simple sentence with 'complete meaning' which is the basic element of natural language, has been suggested as the source of all subsequent symbolic models and is called the 'primary model'. We now examine in more detail the constituents of this form regarding their function in producing symbolic models. The outcome of this exercise is finding the expressions in context which can be considered as the 'elementary constituents' of a systems theory.

The term 'theory' refers to a reasoning scheme with hypothetical components which people put forward all the time trying to understand aspects of their surroundings including their own bodies, to describe, to explain or to predict the 'existence of states of affairs' or 'happening of an event or change of state'. The whole or a part of a sentence can be used for contributing to the construction of such a scheme. The kind of theory that emerges depends on which part of the sentence is selected for its construction. For example, significant, reasoning schemes produced by conventional science consist of 'hypothetical principles and symbolic models intended to expose the former to experiment or observation for their conditional truth values'. The laws of thermodynamics or Newton's laws fall under this category [Rogers, Mayhew, 1957, Burton, 1984, Korn, 2009, 2012, 2018].

Selection of parts of a sentence

1. Properties or qualifiers or *adjectival* and *adverbial* phrases
This selection has resulted in the emergence of 'conventional science physics', the fine and performing arts', conventional, engineering problems and so on. These properties are close to perceptual experience of and can be appreciated by people and their use has been in existence for a long time as natural language has evolved except in science which as we understand it now, may be said to have begun at the time of the Renaissance. Conventional science and the arts have been very successful in creating great human, intellectual and practical achievements leading to the advancement of knowledge and artistic works affecting technology and social changes in direction of increasing complexity. This is so to cater for convenience, higher performance in products and in manufacture at the expense of exploitation of environmental resources and production of material and thermal waste.

Properties attached to noun phrases within a sentence and converting a sentence from 'context – free' to 'context – dependent', are extracted and organised into the structure of a variety of symbolic models sensitive to the senses. However, the mathematical models of science operate in terms of quantifiable properties and variables only and as such lose the identity of agents and objects modelled as noun phrases. Mathematical models can be manipulated in accordance with the rules of mathematics and by computer software.

2. Complete sentences

This selection leads to 'speculative works' like literature, fiction and poetry and is practiced in the current and past 'systems thinking or field'. This choice has been used in every day written and verbal communication and has yielded the vast amount and kind of descriptive literature including professional works such as writing of laws, rules and regulations.

3. Noun phrases

This usage usually employs 'abstract noun phrases' which stand on their own in arbitrary arrangements examples of which are 'purpose, values, ideals, goals, systems etc.' usually connected by directed, or not lines, with vague, or designation. The construction and use of this kind of symbolism is usually practiced by researchers in the 'systems field'. This approach cannot produce any kind of reasoning hypothesis.

4. Qualified diagrams

These are indiscriminate, vague as well as precise linguistic expressions attached to abstract diagrams such as causal loop, systems dynamics notations, SSM, VSM etc. developed in the 1970's but still practiced in the 'systems field' occasionally. They have led to fragmentation to and ignoring the unique field of 'systems thinking' as suggested by the 1st principle of systems [Korn, 2018].

5. Relational or *structural* or *systemic* properties

First, these are precisely defined linguistic expressions usually meaning quantifiable properties of aspects of physical objects such as, for example, 'Volume times density equals mass' and attached to directed lines of 'two – terminal networks' such as engineering, multidisciplinary networks similar to electrical networks and transfer functions of control theory [Korn, 2012]. For example, 'output equals [transfer function] times input'.

Second, 1 – and 2 – place, simple sentences with qualified elements which are the simplest, linguistic expressions making complete sense and can serve as 'elementary constituents' or 'elcons' or the description of *basic, structural elements*, in linguistic modelling [Burton, 1984, Korn, 2009, 2018].

The 1st and 5th selections are the ones considered suitable for use to satisfy the 'requirements' as formulated next for constructing a 'systems theory'. The 1st selection provides the 'elementary constituents' for the mathematical models of conventional science and for those disciplines which make use of quantifiable properties such as aspects of 'management science' using operational research methods [Taha, 1987]. The first in the 5th selection is extensively used in 'network theory' [Korn, 2012]. The second in the 5th selection are the smallest sentences of the 'subject – predicate' form which make complete thought. They are the elementary description of 'states (signalled by static or stative verbs)' and 'events (signalled by dynamic verbs)' which consist of:

- An area of interest or the 'subject' of the sentence, and
- What is alleged about the 'subject' or the predicate which together form the 'elementary constituents' of which more complex structures can be constructed.

GHI. --- Accordingly, 1 – and 2 – place sentences in natural language are the choice for acting as the 'elementary constituents' in the sought after, proposed 'systems theory' which is another name for the 'New Science of Systems' [Korn, 2009, 2018, 2020a,b]. These sentences are the smallest structure in natural language with 'complete thought', removal of any of their elements results in loss of sense. In other words, a 'structure' serves as 'elementary constituent' in a theory of 'structures'. A theory in physics, for example, uses quantifiable, physical properties as 'elementary constituents' of mathematical models or its symbolic structure. ---

For example, the sentence 'The helpful, bus driver called his passenger's attention to get off at the next stop' when modified to 'The helpful, bus driver called......' leaves the reader with a feeling of 'something is missing' i.e. incomplete thought, the description of scenario sounds incomplete.

Following the 1st principle of systems in **ABC.** in section 1.2. any thought expressed in terms of a symbolism and possibly realised as a symbolic model, consists of 'elementary constituents' at a any level of complexity. This is the case in general when constructing a symbolism representing 'concrete' or 'symbolic' or 'abstract' or 'imaginary' part of the world. However, when constructing a symbolism of an 'empirical theory', selection of 'elementary constituents' are subject to the following criteria.

1st criterion: 'Elementary constituents'

Justification for acting as a criterion = 'Any part of the world is seen as a 'structure' which, as such, consists of constituents of which there is always once to act as 'elementary'. An idea similar to that of Russell [Russell, 1972].

In section 1.2. the 1st principle of systems asserts that the 'systemic or structural view' of any part of the world in pervasive or general, there is no alternative, we cannot even imagine one. The function of 'elementary constituents' is to carry this view into a specific kind of symbolism as suggested by points 1. to 5. above. The basis of constructing a symbolism is:

X. Identification of the concepts regarding membership of a 'domain', or
Y. Construction of 'complex structures' out of simpler ones.

The term 'domain' refers to the range or scope of knowledge or awareness about objects sufficiently similar in an aspect or 'point of view' or function. To identify whether an object belongs to a domain, or not, a number of 'properties' needs to be present at the same time. This is perhaps the simplest way of stating such a debatable point subject, for example, to vagueness of terms. The topic is related to classification which is a well developed subject. When two or more objects of the same or different domains are seen to be related or interact with a view to produce an 'outcome' which none of the objects alone can produce, we speak of 'complexity' or a 'system' [Checkland, 1982]. The function of 'elementary constituents' is to create 'domains' and 'complexities'.

For example, there is a piece of matter with 'elementary constituents':

- Geometrical properties – length = 20 cm, width = 10 cm, height = 5 cm,
- Material properties – mixture of cement and sand, colour – orange,
- Function – used for constructing buildings,

which, when related using statements such as 'Length is perpendicular to height' becomes a 'static, complex system' labelled 'brick' when it regularly recurs. and belongs to the 'domain of building materials' as judged by an observer. In its turn, when a number of 'bricks' in a disorganised heap regarded as elementary constituents, are combined by an agent, a 'dynamic, complex system' into an organised, specific arrangement of a 'complex structure or system', the result yields an 'outcome' labelled 'wall'. The function of 'wall' is 'to support the roof' or 'to prevent neighbours from being able to look into my garden'. Neither of these functions can be fulfilled adequately by a single 'brick' alone.

JKL. --- We note a general point here which anticipates the subject matter which follows:

First, a piece of matter is constructed [in general = concrete, symbolic, abstract or imaginary] out of elementary constituents SO AS TO ACQUIRE A FUNCTION TO PRODUCE AN OUTCOME in the form of:

I. *Interaction* in terms of 'physical power' [mechanical (pushing), electrical (voltage times current) and so on [Korn, 2012] or influence such as 'information', 'use' or 'social status' [appearance before a king requires bowing] [Korn, 2010]. The concept of 'information' is described here as 'any sentence or phrase with complete thought following a special, dynamic verb to appeal to mental state to change to state of awareness'. Such verbs are 'to notify', 'to let you know', 'to make a note', to announce and so on.

II. *Physical and/or mental properties* which are intended to enable a piece of matter to fit or to match that or those it is intended to fit or to match. For example, a shoe should have properties to enable it to fit a foot otherwise it is no use. ---

This statement applies to designed 'artificial objects' or 'products'. Living things have evolved so as to acquire the ability to produce *'outcomes'* for contributing to the *resolution of problems* induced by:

'Problem generators' i.e.

1. Survival or continuation of existence,
2. Pursuing purposes through achievements to satisfy ambitions, and
3. Ensuring removal of material and heat waste.

'Pieces of inanimate matter' evolve or change by 'dynamic, natural forces' operating by chance, no conscious outcome or function appears to be involved. They may be given a function by a living thing when, for example, 'The boy picked up a pebble to throw at a nearby swimming fish' [Korn, 2018].

Second, we see the operation of TWO entities = One, a 'piece of matter' which may or may not have acquired a 'function', Two, the entity with the ability to produce the former. This idea will be elaborated later in detail. By 'piece of matter' is meant a 'physical as well as mental and intellectual entity or product' such as a 'writing desk or anxiety or a book' respectively.

Remarks

A. 'Elementary constituents' at any level of complexity can

a. Be used for constructing symbolisms or models which in some aspect are sufficiently similar to be seen to belong to the same 'domain'. For example, the physical properties as 'elementary constituents' like 'hairy skin', 'weight of about 5 tons when fully grown', 'with two large, curvy tusks' etc can be identified as an 'elephant' forming the 'domain' of all 'elephants'. A number of elements or 'elephants' joined comprise a 'herd' which together can overcome a 'pride of lions' which a single elephant on its own cannot do. Perhaps the herd can do this by presenting to the lions a 'formidable image', a mental product intended as 'information'. Acquired as such by the lions, the receivers, if interpreted as intended by the herd or the senders. The 'herd of elephants' forms a 'complex entity' or a 'dynamic, complex system' producing the 'static, complex system'.

We note the operation of the two entities: First, that of the 'complex system', Second, that produced by the 'complex system' called the 'PRODUCT'. Or

b. Act as means for applying such a structure to parts of the world which is sufficiently similar to those which have been used for originally conceptualising the elementary constituents i.e. can be seen to belong to the same '**domain**'.

For example, an 'elastic spring' when subjected to a 'force' expands or displaced. The quantifiable concepts of 'displacement' and 'force' may be adopted as 'elementary constituents' and

- First, used for recognising objects judged to be similar to form the 'domain of elastic springs', and
- Second, organised into the mathematical model of: 'Force equals a constant times displacement' [Korn, 2012]. This model can then acquire the function of being capable of predicting that any 'elastic spring' which is sufficiently similar to those used for generalising the concepts or belonging to the same 'domain', is displaced when a 'force is applied' to it.

B. There is a possibility of methodical construction of complex structures from simpler ones using the relevant 'elementary constituents 'elcon''. This is how the systemic view of parts of the world acquires its 'hierarchical nested feature' or the 'elementary constituents' at one level of complexity are nested or contained in the 'elementary constituents of the next level of complexity. For example, this is seen by the 'atom, molecule, compound, mixture' constructions in chemistry but this feature prevails throughout existence. As a result of 'congregation' of elements in the periodic table of Mendeleyev 'new, perceived properties' or 'outcomes' may emerge. This phenomenon may be referred to as 'emergence' which has caused many debates in circles interested in 'systems thinking', nowadays the matter appears to incite little interest [Nagel, 1968, Korn, 2018].

End of **Remarks**

2nd criterion: 'Model and story languages'

Justification for acting as a criterion = 'A symbolic structure called 'model language' is usually expressed in more general terms than the 'story language' which represent particular cases. A symbolic structure needs consider the relation between these two languages.

Natural language being the 'primary model' is usually used as the first attempt at modelling scenarios. Because of its accessibility, it is perhaps easiest to express thoughts in the symbolism of natural language which is called the 'story language'. However,

1. Imagination is a powerful means for feeding creativity and the desire and need for innovation exercised by human beings to overcome the 'problematic issues' raised by the 'problem generators' as mentioned above or just for self-satisfaction to express themselves. Imagination in the course of producing thoughts has found that it is more efficient, expressive, more suitable for generating emotions and so on to use a particular 'model language' than 'story language'. These languages are 'intellectual products' invented for resolution of problematic mental states and there has been a huge variety of them created over the millennia of human intellectual endeavour. The evolving stages of human intellectual endeavour are called 'paradigm changes' [Kuhn, 1996].

Intellectual products or symbolic models or 'model languages' are:

- Conventional science of physics [testable models such as mathematical models],
- Fine and performing arts [models intended to impress such as paintings, sculptures, literary works, ballet leading to speculative interpretation],
- Social sciences [laws, regulations in social organisations interpreted to be obeyed, theories describing aspects of society, statistics descriptive models],
- Religions [habits, rituals and devotion producing peace of mind],
- Current 'systems thinking' [various speculative approaches, VSM, SSM, UML, systems dynamics inspiring but unsupported ideas],
- Every day practices [symbolic models needed for navigating in the world such as 'road signs', gestures, recipes and so on, can usually be expressed in operational terms].

For example, mathematical models have been invented because they can answer in quantitative terms questions raised in connection with a specific aspect of a part of the world or a road sign 'red triangle with a man using a spade on white background' [model language] means or interpreted as 'there is road works ahead interpreted to take care' [story language].

2. The tendency to identify terms in a 'story language' by searching for their meaning which is equivalent to or **contained** in terms in the 'model language' developed from the former as referred to in point 1. just above and vice versa [Saeed, 1998]. For example, an instance of 'model language' is the term 'product' which can be identified as 'energy converter' in the 'story language' and can be made more specific towards development of an 'operational model' when named as a 'direct current electric motor' or a 'candle which converts fat into light' which all fit into the term 'product'. 'Shoe lace' also fits the term 'product' but it does not fit 'energy converter', it functions as a 'converter of an open shoe into a laced shoe'. The notion described can be summed up by exp1. [expression]

A term in model language $\geq$ A term in story language **exp 1.1.**

which is a requirement since 'model language' must be more general than 'story language' otherwise it cannot be applied to more than one particular case. The process goes the other way: A term in a 'story language' can fit into that in a 'model language', for example, an object labelled 'dining table' can be categorised as 'furniture'.

3rd criterion: 'Conditions of testing symbolic models against experience'

Justification for acting as a criterion = 'Imagination is extremely fertile in producing ideas. If any such idea is to be called 'scientific', its symbolism must be expressed in *operational terms* which can be tested for truth by experiment or observation. This criterion describes how this can be done.

If the 'elementary constituents' are selected so as to aim at producing an *empirical theory* the resulting symbolic structure must be shown to be capable of being exposed to tests of experience or 'confirmation' or 'falsification' by observation or experiment. This demands that such a structure be expressed as a 'predictive arrangement' of a 'logical conditional' as follows [Popper, 1972, Copi, 1978, Korn, 2009]:

The antecedent or hypothesis = 'IF there is a symbolic structure AND it is subjected to a stimulus or solved [if it is a mathematical model capable of solution],

The consequent = THEN there is an observable 'outcome' or 'solution'.

The procedure of exposure of the conditional to test for its truth value is:

First step = The antecedent of the conditional is the 'hypothesis' or the symbolic structure to be described in operational terms and is subjected to a stimulus or solved if it is a mathematical model and **X.** The consequent or the resulting 'outcome' obtained by simulation or 'solution' is seen on screen of a monitor or paper,

Second step = The symbolic structure is reproduced in hardware terms or exists in nature and is subjected to a stimulus and
Y. The resulting 'outcomes' are observed,

Third step = If **X.** [the result generated by the hypothesis], and **Y.** [the result obtained experimentally or observed] are found to be sufficiently
Similar then the hypothesis is verified or confirmed, or
Dissimilar then the hypothesis is falsified.

In addition, a 'conditional' is 'true' if it is 'false' that its antecedent is 'true' and its consequent is 'false'. That is if the 'Third step' is achieved then the symbolic structure may be accepted to provide 'reliable knowledge' subject to the rest of the world remaining unaltered and provided the 'Second step' is sufficiently similar to the 'symbolic structure' or model.

We note that exposure of a 'principle' or 'axiom' as a symbolic model which is expressed in general terms of 'model language' so as to be applicable to a range of particular cases in a domain, to observation or experimentation implies that a *general* model can be falsified by a *single* case.

Examples
First, a symbolic structure or system of mechanical, hardware [Korn, 2012] = This kind of systems exhibit different behaviour depending on the characteristics of their constituents.

If this 'mass, spring, friction' assembly is subjected to a step input then, for given properties of its components and their interconnection, solving the set of differential equations the outcome is oscillatory.

If this 'mass, spring, friction' assembly is actually constructed and subjected to a step input [antecedent] and its observed outcome is oscillatory and sufficiently similar to that given by the solution [consequent] then we can say that the 'hypothesis is 'true'.

Second, a human activity scenario =

Generally speaking in the course of an epidemic people stay at home or stay separated for sufficiently long time then after a time the epidemic peaks.

The mathematical model of a particular epidemic says that: If people stay at home for 14 days then the epidemic peaks 14 days after.

Following the advice based on the mathematical model, the prime minister strongly advises people to stay at home for 14 days to expect the epidemic to peak in 14 days after. If people actually stay at home for 14 days [antecedent (which is by no means certain or to what extent)] then it is observed that the epidemic has peaked in 14 days after [consequent] and we conclude that the 'hypothesis is true [to what extent]'.

'Predictions' and 'explanations' of this kind are commonly made in the course of every day life. Conventional science of physics has formalised this practice. The aim of the 'new science of systems' is to follow the example of conventional science but with 'systemic content' [Copi, 1978, Hospers, 1978, Korn, 2018].

4th criterion: 'Manipulation of a symbolic structure'

Justification for acting as a criterion = 'Manipulation means changing the form or action of a symbolic structure which is desirable in case of modelling dynamic scenarios to be tried to see their producing various outcomes when subjected to different inputs or when any of their constituents is changed. In case of modelling static scenarios manipulation may be desirable as in case of 'algebraic equations', in other cases, may not be. For example, changing the composition of a story or that of a road sign or any other information bearing structure, changes its 'meaning'.

Selection of 'elementary constituents' may or may not lead to symbolic structures which can be 'manipulated' or solved or subjected to a 'stimulus' using software. This need varies depending on application:

1. Modelling dynamic situations or scenarios
In this case 'manipulation' is required so as to predict or to explain. The term 'scenario' usually refers to 'activity' by inanimate, natural and artificial, or living things or their combination such as a 'volcano in eruption', a 'position control system closing and opening large gates in a fence surrounding a property', a 'church congregation' or a 'person hammering a nail into a plank'. Mathematical models can be manipulated towards solution, for example, in an algebraic equation one term can be transferred from one sided of the equation sign to the other.

2. Modelling static situations
This kind of intellectual activity arises in the course of 'modelling announcements', 'works of fine art' and so on. For example, a 'road sign' must not be manipulated because if its configuration is changed it loses its meaning.

Remark

Living things are in more or less constant communication with their environment including their own body, in the interest of evaluating environmental features or physical, mental and intellectual properties and act, or not, accordingly as indicated in Figure 1.1. This kind of intellectual activity is accomplished by means of creating 'symbolic structures leading to models' which aid:

1. Memorising instances of experience,
2. Representation and communication of thoughts, and
3. Invention of new thoughts through imagination.

According to the 1st principle of systems the 'systemic or structural view' of parts of the world is universal so the construction of symbolic structures is no exception i.e. it consists of 'elementary constituents' of hierarchical, nested levels of varying complexity [a molecule is comprised of atoms]. In this chapter we have discussed the nature of this construction including its characteristics of its 'elementary constituents' so that it can be used for creation of any of the large variety of symbolic models that living things have invented. This intellectual activity has been going on in order 'to resolve problems' and 'to construct the systems and structures which actually attempt the resolution'.

We have mentioned the 'physical, quantifiable properties' such as force, speed, current, voltage, temperature and entropy flow acting as 'elementary constituents' in conventional science and engineering systems [Korn, 2012]. Similarly, in section 1.3. we propose the 1 – and 2 – place sentences of natural language which are the smallest entities to make 'complete sense', to act as 'elementary constituents' in the symbolic model of a 'systems theory'. Natural language is the symbolic structure which can match a 'systems theory' in generality but it needs to be transformed into a 'reasoning scheme' called 'linguistic modelling'. The proposed 'systems theory incorporates problem solving', in fact dynamic systems or structures exist for solving problem which is *innate* in living things. This is discussed in later chapters.

End of **Remark**

Figure 1.1. is constructed according to the rules of 'linguistic modelling' with which we are not yet familiar but we can read this figure as follows: 'Living things receive perceptual input from environmental objects including their own bodies and, in case of humans, using their brain/mind apparatus with imagination, transform perceptual input into 'symbolic structures' or thoughts after interpretation [which become 'models' when encoded in a *medium*]. Followed by living things becoming knowledgeable through beliefs by having learnt the symbolic structures about environmental objects including their own bodies. Accordingly, living things prepare themselves for action and become ready for action, or not so as to engage in 'problem solving' which is *innate* in all living things'.

Figure 1.1. shows the general method of creating symbolic models as the product of interplay of 'sensory input', 'imagination' and 'environment'. There appear to be *two* kinds of content of such models:

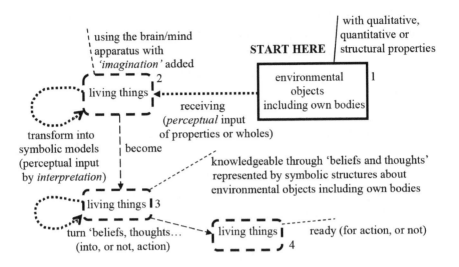

Figure 1.1. Mechanism of converting environmental input into action

1. First kind: Intellectual products mostly of the imagination with sporadic sensory input with a view to create and to maintain *interest* of one or a group of individuals. The question of ascertaining the truth of the subject matter rarely arises.

For example, artistic models, the product of discussions of abstract topics and terms, an activity currently favoured in 'systems thinking' as discussed in CHAPTER 2. and referred to in the APPENDIX, philosophical ideas and simply conversation.

2. Second kind:Intellectual products mostly abstractions of aspects of parts of the world through observation using sensory input and imagination with a view =

- To inventing *actual products* for applications to cater for convenience, to increase efficiency and so on, and
- To creating *'empirical' theories* or *symbolic models* of varying complexity with a view to produce *knowledge* of the empirical world or 'cognitive value'.

For example, we can have a simple physical product like the 'lever' presumably invented by Archimedes or the 'Internet'. Also, there is a simple intellectual product like an 'algebraic equation of multiplication representing the relation between the friction force, speed and friction coefficient' or 'Maxwell's equations'. This kind of models are exposed to tests of observation, experiment and application.

All models are created for affecting *mental state* by acting as intellectual 'product [3]' in Figure 3.1. A particular case is *information* as discussed in section 4.2. In general, we observe the usually sequence of *mental activity* as implied by Figure 3.1.: 'Problem solving' --- followed by --- 'product [3]' --- followed by --- 'User/Producer [2]' = = =

Further to the '4 – criteria' suggested for symbolic models to satisfy so as *to exist as feasible models*, we can say that:

A. All models need to satisfy the 1st Criterion,
B. Models of the 1st kind need to satisfy the 1st and 4th criteria,
C. Models of the 2nd kind need to satisfy all criteria.

CHAPTER 2

CRISIS IN SYSTEMS THINKING AND IN PROBLEM SOLVING

The aim of CHAPTER 2

--- The proposed 'systems theory' is the 'intellectual product' aimed at changing the aspects of current 'systems thinking' the current state of which is regarded as the 'problematic issue'. Before discussing the 'systems theory' we describe this 'problematic issue'.

There are two points which are presented here, perhaps not the first and not the last time because they constitute the basic background ideas behind the current work. Namely:

I. 'Systems thinking' and 'problem solving' are particular cases of intellectual endeavours which, to a large extent, are discussed and practiced separately by professional people and in the course of every day life by the general public. The proposed 'systems theory' integrates these two aspects into a unified whole.

II. The systemic or structural view of parts of the world is universal, there is no alternative. It has been modelled by workers in the field over many decades in a highly speculative manner and in terms of inadequate symbolisms which have made the unique subject fragmented and more or less unrelated to the *empirical view of the world* which is permeated with 'changes regarded as problem solving or change of equilibrium'. Perhaps this has taken place because workers in the field of 'systems thinking' either have not been interested or have not been able to find the connection between the 'systemic or structural view' and 'problem solving' and suitable, 'elementary constituents' which is the precondition for constructing a symbolic structure or any other structure physical [roof of a house], intellectual [book], imaginary [centaur].

It had taken many centuries for 'conventional science of physics' to appear on the scene of development of intellectual endeavours and to hit on the idea of employing the concept of 'quantifiable properties' as 'elementary constituent' leading to the development of the variety of mathematical models. This kind of models enable to expose the hypotheses of conventional science generated in its various domains, to observation or experiment with the view of 'falsification' as suggested by the 3rd criterion in section 1.3. In a similar spirit as mentioned in Chapter 1., we propose 1 – and 2 – place sentences of natural language to act as 'elementary constituents' for 'linguistic modelling'. Linguistic modelling is the basic symbolism of the proposed 'systems theory' which is based on 'natural language', the most generally applicable symbolic structure, can meet the generality of the systemic or structural view of parts of the world.

The objective of this chapter is to discuss the current state of 'systems thinking' in relation to points I. and II. ---

2.1 An outline of the historical development of the human, intellectual endeavour

Further to Figure 1.1. living things have no problem with recognising physical objects in static or dynamic state in their environments in the *entirety* of these objects to begin with,

- First, although this mental exercise is widely practiced today, because, at this stage of their evolution, living things had no mental and intellectual means for creating symbolic structures,
- Second, because this is the most efficient representation as usually there is no or limited time for some kind of analysis or evaluation or appreciation of a scenario with rapid or slow or any event taking place and there is no time for queries. There is urgency to take appropriate action:

To ignore the objects, To make use of them [to shape them into tools], To avoid them [to go round a threatening snake], To run away from them [to escape an avalanche], To fight them [to hit an intruder].

All of these kinds of action can be performed by *thought or impression* alone

Figures to be corrected in 'SCIENCE AND DESIGN OF PROBLEM SOLVING SYSTEMS' Janos korn, 11/09/2022

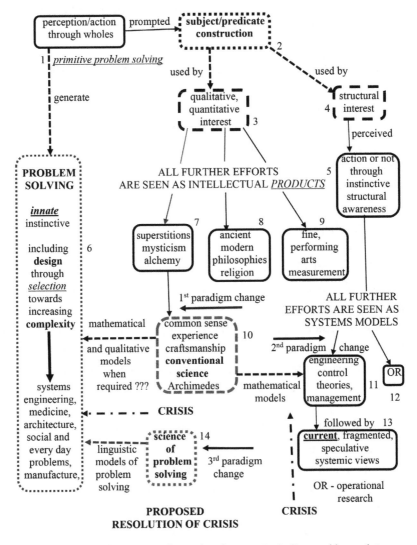

Figure 2.1. Diagram of human intellectual endeavour including problem solving

and to act 'instinctively' [Bronowski, 1973]. This description constitutes a 'primitive sort of *problem solving*' as shown at contour 1 in Figure 2.1.

However, when it comes to communication or satisfying 'curiosity', living things had been forced to invent means of 'description' which must have been:

1. Adequate to contribute to recognition of a part of the world, and
2. Suitable for being converted into *symbolic structures* and implemented or encoded in *a medium* to create symbolic models to be transmitted by a sender to be impinged on a sense organ of a receiver who can then decode them, and
3. Able to provide 'complete sense' so that a part of the world can be appreciated by the receiver. In other words, 'information' expressed as the 'subject/predicate construction' had been invented.

These notions are presented by contours 1 and 2 in Figure 2.1. which shows aspects of the vast and divers 'human, intellectual endeavour' relevant to the current discussion.

Further to the diagram in Figure 2.1. we note:

1. Once the 'subject/predicate' form in contour 2 had been invented, we can say that people became and still are *interested* in aspects of objects in their environments as described:
In contour 3, **either** by using statements with 'qualitative or quantitative' aspects of objects and forming symbolic structures with natural language or employing fingers to point at objects or creating their configurations as in 'sign language'.

For example, 'The [round] table [in this room] is pushed (into the corner 3 m away)' where the expressions in square and round brackets are 'adjectival and adverbial qualifiers' respectively representing the 'qualitative and quantitative' aspects of an object 'table', the subject of the sentence or part of the world. The sentence without qualifiers is 'The table is pushed' is 'context – free', qualifiers turn this kind of sentences into 'context – dependent'. The selection and kind of qualifiers play important part in exposure of a state or event to experiment or observation for 'falsification' of a hypothesis [Popper, 1972, Burton, 1984].

In contour 4, **or** by using statements which refer to the 'structural' aspects of objects describing them in terms of their =

A. 'constituent objects', and
B. their 'relationship',

which together define the 'object in question' being part of entities at a higher level of 'complexity' yielding an 'outcome' as 'emergent property as discussed in section 1.3. in point **JKL.** For example, 'The table consists of [four legs standing vertically (connected to) the horizontal top]'. The constituent objects are 'legs' and 'top' [noun phrases] and their relationship is specified 'connected to' [stative verb]. There is a number of possible and impossible variations of this arrangement, for example, the 'legs' can be 'connected' to the 'top' from below or above. There is one variation which can be called 'table' which can function as the 'product'. This topic is considered in detail in [Korn, 2009] through the notion of 'network analysis'.

2. So, we can say that the intellectual endeavour as presented in Figure 2.1., is divided into 'distinct branches':

X. Most of the 'intellectual products' of this endeavour have been produced and expressed in terms of 'qualitative, quantitative properties' as indicated in contour 3. Perhaps this has happened because people's attention and interest are drawn primarily by perceiving these properties like colour, texture, shape or size and so on, when faced with selection of 'products' like a dress or a car.

Y. Structural interest executed in terms of structural models of structural properties and pointed out in contour 4, are of lesser importance in every day representation and communication. It is mostly of interest to manufacturers of 'products'. Here we have a general point:

MNO. --- A structural property is defined as the elementary structure of one or at most two entities expressed by a symbol and the relationship to itself and between themselves. For example, 'The boxer [hit himself]', 'Mexico [lies below] the USA', 'John [is older than] Mike', 'The 1 – and 2 – place sentences as referred to in section 1.3. under point GHI. the structural properties in the proposed 'systems theory'. ---

Z. The third branch is concerned with 'problem solving' which is a particular kind of 'reasoning or thinking process'. Problem solving thinking:

Begins with perception by a living thing or a human being of a state of affairs [dirty floor in the kitchen] or some aspect of a scenario [generation of waste in a factory or lack of attendance of church services] which is deemed for any reason *unsatisfactory,*

Followed by a 'decision of' **either** accepting what has been perceived **or** taking appropriate action which implies calling on the services of an 'agent'. This agent is called 'system' or 'structure' with the function of producing or employing a 'product' which is intended to convert what has been perceived unsatisfactory into something that appears to be *satisfactory.*

Accordingly, problem solving thinking consists of *two stages*:

A. The 'creative stage', and
B. The 'stage of systems and product design'.

Problem solving is a general activity of living things throughout their existence, it is **innate** and is carried out instinctively ever since a living thing had appeared on this planet and continues today in every day by humans, animals and plants and professional people throughout the living sphere. Contour 6 in Figure 2.1. is intended to demonstrate this notion. A 'systems theory' is a symbolic model which represents this activity to demonstrate how the 'two stages' are implemented in an integrated fashion.

The aim of current work and that of this book is to describe the development of this 'systems theory' based on published material with new features to be introduced. The 'systems theory' is regarded as the 'resolution' of a 'problematic issue' in the field of 'systems thinking'. Accordingly, in this chapter we describe what is seen as the 'problematic issue'.

3. Evolution of intellectual products over the millennia perhaps driven by 'curiosity', 'inspiration' and the 'drive for innovation' to satisfy a 'need' for convenience, higher performance etc, has been going on in terms of 'paradigm changes'. They are indicated in Figure 2.1. by the horizontal, continuous directed lines. The *first paradigm* change after contour 7 points to the beginning of the 'age of reason', especially with the birth of 'conventional science of physics' as indicated in contour 10.

4. The *second paradigm* change is indicated above contour 11 and concerns the change in thinking from being 'aware of structures or systems' as shown in contour 5 to actually constructing structural models as indicated in contours 11 and 12. The content of these contours is outlined as follows with the intention of pointing at the 'problematic issues' which they raise.

People have no difficulty with recognising what may be described as a 'complex structure or system' in static or dynamic state and label it just 'system'. For example, there is a 'sports complex', 'system of components of a shaving kit', 'transport system' or the 'solar system'. The first methodical attempt at creating structural models appeared during the 2nd world war with the introduction of 'control theory' and 'operational research' as indicated by contours 11 and 12. These innovations were called for by the need to hit moving targets using a 'servomechanism' and to find the optimum number of ships in transatlantic convoys carrying supplies from the USA to the United Kingdom.

The structural model called 'control theory or transfer function analysis' is a description of operation in terms of signals, no physical power [mechanical, electrical, etc] is explicitly involved. Perhaps this kind of approach had arisen from

1. The influence of 'information theory' known at the time on the thinking of the pioneering researchers [Hartley, 1928, Shannon, Weaver, 1964], and
2. Control theory operates in accordance with the scheme of 'problem solving' so as to achieve an objective or a 'purpose' or resolving the 'problem' i.e. shooting down a moving aeroplane. Although an every day occurrence, this kind of thinking expressed in theoretical terms, was alien to conventional scientists thinking in terms physics of 'matter and power', no 'purpose' is admitted. The structure of a 'control system' consists of two regions: The region in which signals carrying information circulate and the region in which physical power circulate joined to the former by an 'amplifier' or 'influence to power converter'. So, the way out was to devise the 'mathematical model of transfer function analysis and modern control theory' which could represent the whole structure in terms of 'signals'.

However, this approach had created an anomaly discussed more fully in [Korn, 2009] which has not been resolved and produced problems because control theory did not fit into conventional, engineering courses except in courses in 'electronics'. This is because 'electronics' dealt with hardware assumed to carry signals. Nowadays the application of computers masks the anomaly which was recognised as a 'problematic issue' and attempted to be resolved by 'network analysis of engineering systems' devised by the author, however, this approach did not gain acceptance.

In the 1970's and 80's people in higher education began to recognise the importance and relevance of 'design of systems and product' and 'problem solving' thinking and also saw that conventional engineering courses with their 'applied science' domain dependent teaching was unable to accommodate this kind of thinking. So inquiries were conducted to find the way to resolve this problem but no satisfactory outcome was achieved because at that time there was no 'systems theory' [Finniston, 1980, Lewin, 1981].

Operational research or OR as indicated in contour 12, an intellectual product, was also born during the 2nd WW out of the 'problematic issue' of trying to optimise the number of ships in a convoy carrying supplies from the USA to The United Kingdom. Optimisation can be expressed in terms of a mathematical model which set the direction of development of the subject matter of OR towards using mathematical models for the resolution of problems rather like that in engineering systems. Currently there seems to be a tendency to search for 'soft OR' through considering [again] Soft Systems Methodology and identifying a PSM, problem structuring method in terms of speculative thinking.

The change from just awareness to actual production of structural models merits to be called the *second paradigm change* shown by the directed line below contour 5 and above contours 11 and 12 [Brown, Campbell, 1948, Blackett, 1948, Checkland, 1982, Taha, 1987, Korn, 2012]

5. The *third paradigm change* represented by the directed line pointing into contour 14, implies the change of viewing parts of the world, their concepts and structural modelling from those noted in contour 13 which stand for the current practices. Development of structural modelling of 'systems theory' so as to be called 'Science of problem solving' as written in contour 14, is the central theme of current work by the author and is discussed in this book.

The inscription in contour 13 is intended to refer to current practices in 'systems thinking which form the 'problematic issue' to be discussed and identified as such with a view to accept the proposed 'systems theory' as a supplement. This discussion takes place in the next section.

6. We can say that the topics indicated in contours 7, 8 and 9 have been pursued for as long as man stood upright and engaged in producing 'intellectual products' used for resolving problematic, mental states in the course of survival, satisfying curiosity and communication like cave paintings. Construction of rules, traditions and laws perhaps needs to be added as intellectual products for directing people's minds to act in prescribed manner.

7. Contour 6 is intended to indicate that living things, in particular human beings, have been engaged in 'solving problems' since the beginning of their existence up to the present time. The ability to solve problems as a matter course in every day lives of living things, pursue ambitions and maintain themselves, is *innate*. In the course of this activity they themselves have evolved into the currently observable huge variety of kinds and forms like man, lions, roses and other forms of flowers in direction of increasing complexity and have produced physical, symbolic and intellectual products also in direction of increasing complexity. Comparing chariots with modern fighting vehicles, sending messages through smoke signals with satellite communication and use of papyrus with use books for writing, acts as a testimonial to the validity of the previous statement.

The question arises regarding HOW living things, especially humans, have managed to reach such high levels of complexity of what they have produced thereby propelling themselves into the mode of living at such high intensity like using a 'car' instead of 'walking'.

We can suggest that living things, in particular their human variety, have been able to

1. SURVIVE,
2. EVOLVE, and
3. ACHIEVE,

in the course of their lives because they

A. Posses the *innate* ability of 'problem solving',
B. Can make use of available knowledge at any epoch and invent new physical devices and intellectual products, and
C. Can accumulate, transmit and use *experience*.

We do not know the 'biological' and 'chemical' entities that propel life in direction from simple to complex. Perhaps the first molecule that absorbed another had no other direction but adapt to followed by actively alter the physical environment.

Remarks

The contours in Figure 2.1. diverge into three distinct branches from contours 1 and 2:

- The structural interest branch viewing parts of the world in terms of *structural* properties,
- The qualitative, quantitative interest branch viewing parts of the world in terms *qualitative, quantitative* properties, and
- The problem solving branch which is *innate* and practiced instinctively supplemented by supporting intentional change through *design thinking* for ensuring continuation and betterment of life of individuals and societies.

The structural interest branch has not produced satisfactory symbolic models to understand the operation of systems or structures and to place this empirical phenomenon into the context of human, intellectual endeavour. The qualitative, quantitative interest has been very successful in producing scientific theories for explanation and prediction of states and events in the natural world extended to use in the artificial i.e. technology and society. This branch has also led to the creation of intellectual products for improvement of mental and physical states of individuals and societies as indicated partly by the contents of contours. The problem solving branch has also been very successful in evolving, ensuring and improving lives of individuals and societies.

We note that the branches imply activities by the human intellect operating separately. We propose to outline a 'systems theory' which improves the intellectual products of the structural branch, provides a theoretical background for the problem solving branch and incorporates when there is a need, aspects of the qualitative, quantitative branch.

End of **Remarks**

2.2 Description of the crisis in current, 'systems thinking' and 'problem solving'

We are talking mostly about the content of contour 13 of Figure 2.1. but touching on the topics in contours 11 and 12. Also, we discuss instances of 'problem solving' as generally practiced by professional people with examples found on the internet with reference to contours 1 and 6. We intend to justify the assertion that 'systems thinking' is in *crisis*.

FIRST, discussion of aspects of current 'systems thinking'

The current field of systems thinking consists of a variety of by and large speculative views, inadequate methods and a number of organisations involved in arranging meetings, discussions and publication which suggests a state of confusion and fragmentation of the field when contrasted with the generality of the 'systemic or structural view' of parts of the world [Korn, 2018]. This can be interpreted as a 'crisis situation'. So, how has this situation arisen ???? which is what we intend to outline briefly first.

A resolution of the crisis in the form of a 'new science of systems' is then suggested. Assuming this new science becomes part of the field of systems thinking, a debate of the field is proposed with a view to consider its current state and future developments in relation to currently available methods.

Firstly, people have no difficulty in using the term 'system' or that of 'structure' mostly in an intuitive manner. When the 'computer ceases to work in the office' the staff will usually say that the 'system broke down and we cannot process your application' or when 'we look at a step ladder' we recognise 'its structure and describe it by the sentence 'it consists of 7 horizontal slabs held 40 cm apart by 2 vertical end pieces to which the slabs are attached'.

We can put forward a number of points prompted by the 'ladder' example:

1. The sentence describes 'structure', no reference is made to 'material [colour, hardness...]' or 'geometrical [length, width...]' properties of systems components, however, their 'orientation' is given.

2. We can identify the basic expressions which describe 'structure' such as 'slabs or planks [are held apart] by the end pieces'. This expression consists of 'objects or agents' and their 'relations' given in the brackets.

3. There are two objects indicated 'slabs' and 'end pieces' each having a function which is its contribution to the function of the whole, the 'ladder'. For instance, the function of the 'slab' is to allow a person to step on.

4. The 'ladder' as a whole may be described as a 'product' which is constructed so as to have an 'outcome': It makes it possible for a person to change h/her initial position 'from ground level to a higher level limited by the height of the ladder'. Neither of its two components on its own can accomplish this [Checkland, 1982].

5. The person being at 'ground level' is h/her 'initial state regarded as unsatisfactory' referred to as the *problematic issue* which h/she wants to change to being at a 'higher level' which is h/her 'final, satisfactory state' or *resolution* of the problematic issue. This description is part of the mental process of 'problem solving'.

6. We note that *design of the product* can be seen to follow from a detailed specification of 'part of problem solving'. Properties or *requirements* of the user i.e. the person, dictate properties of the 'ladder' or 'product' as a whole from which detailed properties of the 'systems components' follow. For example,

   - Requirements of user: 'H/she wants to climb to 2 m' and 'H/she can carry 24 kg weight',
   - Properties of the 'ladder' as a whole: 'The ladder is 2.5 m tall' and 'Weighs 22 kg',
   - Properties of 'slabs': There are 7, each 50 cm long, 3 cm thick, 10 cm wide, made of timber,
   - Properties of 'end pieces': There are 2, each to accommodate 7

'slabs' 40 cm apart, 300 cm long, 0.2 cm thick, 14 cm wide, made of aluminium.

7. The observability of the systemic or structural aspects of an entity makes a possible 'systems theory' *empirical*.

Similar considerations apply to description of 'problematic situations' with living or human components which is widely practiced by employers engaged in hiring employees or marriage arranging agencies trying to match couples. The properties are emotive [loving...], intellectual [clever...], mental [adaptable...] and physical [appearance...]. These properties can be vague, with uncertainties and difficult to assign to a person as interpreted from observable properties but the thinking is common with situation involving hardware kind of objects except 'design of systems components' is replaced by 'training or education'.

Secondly, observing activities which appear 'complex' i.e. involving a number of related objects in static or in dynamic state and need to be referred to as a whole, people usually assign the term 'system' to them. There are, thus, 'transport systems', 'educational systems', 'solar system', 'shaving system', 'sports complex' and so on.

However, issues which acutely arose in the 2nd World War began to draw attention of thinkers to problems which appeared beyond those usually found within the reach of conventional science of physics such as 'finding the optimum size of a convoy of ships carrying supplies to reduce the chance of being attacked by u – boats' or 'shooting at moving targets by anti aircraft guns' [Blackett, 1948, Brown, Campbell, 1948, Beer, 1979].

Accordingly, the first organised development using systemic properties i.e. objects or agents in relations, for representation of parts of the world had been in 'operational research' and 'engineering control theory' evolved during and used after the 2nd WW in teaching and industry [Brown, Campbell, 1948, Taha, 1987, Nise, 2008]. This development was followed by the work of thinkers like von Bertalanffy and Boulding who noticed the general applicability of the 'structural or systemic view' to parts of the world including social activities and they called this General Systems Theory. They, however, achieved no further, significant analytical development leading into symbolic structures for applications to the constantly recurring problematic issues in the world. Subsequent workers attempted a development of GST based mathematical modelling or 'discovering isomorphisms in branches of science'.

Mathematical models can take into account the quantitative or quantifiable aspects of a part of the world which is too restrictive to act as a symbolism for a GST. This kind of models do not take into account qualitative features associated with 'social and emotive properties' such as 'rich' and 'angry' which could exert influence on behaviour. For example, 'A person hungry and destitute passes a grand house presumably occupied by rich people and, driven by envy, h/she throws a stone at a window'. Isomorphism or similarities between otherwise different things, can give a limited scope for modelling the 'systemic or structural view' of parts of the world. In addition, if it is restricted to apply to branches of science then the result remains within science, however, the 'systemic or structural view' is a very different matter. Successful application of similarities has taken place in 'network modelling of engineering systems' [Klir, 1969, Troncale, 1985, Korn, 2012, 2018].

The problem with 'operational research' is that its methods use mathematical models which can be identified as 'intellectual products' as implied by contour 12 in Figure 2.1. and are directed at meeting the change of mental state of curiosity but not recognised as being a part of a 'problem solving process' including the human agents engaged in raising the problem and striving for its resolution.

Here we have a *problematic issue*: On one hand, we have the statement of the 1st principle of systems [Korn, 2018] = 'The systemic or structural view of parts of the world is general, empirical, hierarchical [in the sense of objects at a lower level of complexity are contained in those at a higher level ones] and indivisible and there is no alternative' and, on the other hand, against this assertion there is ===

A. The failure of development of an acceptable GST which would meet the 1st principle, and

B. Perhaps the failure of development of an acceptable GST led subsequent researchers to produce their individual approaches to the production of a symbolic model to represent the 'systemic or structural view' which does not meet the 1st principle or its generality,

C. The subsequent spread of the present day variety of extensive and intense activity of producing publications, organising conferences, activities of societies and sporadic teaching at graduate and postgraduate but not at school level of ideas and methods thought to be part of 'systems thinking'.

This development or the current, intellectual field of systems thinking is seen as:

OR (operational research) is a variety of mathematical models,
Engineering control theory is signal based i.e. flow of power is represented as if it was signal flow,
Variety of views and opinions of what systems thinking is about,
A number of unrelated concepts like feedback, boundaries, viable systems, critical systems, interdisciplinarity, functionalism, living systems, cybernetics, open and closed system, holism, emergence etc. are still not clear,
A range of by and large speculative and stimulating views,
A variety of methods of modelling scenarios,
No general approach to systems and product design,
The field is sparsely related to well established branches of knowledge like parts of physics or symbolisms like linguistics and logic,
Concepts from physics like 'entropy' and 'energy' is debated.

The field of systems thinking is, thus, fragmented, speculative i.e. views without adequate foundations, and it is confused. This is contrasted with the unique view of systems thinking which says that any part of the world has a structural nature which is pervasive, empirical, indivisible and hierarchical [Korn, 2018]. This view corresponds to the observation that the phenomenon of structure or system is *empirical* and *universal*, there is no alternative capable of interpreting existence in its variety and diversity, we cannot even conceive one. If this is the case, the question arises whether it is possible to resolve the *crisis* while carrying on admitting new, constructive, debatable ideas.

This view of the field presents a confusing and disjointed picture and may be interpreted to be 'in crisis' which is described as 'time of aggravated and intense difficulty with little prospect of production of an outcome or of danger [physical], confusion [intellectual] or harm to the image or reputation of an organisation [organisational]' [Korn, 2018a]. Intellectual crises had been seen to happen before in the history of human thoughts with *paradigm* changes as their resolution as indicated in Figure 2.1. [Kuhn, 1996]. The period of the Renaissance may be regarded as the resolution of the intellectual crisis of Middle Age thinking of believes and attempts at creating explanatory hypotheses like the 'phlogiston' and 'caloric' which were later substituted by a 'theory of combustion' and 'heat as a form of energy', a more rational account of the same experience [Pledge, 1966].

PQR. --- Creation of a new domain or discipline is creation of a new 'symbolic structure' which may be called a 'new paradigm'. Like any structure, physical [table], abstract [problem], imaginary [fairy], involves finding the 'elementary constituents' of the structure of which more complex structures can be constructing. The search for elementary constituents is age old such as earth, water, air, fire of ancient Greece or the atomic theory of matter, for example. Conventional science of physics uses quantifiable, physical properties like force, electric current, temperature or entropy flow leading to the structure of mathematical models. Multidisciplinary engineering systems uses the classification of variables into 'through and across' to cope with 'energy conversion', for example, together with the elementary constituents of 'networks' [Kuhn, 1996, Levene, 2010, Korn, 2012]. ---

The basic problem with 'systems thinking' has been the failure to find suitable 'elementary constituents' until current work which identifies 1 – and 2 – place sentences of 'linguistic modelling' as such constituents [Korn, 2009, 2018, 2018b].

The description of the current state of affairs of 'systems thinking' is interpreted as an intellectual crisis situation because it is fragmented apart from deficiencies of its methodologies such as VSM, SSM, System dynamics or Causal loop diagrams because they do not satisfy the criteria in section 1.3. More concretely, a view of the constituent parts of the 'current symbolic structures' of 'systems thinking' are:

Engineering Control Systems Theory [Brown, Campbell, 1948],
General Systemic view [Bertalanffy von,1950]

Systems Dynamics [Forrester, 1969],

Soft Systems Methodology [Checkland, 1982],

Viable Systems Model [Beer, 1979],

Autopoiesis [Maturana, Varela, 1980]

Systems thinking [Senge, 1990]

Use Cases [Bittner, Spence, 2001]

Systems Engineering [Anon, INCOSE, 2004]

Appreciative inquiry [Witney, Coppervider, 2005]

Network Representation of Engineering Systems [Korn, 2012]

Petri nets [Murata, 1989]

UML (Unified Modelling Language) [Jacobson, et al., 1998]

Agent-based models [Gilbert, 2007]

Systems maps [Penn, Barbrook-Johnson, 2016]

and a number of diagrams (business modelling etc] plus methodological and philosophical approaches are described in [Jackson, 2000].

Another sign of crisis in the current intellectual scenario is the number of organisations concerned with aspects of the essentially unique systems thinking such as:

Business Systems Laboratory, Cybernetics Society, International Society of Systems Science, United Kingdom Academy of Information Systems, United Kingdom Systems Society, Operational Research Society, European Union for Systems, university teaching schemes of 'systems' and so on.

Over the past 70 or so years the single but vague notion of 'system' has produced a large amount and variety of intellectual output of which the above list is a sample, supplying material for publications and debate but not *critical* debate. If this kind of activity is the objective of the 'field of systems thinking' then there is no crisis. However, if the intention is to recognise the:

1. Empirical nature of the systemic phenomenon and to notice the lack of more rigorous and scientific appearing methodology with integrated 'problem solving' and aiding design of systems and products,

2. Need for a more precise and unified approach in place of fuzziness and multiple strands,

3. Need for a systems theory that has a more fundamental basis with roots in branches of well established knowledge, can be applied to 'problematic scenarios' following a well defined procedure and is teachable at class level ---- then there is *crisis*. The 'new science of systems' is suggested as a possible resolution of the *crisis* subject to critical debate and perhaps using the suggested criteria as the ways of assessment considered in section 1.3.

These *criteria* are now applied to two methods currently available and used in the field of *systems thinking*:

Soft Systems Methodology (SSM) [Checkland, 1982]

1. Application of natural language
The story is as follows: 'A householder having inspected his garden fence, concluded that it needed painting. He decided to do the job himself so as to ensure that it will enhance the visual appearance of the property'. This is usually followed by construction of 'rich pictures'.

2. Elucidation from the 'story' of what may appear to serve as elementary constituents

> C Customers = Victims or beneficiaries of a T (transformation):
> Householder
> A Actors = Those who would do T:
> Householder
> T Transformation (process) = Conversion of input to output:
> To paint
> W Weltanschaung = The worldview which makes this T meaningful in
>   context:
> Job is to enhance the ....
> O Owners = Those who could stop T:
> Householder
> E Environmental constraints = Elements outside the system of actors
>   performing T:
> Need to enhance property affects selection of paint ?

3. Construction of 'relationships' of elementary constituents or 'root definition' of an envisaged system using CATWOE

'The householder having inspected the garden fence [actors (A) with point of view (W)] paints the garden fence [interaction (T)] by hand [means (Y)] to ensure that it will enhance the visual appearance of the property [final state (Z)] for his own benefit [User/utiliser (C)]'.

The X-Y-Z scheme was mentioned in section I.1.

4. Construction of a complex structure using the 'root definition'

Figure 2.2., the conceptual model, shows the envisaged system which is supposed to alleviate the problematic initial state or the 'garden fence is unpainted'.

5. Testing the relationships for their truth value

The intention of doing this is indicated in Figure 2.2. by labels 6, 7 and 8 which are added arbitrarily.

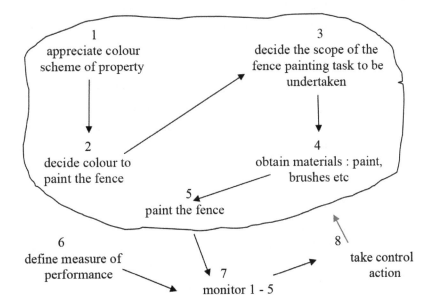

Figure 2.2. Model of root definition

Application of criteria from section 1.3. =

1. First criterion = Selection of elementary constituents
There is no awareness of the concept of 'elementary constituents' by the creators of SSM. The components of CATWOE are identified as such by the author and used in further development of the method.

2. Second criterion = Relationship between 'story' and 'model' languages
A 'story of the perceived scenario' is given by the author instead of using a 'rich picture' as a means of extracting one or more 'problematic issues'. Such 'issues' can usually be identified from the way linguistic expressions are formulated. For example, in 'The butler looked into the cupboard and found the level of wholemeal flower in its container was low.' which indicates a possible 'problematic issue': 'The wholemeal flower may need to be topped up'.

The items in the CATWOE scheme are 'model language' which, when their meaning is briefly clarified, can be related to terms used in the 'story language'.

3. Third criterion = Testability of the resultant scheme of a structure or system
Setting up experiments or exposure to deliberate observation is not part of the SSM but assessing the effects of intervention using results of application of the method can be.

4. Fourth criterion = Manipulation of the symbolic structure
There is no mechanism in SSM for subjecting a diagram such as in Figure 2.2. to input stimulus. Qualitative considerations of the effects of changing components of a diagram is a possibility.

Remarks

At the time of its introduction into academia in the years of the 1980's, SSM was a pioneering initiative because its was the first attempt at constructing a comprehensive scheme for 'problem solving'. It considered both parts of 'problem solving': One, the statement of the 'problematic issue' and its creatively suggested resolutions, and Two, the structure or system and product intended as the means of putting the resolution into effect. We note that in

SSM the function of the 'product' in 'problem solving' which is the immediate means of changing the 'problematic state' into an 'acceptable, resolved state, does not enter into considerations.

SSM is supposed to be a 'problem solving scheme' but, in addition, its creator claimed it to be some kind of learning mechanism as well which like any attempt at modelling a scenario, it may have been. It meets the generality of 'systems thinking' because it is concerned with 'problem solving' which is, when connected with the concept of equilibrium, is probably the most general concept reflecting an aspect of existence. Otherwise SSM uses vague, poorly defined terms, it is not based on excepted branches of knowledge all of which perhaps make it difficult to apply to problem solving of scenarios. A diagram such as Figure 2.1. uses the 'imperative mood' of dynamic verbs which is the language of computer algorithms. The usual form of representation of scenarios is the 'declarative mood'.

End of **Remarks**

Viable System Model (VSM) [Beer, 1979]

The VSM asserts or claims that it specifies the necessary and sufficient structural, preconditions for the *viability* of any organisation [Jackson, 2000, Schwaninger, Scheef, 2016].

Application of the criteria from section 1.3. =

1. First criterion = Selection of elementary constituents
There is no awareness of the concept of 'elementary constituents' by the creators of VSM. However, the 'five systems' could be considered as 'elementary constituents' interconnected by unspecified, undirected lines.

2. Second criterion = Relationship between 'story' and 'model' languages
There does not seem to be awareness of a need to consider this aspect of constructing symbolic structures.

3.Third criterion = Testability of the resultant scheme of a structure or system
Setting up experiments or exposure to deliberate observation is not part of

the VSM. A kind of statistical test of the theoretical claim versus empirical evidence was attempted but this work is based subjective evidence [Schwaninger, Scheef, 2016]

4. Fourth criterion = Manipulation of the symbolic structure
There is no mechanism for subjecting a diagram of VSM to input stimulus or variation, it may be seen as a suggestion for assessing viability.

The question is 'what is the justification of the VSM's claim ???' It seems that the proposed method of falsification of VSM by the authors [Schwaninger, Scheef, 2016] is seeking opinions using a questionnaire. This is not direct falsification of a symbolic structure by exposing it to the rigours of a properly set up experiment or a properly conducted observation. The diagrammatic representation of VSM is consists of vague, undefined symbols such as the amplifier, triangle symbol and the connecting lines which makes it difficult to apply although reference [Schwaninger, Scheef, 2016] tries to impart meaningful content to a few of the symbols.

Similar tests could be conducted with the 'current symbolic structures' of 'systems thinking' as listed above using the 'set of criterion' which are justified to some extent for use as 'criteria for acceptability' of a symbolic structure to act as representation of scenarios with fidelity. However, use of 'current symbolic structures' except, UML, for example, makes 'systems thinking' fragmented and as such contradictory to the original insight of researchers in the 1950's of the generality of the 'structural or systemic view' to be expressed in terms of the frequently attempted General Systems theory [Bertalanffy, 1950].

SECOND, discussion of aspects of current views of 'problem solving'

The subject matter of 'problem solving' is vast and spreads over 'psychology, cognitive science, computer science, engineering etc. and more recently to the notion of 'problem structuring methods' [Mingers, Rosenhead, 2004, Anon. Wikipedia, 2018].

We look at a few suggestions for what is understood by the term 'problem' and 'problem solving'.

1. 'Problem' is a source of perplexity,
2. 'Problem solving behaviour' is the use of various strategies to overcome difficulties in attaining a goal or resolution of the 'problem' if any,
3. A 'problem' is the distance between how things currently are and the way they should be,
4. 'Problem solving' forms the 'bridge' between the two elements in points 2 and 3. In order to close the gap, we need to understand the ways things are (problem) and the way they ought to be (resolution) [Anon., 2014].

The suggestions seem to confirm the idea that the mental process of 'problem solving' consists of *two parts* as discussed in section I.1:

A. Identification and agreement of a 'problematic issue' or an initial state of affairs regarded as unsatisfactory for some reason or other and an envisaged, satisfactory, final state of affairs,

B. The means or dynamic structure or system that is seen to bring the change about.

Both parts are concerned with *creating, material things* that **satisfy expectations** and did not exist before the human interference had taken place and as such much analysis, discussion, creative effort and agreement are needed before the results can be finalised if at all.

We recall from section I.1. that the mental activity of 'problem solving' is *innate* in living things and is operated 'instinctively'. Our intention is to develop a *basic scheme* which emphasises what is regarded as the **fundamentals** of 'systems thinking' in the form of a 'systems theory' that can

1. Provide a scheme for 'conscious, deliberate' activity to supplement the instinctive activity of 'problem solving', and
2. Integrate the two aspects of 'problem solving' and, in particular, to suggest that part A. can fit into the general concept of 'equilibrium' well recognised in conventional science.

Detailed steps to accomplish the activity of 'problem solving' is given in [Anon., 2014] which is summarised here with the title of each step:

1. Define and understand the problem
2. Assess the scale of the problem
3. Gather relevant information
4. Identify the root causes
5. Test the hypothesis
6. Involve others
7. Consider the proposed solution(s)
8. Test the proposed solution
9. Champion your decision
10. Monitor the results

A detailed description of activities under each step is given in the reference.

'Problem solving' schemes are also given as diagrams and an example is shown in Figure 2.3.

Figure 2.3. shows a symbolic model of contours with 'instructions' connected by unlabelled, directed lines. The 'instructions' are given by dynamic verbs in imperative mood followed by noun phrases describing what is to be done. Both, the verbs and noun phrases are expressed in abstract and vague terms which are difficult to implement in any problematic scenario. As far as the brief survey shows this is the feature of approaches to 'problem solving'. This is a 'problematic issue' and it arises because 'problem solving' as an intellectual activity is not connected with a suitable 'systems theory'.

Remarks

Perhaps because the activity of 'problem solving' is 'innate' in living things,

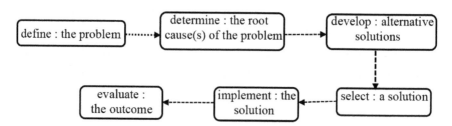

Figure 2.3. Diagram of a 'problem solving' scheme

in particular in human beings, attention to the development of formal approaches to problem solving is more recent. Human achievements over the millennia have been immense and progressive such as from a horse drawn chariot towards the higher 'complexity' of the *artificial* of a Formula 1 racing car. The drive behind this kind of progress appears to be to satisfy the needs for survival, convenience, higher productivity, increased performance and *variety* of machines, improving health, means of entertainment and so on, driven by human ingenuity, inventiveness and creativity.

The development of technology as just referred to at an increasing speed has led to increasing population in practically all countries, increased and more diverse manufacture including agriculture, huge distribution and commercial enterprises and financial institutions. The increased tempo and size has resulted in increasing pace of exploitation of natural resources in the environment to feed the appetite of production and supply of goods to sustain the population, increasing variety and scale of social activities taking place within a *limited space* available.

This development may have taken place because of the:

1. Ability of 'problem solving' by living things, in particular man, is innate and is practiced instinctively throughout the species, to facilitate their survival and to succeed in life, all depend on this ability,
2. Ability of human beings to make use of available knowledge at any given epoch and to invent new devices,
3. Ability of accumulating, transmitting and using experience.

STU. --- The hugely increased number, magnitude and intensity of activities within a limited space that has made the nowadays ever present interactions among instances of activities so noticeable which is called 'joined up' state of affairs. However, interactions take place not among activities but among the 'results of activities if any' or the 'changes of state' which is called in the current work 'acquired property' [Korn, 2009, 2013, 2016]. ---

For example, in the sentence 'The escaped convict took the train and arrived at the railway station at 11.30 hours and was intercepted by the police' 'the arrival' of the escaped convict" is the 'acquired property' which the 'police noticed', thus, interaction can take place.

End of **Remark**

A statement like **STU.** would not be applicable to what appears to have been going on the planet 3000 years ago. At that epoch the activity of a group of people would have been unlikely to have caused a 'problem' in the form of an undesirable interaction to another group. For example, a more recent but relevant event 'The Mongol invasion took place around the years of 1230 of eastern and central Europe led by the descendants of Genghis Khan'. This resulted in devastation of property and death of millions of people but there is no historical record of countries such as Germany, France or England took the slightest notice assuming they existed at that time as coherent countries. Nowadays any such or more minor event would not go unnoticed and would provoke some form of retaliation by other countries.

In any case, the statement **STU.** is generally applicable and makes the development of 'problem solving schemes' as symbolic models, relevant.

Remark

The first point ===
We again reassert that the 'structural or systemic view' of parts of the world is an **empirical view** i.e. we can perceive the structure of an object or an entity by the sense organ of vision and touch, perhaps, and transmit the result of perception to the brain/mind mechanism for creating symbolic structures or ignoring the results.

The second point ===
The 'structural or systemic view' of parts of the world is a view of an aspect of an entity, concrete, symbolic, abstract or imaginary, just like any other view. In other words, viewing a part of the world needs a symbolic structure.

VWX. ---We have asserted before [Korn, 2018] that 'We can make an **infinite number of statements** about any part of the world which means that perfect knowledge is impossible. We, therefore, select a few statements and the selection is directed by a 'point of view' which is called the **symbolic model**. Accordingly,

1. Knowledge is subjective and conditional on circumstances surrounding the selection prevail, and
2. Knowledge, when encoded in a medium and transmitted, interpreted by the receiver.

It then follows that knowledge is 'uncertain', subject to 'prejudices' and serves the furtherance of individuals or groups of people. ---

In current work we take or 'systems thinking' takes the 'structural view' or 'structural aspect' of a part of the world just like, for example, the 'discipline of mechanics'. However, mechanics has a distinct selection of properties and variables or 'elementary constituents' which enables us to:

1. Identify an object as part of the domain of mechanics, and
2. Construct symbolic structures.

For example, the 'elementary constituents' of *mechanics* or the mechanical properties: Density, viscosity, elasticity and the mechanical variables: Force, speed etc. the appropriate combination of can be seen as a mathematical model. Thus, we can say 'This jug of water has density = 1000 kg/m^3 and volume = 0.1 m^3 which makes its mass = 1000 times 0.1= 100 kg and which makes it part of the domain of mechanics [Korn, 2009.

We can regard 'systems thinking' as a discipline if we so choose because, at least in case of concrete objects like an armchair, we can perceive their 'structure' but *we cannot do a similar reasoning with 'systems thinking' because this discipline has NO IDENTIFIED and AGREED on 'elementary constituents'* [elcon].

The third point ===
It appears, by and large, that aspects of 'systems or structures' and those of objects with 'problematic issues' are discussed on their own. Or 'systems' and objects with 'problematic issues' are regarded as separate entities. Our **intention** is to develop a 'systems theory' which discusses theses two topics as

a part of an unified whole in the rest of this book.

Or

'Problematic issues cannot be *resolved* on their own', and

'Systems have a part in the process of *resolution* or systems have a purpose of existence'.

End of **Remark**

CHAPTER 3

DEVELOPMENT OF THE FUNDAMENTALS OF 'SYSTEMS THEORY'

The aim of CHAPTER 3

--- We have now discussed that, judging from the angle of empirical nature and generality of the 'structural or systemic view', the current, field of 'systems thinking' is speculative and fragmented. Also, from the angle of *'innateness'* of 'problem solving' in living things the current field of 'problem solving' methods are descriptive with a variety of detailed recipes and there is no acceptable 'problem structuring method'.

Against this background we propose to suggest a 'systems theory' which

1. Integrates 'problem solving' and the 'systemic or structural view' of parts of the world, thus, justifying the creation and activity of an agent, the 'system' which is to act so as to resolve problems, and

2. Brings both these intellectual efforts closer to branches of accepted knowledge, thus providing them with a fundamentals rather than their being unrelated to what already exists,

The aim of this chapter is to develop points 1. and 2. The method is to begin using general terms as suggested in point 2. of 'Selection of parts of a sentence' in section 1.3. ---

3.1 Introducing the empirical background to 'systems theory'

We begin by describing the general, empirical concepts as a basis for generating models of scenarios including human activities with their *emotions, interests, prejudices, preferences, ambitions* and so on which can lead to expressions in operational terms. Once a symbolic structure is offered in such terms it can be exposed to observation or actual or thought experiment as described by the 3rd Criterion in section 1.3.

Observation of parts of the world tells us that there are 'objects' [label usually attached to entities considered to be in static or dynamic state, inanimate, natural or artificial] and 'agents' [label usually attached to entities judged to be in dynamic state, animate, natural] in relationships recognised as wholes and seen as systems or structures in static (A) or in dynamic (B, C) state, the systemic view (Korn, 2018). Here they are classified into:

1. Inanimate
Static, natural [A. rock, bird's nest],
Static, artificial [A. hammer or a book [Simon, 1996]],
Dynamic, natural [B. hurricane, volcano],
Dynamic, artificial [B. control and computer systems, manufacturing systems].

2. Animate
Dynamic, natural [B. plants, animals (at micro, macroscopic scale as individuals or groups)], man (as individuals at the biological level)
Dynamic, natural [C. man (at the social level)].

Remarks

A. An arbitrary distinction which can serve to facilitate understanding:
Any object consisting of a number of repeated constituents forming a structure like a 'salt crystal', a 'pebble' or a 'wall' is designated as a 'simple system'. Objects consisting of a number of constituents performing different functions like a 'bed', a 'cell' or a 'control system' or a 'religious community' are called 'complex systems'.

B. Inanimate, dynamic, artificial [B] and animate, dynamic systems [B, C] make use of other systems for their operation such as importing 'Raw materials' for carrying physical properties like paint [colour] or like a screw [geometry], 'Energy' like an elastic spring or 'Information' like a letter.

C. Animate and artificial, dynamic systems when operate in states B. and C.

do so because of the *'complex networks of processes'* forming a whole that go on within. These processes have the *characteristics* of:

I. At levels B. and C. animate processes go on at molecular as well as macroscopic level in order to ensure *survival* or homeostasis as individuals or groups,

II. In addition, at level C. animate processes operate so as to achieve *ambitions* towards convenience, power, high performance, new constructions of artefacts, machines, buildings, works of arts, intellectual works and manufacturing entities and so on at individual and group levels which drive, or vice versa, inventions of artifacts and developments of novel ideas,

III. At levels B. and C. all processes produce *irreversibility* due to losses and imperfections resulting in generation of material waste and heat or entropy production [Prigogine, 1955, Korn, 1981, 2012].

These *characteristics* present animate and artificial dynamic systems with the **'problematic issues'** of 'how to survive, how to achieve ambitions and how to operate at constant temperature higher than that of their environment so that heat transfer can take place'. These 'issues' call for 'resolution', the alternative is extinction.

End of **Remarks**

Consequences of the **Remarks**

First, perception and statement of a 'problematic issue' and its suggested ways of 'resolution' is called 'problem solving'. At the molecular as well as at macroscopic levels, 'problem solving' is carried out by systems in **purposive configuration** (Brown, Campbell, 1948, Wiener, 1948, Monod, 1970, Nise, 2008, Korn, 2012, 2018). Plants, animals and human beings convert environmental resources into their own use according to plan to facilitate 'survival'. In addition, human beings accomplish this kind of conversion to pursue 'ambitions'. This point could suggest a dividing line between the capabilities of plant/animal and human brain/mind if criterion between activities directed at 'survival' or 'ambitions' could be formulated. The task of the human brain/mind over the ages of its existence has been to generate the 'intellectual processes' to create views or models for understanding aspects of 'problem solving' as indicated in Figure 2.1.

In this figure by 'intellectual product' is meant any object created so as to accomplish the change of mental state from being 'curious' or 'interested' to being 'curiosity' or 'interest' satisfied. For example, a 'book', a 'scientific article' or 'the result of looking round the corner' are such products.

Second, essentially 'purposive operation' is about stating an objective expressed as a property or an envisaged state of affairs to be achieved, comparing this with the current state and if there is a difference, taking action to bring the current state into line with that envisaged. The purposive structure to accomplish this consists of two regions: one in which energy and the other in which information circulates, the two are connected by an *amplifier*. The ability to 'amplify' information or ideas and converting them into *action* is perhaps the most significant 'invention' by living things because using their brain/mind for generating ideas they can bring about physical changes in their *environment* including their own bodies.

The operation of purposive activity extends from the well known 'engineering control system' using electronic, electrical, mechanical, fluid, thermal and chemical components to throughout the living sphere. We recall: 'Purposive activity is as common in the living sphere as gravity in the material sphere'. For example, in social situations a 'number of people (with ideas) can organise demonstrations by a large group with influence (amplifier) which can force the government to resign (action)'.

Third, purposive activity involves changing a current or initial state of a 'property of an object' because it does not correspond with the 'stated property or objective', into or near the 'stated property', the final state. This feature is shared with 'problem solving'. We have an 'initial, judged to be unsatisfactory state' which is in *equilibrium* or undisturbed until an agent enters the situation and attempts to turn it into a 'final state' or a *new state of equilibrium*. Accordingly, we have linked the concept of 'problem solving' with that of 'equilibrium' which extends the application of the 'systemic or structural view' and 'problem solving' to 'inanimate objects'.

Based on the preceding discussion and previous work, we introduce the following **hypotheses** or *principles of systems* which are the speculative part of the proposed 'systems theory' [Korn, 2018] =

1. The nature of the world: The systemic or structural view of parts of the world is *general, empirical, hierarchical* [nested] *and indivisible* and 'there is no alternative',

2. There is no change by itself: Systems or structures are created to *change equilibrium* states from initial to final by **chance** or in accordance with **purpose** or the change of equilibrium state calls for the creation of a system or structure,

3. The purpose of change is problem solving: The concept of *change of equilibrium* from initial, unsatisfactory to final, satisfactory, is at the basis of *problem solving,*

We note that

A. In the 1st hypothesis the terms 'systems or structures' signify the means capable of and designated to producing the entity called *product*, itself a structure or system, the function of which to create the 'interaction' capable of changing the state of equilibrium. 'Interaction' can have some physical form like exertion of 'force' or 'fluid power' or mental like 'information flow' or 'influence' such as 'temptation' at the sight of a comfortable bed all of which is created by a 'product'. A product is created by a 'producing system' like a 'manufacturing system' or an 'information system' creates a 'public announcer'.

B. The 1st hypothesis also tells us that the proposed systems theory is to be 'empirical' which, in this sense, relates it to conventional science of physics. The term 'empirical' means that the theory is *based* on abstraction or interpretation of results of perception obtained by means of the sense organs which may or may not be transmitted to the brain/mind which does the abstraction. It also means that the 'structural aspects' of a part of the world is a 'property' of that part just like the 'colour red' is a physical property. The 'structure' describes the 'syntax' or 'topology' of that part, its content or 'semantics' is a matter for further perception of 'qualitative and/or quantitative properties', the subject matter of conventional science,

C. The 2nd hypothesis tells us that the existence and operation of systems or structures are justified by the need to bring about change which would not happen otherwise. This is a different way of stating Newton's 1st law of motion.

D. The 3rd hypothesis tells us that the 'initial state' of a part of the world can be regarded as the 'problematic issue' carried by that part and is driven to change to the 'final state' of that part or resolution of the problem by initiative, creativity of human operators using the means of systems or structures. Thus, 'problem solving' is an integral part of and linked to the concept of equilibrium.

E. The concept of equilibrium is a *general* concept of material existence, therefore, the 'systemic or structural view' of parts of the world is also *general* because it is the system or structure which exists and operates so as to change the equilibrium states. This is the *unifying idea* of the proposed 'systems theory'.

F. The 'systemic or structural view' of parts of the world is 'hierarchical' in the sense of 'nested' i.e. constituents of any level of a structure or *complexity* are contained in the next level which applies from subatomic particles, atoms and molecules to the universe as far as known.

3.2 Introducing the basis of 'systems theory'

The hypotheses in section 3.1. imply that the 'systemic or structural view' of parts of the world refers to a universal, empirical phenomenon which follows from 'systems and structures' acting as the agents or instruments of change of equilibrium states. The notion of equilibrium is assumed to refer to a universal phenomenon which is at the core of the 'variational principle' i.e. the dynamic equilibrium maintained throughout any *change of state* i.e. 'forces' created by 'systems or structures' arise so as to maintain the state of equilibrium [Korn, 1981, 2012]. Following this kind of general assertion we need now search towards increasingly detailed considerations leading to a symbolic model, here the sought after 'empirical systems theory', which can be exposed to observation, experiment or applications to confirm or falsify the assertion. This is suggested by the 3rd criterion described in section 1.3. Presumably this kind of 'systems theory' was on the minds of early researchers in 'systems thinking' but never actually realised. A likely reason for this was that they did not realise that for any 'theory' construction suitable elementary constituents are needed since a 'theory' is a mental or intellectual structure which, for its construction like any structure, needs 'basic building blocks' or 'elementary constituents' [Boulding, 1956].

Achievements of living things and problem solving

We consider the First and the Second part of the Fifth point from 'Selection of parts a sentence' in section 1.3. as candidates for construction of symbolic structures. This is usually done for description or communication of chosen aspects of a part of the world or 'empirical object' following a 'thought' generated by 'imagination' or processing sense input by the brain/mind apparatus.

I. The First point: As suggested in section 1.3. 'Selection of parts of a sentence', the *parts* of the 'subject – predicate' form or the grammatical 'sentence', the carrier of 'complete thoughts', can be qualified by (Burton, 1984):

QUALITATIVE/QUANTITATIVE properties which are regarded as the source of symbolic structures such as mathematical models, for describing 'objects [concrete, symbolic, abstract, imaginary (fairy), emotive (anger)]'.
These 'properties' qualify designations of 'empirical objects' such 'table', 'plus or minus', 'productivity', 'witch' or 'hate' which perform specific *functions* in a sentence. Using 'case grammar' terms [Fillmore, 1968], these functions which contribute to 'completion of the meaning' of a sentence are described as follows

A. Subject: Of the sentence which stands for qualified designation of a concrete, abstract, symbolic, imaginary [centaur] or emotive object for locating the interest of the 'producer of thought' in a quiescent or changing part of the world,
1. Agentive: In describing dynamic scenarios, this is the case of the cause, source, instigator or initiator of the process or action identified by the verb,
B. Predicate: The qualified designations and the *verbs* which connect A. and B. In particular,
1.   Instrumental = This is the case of the typically inanimate element representing the 'means' whereby the action is performed,

2. Locative = This is the case of the noun phrase representing the location where the action or static scenario takes place or situated,

3. Dative = This is the case of the animate or inanimate noun phrase affected by the process or action or state,

4. Objective = This is the case of the affected object identified by the semantic interpretation of the verb itself as distinct from the effective object whose case is:

5. Resultative = This is the case of denoting the thing resulting from the action or process.

The qualitative/quantitative **properties** [adjectives and adverbs] make the sentence elements thus the sentence itself, specific or turn a 'context – free' sentence into a 'context – dependent' one which can be tested against experience if the qualifiers are sufficiently precise [Popper, 1972, Magee, 1985].

Sentences with more than two 'cases' operate with 'three or more-place' verbs i.e. verbs which attract three or more noun phrases. For example: 'The (powerful but safe) car [agentive] carries (with ease) its (young) passengers [dative] at a speed (of 110 km/h) [resultative]', 'John (who was hungry) [agentive] went (out to eat) to a (cheap) restaurant [locative] where he had a table (reserved) [objective]', 'The men [agentive] obtained food [objective] from the canteen [instrumental] at the station [locative] (during their lunch hour)' in which the round brackets enclose 'properties [adjectival and adverbial]' and the square brackets carry functions.

II. The Second point: The second part of the Fifth point in 'Selection of parts of a sentence' or the 'subject – predicate' form itself can be used so as to lead to:

RELATIONAL or STRUCTURAL properties which are regarded as the source of symbolic structures of 'scenarios' and consist of

A. Subject: Designates a concrete, abstract, symbolic, imaginary or emotive object, and

B. Predicate: Uses a 'stative' or 'dynamic' verb to indicate 'static' or 'dynamic' state of the 'subject', and the rest of the predicate of the sentence. A. and B.

combined serves as the description of a scenario with the restriction that only 1 – and 2 – place sentences i.e. those which contain 'one and two place' verbs attracting one and two noun phrases respectively, are used.

For example:
'The dog barked (noisily)' describes a dynamic state, 'The patient understands (perfectly well)' describes static state, they are 1 – place sentences describing static states,
'John jumps into the (ice cold) water', 'The prime minister announced (severe) restrictions in (physical movement of) the population' describe dynamic states, 'The (piece of) cork floats on the (wavy) water', 'Mexico lies below the USA', describe static states. These are 2 – place sentences.

1 – and 2 – place sentences are the smallest linguistic entities to make 'complete sense'. They can be seen as 'ordered pairs' [Burton, 1984, Korn, 2009].

Descriptions A. and B. together comprise the 'systemic or structural properties' or the 'elementary constituents' of the symbolic structure of the proposed 'systems theory' which express the 'relationship' between the 'subject' of a sentence and the predicate created by the 'verb'. This selection has been pointed out in the second part of point 5. in 'Selection of parts of a sentence, section 1.3. 1 – and 2 – place sentences are the basic linguistic structures in *linguistic modelling* [Korn, 2009].

Thinking in terms of relational properties of an object or a scenario is called **SYSTEMS THINKING**.

In section 3.1. we proposed three hypotheses which serve as a kind of 'axioms' in the development of 'systems theory'. In this section we have begun to produce the symbolic structure leading to the symbolic model which is intended to expose the hypotheses to the rigours of experience.

Natural language or the 'primary model' is the ground which provides the raw material for the creation of the symbolic structure. The likely candidates for elements or 'elementary or basic constituents' for this structure were considered in 'Selection of parts of a sentence' in section 1.3. In this section we have discussed two of these:

A. Qualitative and quantitative properties, and

B. Relational or structural properties.

These have been selected because they lead to symbolic structures which can be manipulated to result in *predictive models or systems or structures*:

A. Mathematical models and

B. Linguistic models [Korn, 2009, 2012].

We look at a couple of simple examples:

First = 'There is a length of copper wire wound into a coil of length, l, cross sectional area, A, number of coils, N, and permeability of the medium around the coil, n. The *mathematical model* of this kind of arrangement is 'L = (n A N^2/l)' where 'L' is called the 'inductance of the coil'. This is an algebraic equation which can be manipulated, for instance, into 'A = (l L/n N^2) which tells us that if 'the length, inductance, permeability and the number of coils of a piece of copper wire are given then the 'resulting or 'predicted' cross sectional area' of the wire to produce this arrangement is 'A, m^2".

We have considered a scenario which has led to a 'mathematical model' capable of being manipulated by the relevant rules of mathematics. We note that the mathematical model handles perceived and conceptualised by the brain/mind apparatus, 'quantifiable properties'. The 'empirical object' or 'part of the world' and its designation as a whole has disappeared from the scene, its identity has been taken over of a *combination of its quantifiable properties* presumably arrived at by investigation by the methods of physics.

Second = We have the following scenario described in 'story language' as considered in section 1.3. in the 2nd criterion: 'Person comes up to the counter in the shop and the sales lady says: 'I like your hat', the person responds 'I am glad to hear it' to the sales lady's impression of the 'hat' presumably as a whole and the matter rests at that. However, following on, the person can say: 'What particular aspects you like about it ??' and the sales lady replies: 'I like the colour of the material of the hat which is bright red, its shape which is a kind of round, its short peak and decoration which is 15 small, gleaming stars'.

The scenario which is described by declarative sentences, can be expressed as: 'IF there is a hat either seen as a whole or in terms of properties (with material of bright red colour, kind of round shape, having a short peak, decorated with 15 small, gleaming stars) AND the sales lady likes it and she says so THEN I am glad to hear the sales lady's opinion'.

The story language has been expressed as a *logical conditional* which may be seen as a 'linguistic model' [Copi, 1978]. The advantage of this kind of language is that it clearly expresses under what conditions the mental state 'I am glad' prevails. Moreover, it is possible to vary the conditions and to find relations among them similar to the one in the mathematical model.

We note that the 'elementary or basic constituents' of

X. Many mathematical models are quantifiable properties and variables, and that of
Y. Linguistic models are elementary, linguistic structures.

Accordingly, we can say that both kinds of models can predict states based on prevailing conditions.

We are now going to develop the comprehensive *problem solving scheme* into which the following symbolic structure ==

1. Linguistic modelling of linguistic structures,
2. Mathematical models,
3. Creative thinking, and
4. Systems and product design,

fit so as to form an integrated whole of which particular cases can be derived.

*Practically the WHOLE of human intellectual and material **achievements** have been expressed using 'qualitative/quantitative' properties.* This statement is supported by the diagram in Figure 2.1. A 'reason' for this may be given by:

AMBITIONS or objectives of living things are formulated to achieve: Survival, convenience, power, influence, improvements in physical and mental well being [own and of others], feelings, emotions, desires, wishes etc. are **accessible** in the first place by means of the 'senses' and instruments through qualitative/quantitative properties. These are then interpreted by the brain/mind as 'thoughts' and can be formulated in terms of a suitable symbolic model such as writing, mathematics, painting as indicated in general terms in Figure 1.1. Any **ambition** is realised by means of **achievement**

For example,

Ambition	Process of achievement
To survive	Seeking to *have food, drink and shelter*
To have convenience	Ensuring to *use transport* instead of walking
To have power	Conspiring to *depose the government*
To have mental well being	Going to a museum to *look at paintings*

where the words in italic designate the *achievement* which can convert a deficient state into a 'state of ambition'. The present participle of dynamic verbs indicate *action* to produce the 'new state'.

Consideration of the notion of **ACHIEVEMENT** in its widest sense leads to:

I. The concept of *achievement* is 'identified' with the notion of intellectual and material *product* as an artefact. Both concepts have a common meaning as 'that created by an agent'. The term 'achievement' usually means: Created by self, the term 'product' means:
Produced by a third party,

II. As it says in point E. from the 3rd hypothesis, the function of the *product* is to change the state of an object [the term includes processes like flowing water or viruses infecting plants, animals or people]. The 'object' carries a 'problematic issue', designated as *OPI*, which arises in a 'problematic situation' described by a 'story' and generates 'requirements' which needs to be satisfied so that change of state can take place,

III. The 'product' can do this by being manufactured, assembled and/or delivered by a *producer* to a 'notional' or 'actual' 'market' according to 'specifications' which should satisfy the 'requirements' of an OPI and other objects involved in a scenario such as 'stakeholders' or 'environmental objects',

IV. The 'producer' in producing a product operates according to a plan as directed by a *brain/mind*,

V. The 'brain/mind' directs the 'producer' so as to result in a 'product' that can change the state of 'OPI' to lead to *satisfaction* of expectations of another object or agent referred to as *User/consumer* which is monitored by the brain/mind. The cycle can go round until the User/consumer is satisfied.

Points I. to V. describe the mental process of 'problem solving' operating as a 'purposive system' the structure of which is shown as a diagram in Figure 3.1.

For example, the story: 'People in a village would like to cross the river more easily than at present'. We interpret the terms in the 'story language' to fit into those in the 'model language' as suggested by the 2nd Criterion in section 1.3. as follows:

- 'People' identify or see the 'uncrossed river [OPI]' as the carrier of the 'problematic issue' which is the IS [initial (problematic) state] of this object at contour 5,
- The 'not yet existing means of crossing' is seen as the 'product' at contour 3,
- The 'product' is produced by 'producers' or 'designers and manufacturers' at contour 2 in accordance with a '*plan*' or '*design*'. Its stage of execution is monitored by the 'product feedback' and acts as reference generally known as 'objective' or 'ambition' of the brain/mind at contour 1,
- The 'people' also play the part of the 'User/consumer' with 'expectations' to be satisfied at contour 7-8,
- The 'requirements' of OPI, expectations of User/consumer and other interested parties should be met by 'specifications' for the 'product' at a real or notional MARKET at contour 4,
- The 'crossed river FS [final state of OPI' at contour 6 achieved by choosing a product, should be such as to satisfy the 'expectations' or 'need' of people,
- The state of User/consumer at contour 8 is monitored by the brain/mind at contour 1.

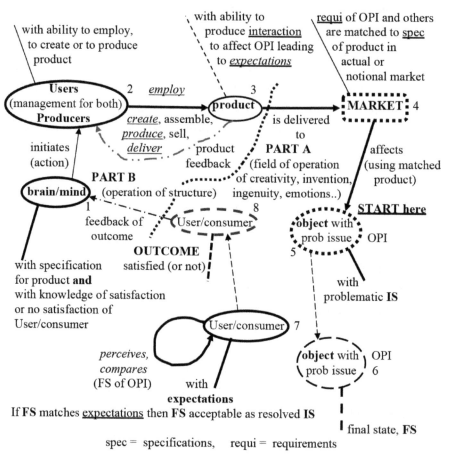

Figure 3.1. Diagram of problem structuring scheme

XYZ. 2 --- Here we have another inductive generalisation: 'Whenever there is a description or perception of a scenario a 'problematic issue' in it can usually be identified by a living thing. Its resolution, or not, takes place in accordance with the purposive scheme as shown in Figure 3.1. The identification is carried out either from the wording of the description by human individuals or from subjective dislike of what is perceived by living things'. ---

For example, we have a story 'There is a single decker bus serving this route which has two schools, a shopping centre and a large housing estate along its winding streets'. [The wording in this description suggests that the single decker bus is likely to become crowded because of the large scale movement of people which is seen as the 'problematic issue'.], We have another story 'In a large car showroom, cars are arranged in descending order of prices i.e. the most expensive cars are located next to the entrance to the showroom'. [There is probably nothing wrong with this but the managing director thinks the arrangement can deter customers, for him the arrangement of cars presents a 'problematic issue'.], Or another story 'Cattle grazing on a field when they come across a patch of grass contaminated by artificial fertiliser, a 'problematic issue' so they go round the patch when further grazing'. [The cattle perceive and instinctively conclude that there is something not right.]

All stories can be analysed so as to identify terms in them with those used in describing the scheme in Figure 3.1. as suggested by exp 1.1. in section 1.3.

Remarks

1. The diagram in Figure 3.1. is a representation of a 'problem solving structure'. It can help in resolving 'problematic issues' in 'straightforward' as well as in 'wicked problems' by providing a procedure for 'thinking' [Rittel, Webber, 1973].

2. Requirements expressed in terms of 'physical and/or mental properties' are generated by:

OPI and other interested agents like stakeholders, the User/consumer and environmental features [physical like road surface or living like people's wishes and interests]. They are matched to specifications also expressed in terms of 'properties', for products and producers at a notional or real MARKET. Products are manufactured so as to exhibit 'specified properties' so as to generate 'interaction' for the accomplishment of change of state of OPI [5-6].

3. The scheme in Figure 3.1. includes *four* kinds of 'systems' or structures as particular cases [Korn, 2020a,b]:

A. 'Utilising systems' which are recognised by their use of 'existing products'.
B. 'Producing systems' which are recognised by their activity such as designing, manufacturing, assembling, delivering, selling 'products' to 'Market'.

C. *'Trouble shooting systems'* existing through perception of a 'OPI, 5-6' through 'symptoms' manifested by a breakdown [of a car] caused by lack of fuel, anaemia [of a child] caused by deficiency of iron, difficult to climb [up stairs] caused by weak heart and seeking **product, 3, producers, 2** to 'restore fuel supply', 'supply of iron' etc. to eliminate cause so as to satisfy a 'User/consumer, 7-8', once a cause can be found.

D. *'Inanimate systems'* which are recognised by the presence of 'producers, 2' (with no management) producing 'product, 3' and possibly affecting a 'User/consumer, 7-8' such as a volcano producing 'lava' and 'ashes' can affect the surrounding countryside and people living nearby. No brain/mind,1 and OPI, 5-6 [Korn, 2020a].

4. A 'story' or 'narrative' in natural language is expressed in terms of 'story language' which is the first step in 'linguistic modelling' to be transformed into 'homogeneous language' of '1 – and 2 – place sentences' by 'meaning preserving linguistic transformations'. Using concrete terms closer to experience can lead to expressing the scheme in Figure 3.1. in 'operational terms' (Korn, 2009, 2016, 2020a).

End of **Remarks**

The scheme in Figure 3.1. consists of two parts:

Part A

This is outlined now. This is the *creative* part where vision, initiative, inspiration, imagination or methodical thinking play a role in recognising a 'problematic issue' followed by convincing others that there is a change needed for

1. Accomplishing a thing, or
2. Thinking about parts of the world in a different way. Convincing does not necessarily follow when an individual exercises h/her 'innate' ability to solve a problem.

Thus, the operation of the scheme begins with perception of an object, OPI [5], (material or mental) carrying the 'problematic issue' which is its initial state, IS. For example, corresponding to point 1. and 2. above

1. 'The driver increases the speed of the train from 30 mph to 50 mph', or
2. 'The eruption of the volcano is not due to anger of gods but is the result of molten rock called magma rises to the surface of the earth'.

OPI emerges from the description or 'story' of a 'problematic situation' or scenario as mentioned under **XYZ 2.**

1. As a result of subjective judgement of a living thing with preferences, likes, dislikes, prejudices and so on, or
2. The 'text of the story' is composed so as a 'problematic issue' is evident.

A consistent final state, FS, of OPI is proposed to see if it satisfies the 'expectations' of a User/consumer identified from the 'story', which is monitored by brain/mind. If satisfaction has been achieved further activity stops.

Part B

Based on requirements matched to specifications at a notional or actual MARKET a 'product' is proposed such as to be capable of generating an *interaction* to accomplish the change from IS to FS. The task of the 'producer' is to keep on producing the 'properties' of 'product' until it attains a state when it becomes capable of 'generating the required interaction'. The production of the product is monitored by the brain/mind through the 'product feedback' in Figure 3.1. with reference to a 'plan' or 'design' generally called the 'objective'.

For example, the 'story' describes a scenario: 'On an assembly line 'operator A' delivers four bed legs and 'operator B' carries a mattress to 'operator C' who screws the legs at each corner of a bedstead [property 1 = bedstead has four legs attached], places the result on the floor [property 2 = bedstead is now the right way on the floor], positions the mattress on top of bedstead [property 3 = bedstead is covered by mattress]. It is now declared by a person that the product 'bed' has acquired sufficient number of properties to be seen ready for 'generating temptation' [*interaction* as impression or influence] perceived by the same or another person to induce h/her to lie down'.

Further to Figure 3.1. and the 'story' we note that the 'product' bed has been constructed so as to be capable of influencing or changing the mental state of a person by having been constructed so as to exude 'temptation' to be picked up by a relevant human being. Whether h/she will succumb to the 'temptation' is a matter of uncertainty introduced into the analysis of the 'problematic situation'.

This example may be seen as a particular case of 'B. Production systems' listed in 'Remarks concerning Figure 3.1.' in section 3.2. The same example can be viewed from a 'design angle' as follows: 'There is a person in an upright position which h/she considers undesirable and h/she thinks that a lying down position would be desirable. H/she then sees a 'bed', a product', which appears to radiate 'temptation', an influence, to lie down' which h/she puts into practice or not depending on 'how undesirable the upright position is judged to be and how strong the temptation is felt'.

This is a very simple example but should give an idea about how the scheme in Figure 3.1. works which is subject to further implementation in subsequent chapters.

CHAPTER 4

CONSIDERATION OF DETAILS OF
'SYSTEMS THEORY'

The aim of CHAPTER 4

--- Having introduced the intention of current work inspired by personal experience in teaching control systems [Middlesex University] and human activity scenarios [Open University] and observing the current state of the 'systems field' or 'systems thinking', we have described the basic notions underlying the proposed 'systems theory'. In this chapter we introduce details into which these notions can be implemented so that they can be seen in terms of a symbolic structure leading to appropriate models. The details consist of:

1. Implementation of Part A. of the scheme in Figure 3.1., and
2. Modelling of systems and products in Part B. so as to realise the implementation of what has been found, proposed and agreed in Part A., the task of *systems engineer*. This exercise leads to the emergence of 'parameters' for detailed design of systems and products, the task of *product engineer*,

The fundamental approach to the development of the 'systems theory' uses the symbolism of *natural language*, the basic model. To describe a scenario, this is expressed in the first instance as a narrative in 'story language' considered in section 1.3., which, when processed into *linguistic modelling* [Korn, 2009] can suggest the application of:

- Mathematical models,
- Knowledge of aspects of conventional science of physics, management and social science and other fields of human intellectual endeavour as required, and

• Design thinking.

Accordingly, the 'systems theory' can be seen as an integrated whole to form the basis of 'systems science'.

In this chapter, therefore, we develop the details of 'natural language' mostly used in Part A. of the scheme in Figure 3.1. followed by the same of 'linguistic modelling' used in Part B. ---

4.1 Identification and qualification of nouns and verbs

We have referred to the 'subject – predicate' construction expressed as a sentence preferably with 'complete thought' and used as the basic symbolism to describe scenarios as interpreted by the brain/mind based on sensory input or created by imagination and indicated in contour 2 in Figure 2.1. Here we consider the 'sentence elements', the topic which was already introduced from a different point of view in section 1.3. under 'Selection of parts of a sentence'. In particular, the consideration touches on:

• How to identify 'nouns and verbs' as needed for further development of Part A. of the scheme in Figure 3.1. and modelling of Part B.,
• To facilitate relating 'model and story languages' and vice versa as described in section 1.3. in the '2nd Criterion',
• Showing how to qualify sentence elements 'nouns and verbs' and the nature of properties the means of qualification.

Viewing things as wholes through perception/action

At the most fundamental level human and perhaps other animate beings appear to perceive through their sense organs chosen 'parts of the world' or 'things', concrete, symbolic, abstract, imaginary [when modelled such as a painting or sculpture of a monster], permanent or changing, not so much in detail as in their *entirety*. Any instance of these is called the 'empirical object or agent or event' where the term 'object' usually refers to an 'inanimate thing' or 'part of the world' whereas the term 'agent' refers to an 'animate thing' operating in accordance with 'purpose' [Korn, 2012, 2018]. We speak of an 'event' when a changing pattern is observed. In many cases, human beings are capable of recognising and reacting to such impressions, or taking action usually appropriately and perhaps intuitively. This idea is shown in contour 1 in Figure 2.1.

Already using the known symbolic model of 'natural language' because for communication a model is needed, examples of the 'subject of perception (awareness and/or no, action)' view are:

Enemy [fight or flight], snake [jump], thunder [hide], hated by man [dislikes him], marking boundary by deer [urinate], newspaper [read or not], book [interesting] etc. This method of rapid processing of information and subsequent action, if any, may have evolved as a result of need for *survival* i.e. in face of danger or any other stimulus, there is no time for contemplation or analysis.

Viewing things as theoretical wholes

This notion is the further development based on the symbolic structure of 'subject – predicate form' indicated in contour 2 in Figure 2.1.

We introduce an empirical generalisation to which we have already alluded in section 1.3. in Figure 1.1. and which governs the mental process of creating symbolic models:

123. --- 'A function of the brain/mind apparatus is to process or to make sense of features of parts of the world external to it but including itself by preparing symbolic models but it has access to such features indirectly through the sense organs. The sense organs themselves are sensitive to material input which they derive from interacting with a part of the world through a *medium* [light, air vibration etc] the result of which is transmitted to the brain/mind as electrochemical signals, for interpretation. The interpretation, if any, is then converted into 'thought' which can be cast into a *medium* [paper, sound etc] chosen for a symbolic model for representation or communication'. ---

In the 'subject – predicate form' of sentences the 'subject or topic' stands for a part of the world which is the subject of interest of an observer or investigator about which the 'predicate' alleges an opinion or view or belief usually making a 'complete thought'. This assumes that all parts of the sentence are internally consistent, there is no contradiction and they are put together in a grammatically correct way. For example, 'John falls upwards on the surface of the earth' is logically inconsistent because it says 'John moves down upwards on the surface of the earth'. The generalisation **123.** uses the 'subject – predicate form' for the purpose of assigning:

A. *Identifying* statements to parts of the world in static or dynamic state or 'objects or agents or events' so as to name them in terms of 'nouns or noun phrases or verbs', or

B. *Contingent* statements to parts of the world including 'adjectives or adjectival phrases or adverbials or adverbial phrases'.

The term 'part of the world' refers to 'objects or agents or event'. Objects or agents are represented by 'nouns or noun phrases or other linguistic forms' such as 'infinitives' as in 'Darkening can give the sky an ominous look'. Stative or dynamic events are modelled by 'stative [to be, to float] or dynamic [to kick, to plough] verbs' [Burton, 1984, Korn, Huss, Cumbers, 1988].

This exercise corresponds to the usage of the verb 'to be' which has a single meaning in English and other languages but in Spanish it has two usages:

1. The word 'ser' is used to talk about 'permanent traits' of something or 'identifying statements',
2. The word 'estar' is used to talk about 'temporary conditions' of something or 'contingent statements.

We are now going to describe an application of the TWO kinds of statements:

A. Use of identifying statements

Identifying statements enable to associate a 'designation' like a name with a part of the world. In particular, development of the concept of 'theoretical object or agent or event' or a designation is derived by making 'statements' about a chosen part of the world or topic, static or dynamic. Such statements carry 'traits regarded as permanent', they define a 'theoretical object or agent or event'. The simultaneous presence of these 'statements' carried by sentences which are arranged in identifiable patterns according to the *meaning* of their contents. The patterns are then labelled by a 'word' which is a *noun phrase* or a *stative verb* if the pattern reflects a 'static or stative' or a *dynamic verb* if the pattern can be seen as 'dynamic'. The patterns are assumed to regularly recur. This exercise assumes familiarity with the use of natural language.

For example: The following statements are all written at random about the same topic:

1. person wears a hard helmet
2. person cuts grass
3. person gets paid
4. person's hands rough skin
5. person digs the soil
6. person likes reading
7. person trims hedges
8. person borrows books
9. person has a membership card

All statements of the 'subject – predicate' structure kind as referred to in contour 2 in Figure 2.1. by definition contain a 'grammatical subject'. Statements with the same grammatical subject refer to the same *topic* expressed as a 'noun phase' or any other grammatical form functioning as a noun phrase such as an 'infinitive' in the following sentence 'Sewing is a skilled activity' [Burton, 1984]. Thus, the topic is identified by the subject of a sentence.

The same statements refer to the same topic but now classified into TWO groups by considering the *meaning* of the statements:

1. person digs the soil
2. person cuts grass
3. person trims hedges
4. person gets paid
5. person's hands have rough skin
6. person wears a hard helmet
   where the first four statements include dynamic verbs, they refer to 'events' but they describe 'permanent traits' which are habitually worn and statements 4. and 1. are static, they refer to 'states'. Also

7. person likes reading
8. person borrows books
9. person has a membership card

where 6., 9. are static statements and 8. includes a dynamic verb but expresses a 'permanent trait or habit'.

All nine statements describe a single 'topic' performing two functions at two different times expressed in terms of two symbolic structures or 'models' which are 'He is a gardener' and 'He is a member of a library'. We note that the statements are replaced by two *abstract words* in the interest of economy of representation and communication which is a significant feature of natural language.

The idea outlined through an example can be expressed symbolically by exp 4.1. to suggest a generalisation as follows

well read gardener $= \pi \left(q_i\right)_i$ **exp 4.1.**

where 'π' is the logical 'and' function, q_i is in a set with '$i = 1,2,...I$' statements.

Perhaps all linguistic considerations are based on the idea that 'natural language' is a 'model'. Parts of it i.e. 'words', stand for some part of the world as we see above, concrete, symbolic, abstract or imaginary, other parts perform the functions of 'connecting', arranging or structuring the first parts so that the whole i.e. a sentence, can also stand for something. For example 'The gardener [the first part] although [second part] having cut himself, carried on working]'. The model part (gardener) stands for a person who is understood 'to perform well defined activities in a well defied location at specific times', the second part (although) connects and signals 'contrast' through a phrase so as add more *meaning or thought* to the whole sentence.

The following statement describes a 'dynamic event':

1. Liquid is in motion,,,
which refers to the 'dynamic verb' 'to flow' or 'to fall'.

The following statement describes a 'stative event':

Stationary solid object is on top of the surface of motionless liquid, which refers to the 'stative verb' 'to float'.

Remark

These examples demonstrate that the method of describing a part of the world by sentences applies to 'objects or agent or event [static or dynamic] which are designated by 'nouns and verbs'. Also, the method used in the other way i.e. expanding a 'noun or verb' in a 'story' or in a formal model, into statements, is applicable to expressing such 'noun or verb' in *operational terms*.

End of **Remark**

Interpretation of exp 1.1. through statements
The introduction of the idea of 'theoretical object or event' viewed as a set of statements helps to put exp 1.1. in section 1.3. into practice. For example, we can have 'working persons' as a term in a 'model language' defined by one of the number of possible statements such as 'working persons are engaged in skilled, manual labour' then using the linguistic device called 'meaning' we can assess the term 'gardener' to belong to the 'story language' because statement 2. 'he cuts grass', can be understood to be contained in or covered by the statement of 'working persons'. There is an element of containment in the concepts of 'model' and 'story languages' [Saeed, 1998].

In general, we have two *sets* of single or complex statements as shown by exp 1.1.: One applied to a term in 'model language' and the other describes a term in 'story language'. If one or more terms can be identified which share 'meaning' in the sense of one can be understood to be contained in the other then we have the 'model/story language' relationship. Symbolically

statements in 'model language' $\geq$ statements in 'story language'   **exp 4.2.**

'Meaning' as outcome of words and sentences
In point 2. of **Remarks** in section 3.2. we have asserted that the 'function of a 'product' is producing interaction'. If a 'word' or a 'sentence' can be seen

to function as a 'product' then its 'interaction' to be produced is *meaning*. The structural aspects of a symbolism, in this case a word or a sentence in natural language, is an important part of modelling, the 'meaning of the model' depends on it. For example, 'The symbol 'triangle' when used as part of a road sign, means 'warning' as understood by human beings suitably qualified. Changing the topology or the structure of the 'triangle' by opening it until any two of its sides become parallel, will lose its meaning. Therefore, it may be an idea to consider a very simple example to demonstrate this point more formally. So, we look at a word 'mile' spelt into:

Parts = letters --- m, i, l, e
Description of structure = m [is before] i, i [is next to] l, e [is just after] l, which is shown in Figure 4.1.

The rearrangement of the relational properties of the same 'letters' leads to:

Description of structure = l [before] i, i [before] m, e [after] m, which is also shown in the same figure and means 'lime'.

We have related simple sentences to intuitive consideration of diagrammatic representation of structures which raises the question of network representation which is introduced later following the details described earlier [Korn, 1995, 2009, 2012]. The effect of changing structures on the meaning of noun phrases has been demonstrated.

B. Use of contingent statements

Contingent statements increase the meaning of an already existing designation i.e. a noun, noun phrase and a verb. This is useful when the

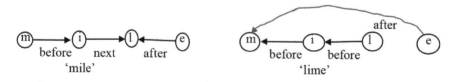

Figure 4.1. Effect of topology on meaning

'precision' of a vague word needs to be changed, perhaps increased. They impart 'temporary conditions' to 'theoretical objects or agents or events' through their designation of 'nouns and verbs'.

Natural language is the 'primary model' accessible to all and used most often in representation and communication of aspects of parts of the world or 'thoughts' which are the results of imagination, an ability of the brain/mind apparatus or of processing the output of sensory organs. This is diagrammed in Figure 1.1. and composed in the generalisation **123**. Parts of the world seen in static or dynamic state, may be seen as 'objects or agents or events' constantly *performing specific functions* as described in 'case grammar' terms which was considered in section 3.2. and these functions are reflected in their role in sentences. We have looked at how to elaborate their meaning by using simple statements an exercise which assumes that the meaning of these sentences themselves are known.

Contingent statements are assigned to 'nouns and verbs' when they are parts of sentences which are already part of a 'story'. These statements explicitly carry

Adjectives and adjectival phrases   ⟶   Nouns and noun phrases
                                             which qualify

Adverbs and adverbial phrases   ⟶   Verbs
                                             which qualify

We note that
1. This rule is not categoric because adjectives can qualify or add to the meaning of nouns and pronouns, adverbs can as well. Adverbs add to the meaning of verbs as well as that of adjectives and adverbs, adjectives do not [Burton, 1984],
2. Adjectives and adverbs, the means of qualifying nouns and verbs, are called collectively *properties* or 'qualifiers',
3. Qualifiers are usually assigned to nouns and verbs directly without being part of a sentence. For example, in 'John jumped off the moving train' not 'John jumped off the train [the train was moving (contingent statement)]'.
4. Qualifiers are used in turning a 'context – free sentence' into 'context – dependent' which is required to achieve 'precision'. For example, we have

'The soldiers searched the room' which becomes a context – dependent sentence when we assign qualifiers to sentence elements 'The extremely [adverb] hungry [adjective] soldiers thoroughly [adverb] searched the room [which was in the attic adverbial of place].'

A summary of 'properties' which are frequently used for qualifying noun phrases performing in the various 'cases' as referred to in section 3.2., is given.

1. They turn a context – free sentence into a context – dependent one and figure as 'adjectival phrases' to enable a description of a scenario to be judged for precision or liked or disliked,
2. They can be used to exert influence. For example, the colour can influence a customer to buy or not a dress or there is a sentence "Inflation is the consequence of rising demand' which could result in companies paying out higher dividends as profits rise leading to higher values of shares'.,
3. They can be graded and assigned certainty factors or fuzzy sets, they can also impart a measure to a noun phrase [Zadeh, 1965, Durkin, 1994, Korn, 2009].

A 'summary of properties' is given below.

X. Adjectival
Physical:
Material [hard, heavy], Geometric [long], Numerical [two], Energetic [speed, current], Biological [hungry, sensual],
Chemical [flammable, reactive],
Mental:
Emotional [happy, revolting], Intellectual [clever, informatic], Stately [alert],
Social:
Relational [friendship, neighbour], Financial [investment, property, shares, salary, money], Ethical [moral, just, charitable], Occupational [physical, intellectual, retired],
Structural:
Relational [geometrical, below, next, neighbour to], Linguistic [1 and 2 place sentences, adjectival phrases ['My next door neighbour' John],
Complex:
Sentences and phrases playing the part of adjectival and adverbial qualifiers

of nouns and verbs ['John (wearing his hair long), approached the wind with caution' or 'The patient (recovering from an operation) is (capable of mild physical activity)].

Y. Adverbial
a. Of manner, degree, time, cause, purpose, reason, assertion, information, energy, money,
b. Of place, object, thing.

Information, energy and money are treated as 'adverbials' and carried by 'specific dynamic verbs'. For instance, 'to push' carries 'mechanical energy' or physical power implying the capability to accomplish an action or 'to notice' which carries 'information' as a subordinate clause as in 'The boy noticed that [the ball is stuck in the roof]' [Burton, 1984, Korn, 2009].

Remarks

A method of identification and qualification of two of the parts of the speech or sentence elements have been considered. Identification in terms of statements is useful when it comes to expanding a noun or a verb into 'operational form' so that it can be used in a 'Utilising' or manufactured in a 'Producing system' as described in section 3.2. Qualifiers of nouns and verbs are acquired when they are used in a 'story' or 'narrative' and the writer or investigator wants to add additional meaning to a noun or verb. The additional meaning can make a term more/less precise, desirable, repulsive, emphasising its size, strength, weakness, emotions and so on.

End of **Remark**

4.2 Relations between grammatical and systemic terms

People use a large variety of symbolisms to carry their thoughts to recipients in the outside world at large regarding aspects of parts of the world including own mind and body, they are 'thought generators'. We have called the means to do this the 'symbolic model' which is such as to be intelligible to the recipient of thought. We have now the three components of a scheme of

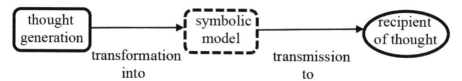

Figure 4.2. Thought generation, transmission and reception

'thought generation, transmission and reception' as depicted in Figure 4.2. which is another version of Figure 1.1.

In Figure 4.2. we have made a view of communication explicit. In order for this communication to be successful or not, in other words, for the 'recipient' to accept or to reject and to act on or to ignore the meaning of the 'message', the features of the model must be understood through a 'medium' and interpreted, by the 'recipient'. The recipient then may convert the result of interpretation with all its subjectivity, bias and prejudice, into h/her own symbolic model for further communication. This highly uncertain mental process can take place in TWO cases:

1. 1st case = Features of the model are arbitrarily generated by the 'thought generator' using h/her imagination. For example, 'There is an artist who has created a sculpture which, according to its title, depicts the demise of the world'. It may not be possible to understand and to interpret the resulting work of art and it may not be possible to assign 'identifiable statements' to it since 'it may not appear to make sense' but, according to the note E. in section 3.1., it has a material structure.

2. 2nd case = The 'thought generator' intends to communicate h/her view about the chosen *aspects* of a part of the world, thus, h/she is engaged in an *empirical* exercise. In this case, h/her brain/mind is in receipt of input from the sense organs to serve as the basis for the generated thoughts, if any. The structural elements or *elementary constituents* [elcon] of the resulting symbolic model are not arbitrarily formulated but they must '*tell something to an observer* or *express a belief* about an *aspect* of the part of the world about which the view is to be communicated. There is a long historical evidence of this kind of intellectual exercise taking place as indicated in Figure 2.1.

Examples for finding elcon for constructing intellectual structures are:

a. The age old 'ayurvedic system of medicine' hit on using the concepts of 'vata, pitta and kapha'. Each of them comprises of a different list of characteristics [elcon] such as for example: 'A characteristic in vata or s criterion to be considered to be a vata person: Has constantly changing thoughts'. The elcons are considered 'indicators' of the kind of physical and mental personality [belief] of human beings [aspects of parts of the world]. The ayurvedic doctor then attempts to fit h/her patient approximately into one of the concepts, a view to be communicated to the patient and may serve as the basis for treatment.

We note that the concepts 'vata (space/air), pitta (fire/water) and kapha (water/earth)' are 'complex structures' constructed from elcon as suggested by the 1st criterion in section 1.3. Elucidation of elcon or characteristics was a matter of observation but their ordering into the concepts must have taken a great deal of intellectual effort although the qualities of phenomena in round brackets might give a lead.

b. The ancient Greeks proposed the idea of 'atom' [elcon] which was considered a part of all structures [belief] of matter which is understood to exist in the form of 'structure' [aspect of parts of the world].

c. They also proposed the generalisations of 'earth, water, air and fire' [elcon] to indicate the different states (solid, liquid, gas and energy presumably) [belief] in which matter was perceived to exist [aspect of parts of the world].

No further development of this intellectual exercise took place until the foresight or vision of the 'atom' as elcon had been studied and reproduced experimentally in the early 20th century.

d. Superstition and mysticism have their structural elements such as 'graphology' has its lines each with its descriptive, geometrical features [elcon] in the palm of the hand [aspects of parts of the world].

The geometrical features indicate the nature of a line [belief] which is a 'complex structure' and enables deductions to be made about longevity of life, family circumstances and so on.

e. Conventional science had adopted quantifiable properties and variables which are amenable to act as [elcon] of mathematical, symbolic structures. For example, 'Friction force [elcon] = (friction coefficient) times (speed between moving parts [elcon])' [Korn, 2012]. These properties express a [belief] about mechanical parts of the physical world [aspects of parts of the world]. Mathematical models lose the identity of the part of the world or object about which a *belief* is expressed. It is the immense predictive power which gives mathematical models their significance. The truth of prediction depends on how faithfully the mathematical model represents a given part of the world.

f. When we come to the 'structural branch' in Figure 2.1., in 'engineering control theory' in contour 11 'transfer functions [elcon]' tell us that if an 'object [part of the world]' receives an 'input' it has an 'output' [belief]. A 'transfer function' is a mathematical model constructed of 'variables and constants'.

Transfer functions can be organised into 'block diagrams' which are 'complex structures'. Operational research (OR) in contour 12 makes use of a variety of mathematical models.

g. The 'systemic views' in contour 11 had come about in the 1950's as a result of efforts by early workers in the field who identified the *generality* of these views of parts of the world [aspect of parts of world] as summed up by the '1st hypothesis' in section 3.1. However, they could not or were not interested in identifying either the 'elcon' or the 'belief of what is alleged about an aspect of a part of the world'. However, later attempts at development of a 'general systems theory' followed along mathematical and speculative lines [Bertalanffy, 1950, Korn, 2018].

Accordingly, no general systems theory has been developed and the 'systemic views' have evolved into a variety of particular, intellectual efforts a sample of which has been briefly considered in CHAPTER 2. This fragmentation has been supplemented by a diversity of speculative endeavours [Klir, 1969, Troncale, 1985, Jackson, 2000, Rousseau, 2017].

h. The pioneering thinkers recognised the generality of the 'systemic view' which is supported by the proposed 'systems theory' and is embodied in the 'hypotheses' put forward in section 3.1. The 'systems theory' is based on the symbolic model of *linguistic modelling* derived from processed natural language which is the 'primary model' sufficiently general to cope with the generality of the 'systemic view'. The elcon of linguistic modelling are '1 – and 2 – place simple sentences' as already mentioned in point 5. of 'Selection of parts of a sentence' in section 1.3. for representing the elementary structures of which complex structures can be built up for modelling static and dynamic scenarios [part of the world]. They are intended to act as Part B. in Figure 3.1. [belief].

Remarks

The preceding discussion leads us to the Remarks:

A. We can represent as a diagram in Figure 4.3. the assertion in the '2nd case' and the abstracted, common structure in the preceding examples of intellectual developments. The shape and size of components of this figure are arbitrary.

Further to the '2nd case' and the examples, we find in practice the elements in Figure 4.3. as follows:

'Deliberately or by chance one of our senses strays to a 'part of the world' and, after processed by our brain/mind, one or more of its features arouses our interest. Alternatively by exercising our curiosity, creativity or inspiration we find the same or other features inspiring or objectionable. We may or may not formulate the 'thought' into a 'belief' using an elcon through a *contingent statement*. A number of thoughts may or may not be organised into a 'complex belief' guided by a symbolic model. The intellectual endeavours depicted in

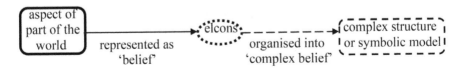

Figure 4.3. Diagram of construction of believes

Figure 2.1. are likely to have been arrived at in this way together with the scheme in Figure 3.1. and the background 'systems theory'.

For example,
'There is a container [number 1354, which has an area of $2 \times 5 = 10 \text{ m}^2$, weighs 3000 kgf and is situated at the end of a row of containers]'.
We note that a 'subject of the sentence' or the object of interest and the four beliefs are needed for the interested parties to select a suitable truck to pick up the container. This example describes a 'situation meaning objects in static state' which can develop into a 'scenario meaning objects in dynamic state or event'.

Another example,
'An [international, well known] bank [intends to launch a new type of account] engages a [large, opinion poll] company [to conduct a survey to find out the likely reception of the new account]. The company carried out [the survey] and reported [the results] to the bank.'
This example describes a human activity 'scenario'.

The square brackets enclose the elcons, beliefs or contingent statements. Both examples are 'stories' carried by the symbolic model of 'natural language'. The 1st example concerns a *single* 'subject of interest', it is the subject matter of 'conventional science of physics'. The 2nd example presents two, the 'bank' and the 'company', 'subjects of interest', it is the subject matter of 'systems science' [Korn, 2018].

B. Our discussions so far have concerned *declarative sentences* describing 'objects or agents or events' singly or in groups. Such descriptions are aimed to produce 'stories' for 'representations' and for 'communications'. However, as mentioned in section 1.1., declarative sentences can be used for constructing linguistic structures with 'explanatory' or 'conditional' meaning. Here we are interested in *conditional structures*. A pair of declarative sentences can be converted into a conditional construction [Copi, 1978].

The '1st **advantage**' of this construction is that it:

'Explicitly demonstrates the dependency of two statements = The first ('if', antecedent) displays the conditions on which the state of affairs described in the second ('then', consequent) depends'. Thus, it is possible to investigate a description of a state of affairs in the consequent regarding its certainty of occurrence subject to the variation of conditions expressed in the antecedent [Copi, 1978, Korn, 2009].

In case of 'context – free' sentences this kind of investigation is not possible because the sentence elements are not qualified. For example, we can say 'If John jumps then Mary cries' which, due to lack of specificity, carries much uncertainty regarding 'Mary's crying'.

However, in case of 'context – dependent' sentences the *adjectival* and *adverbial* qualifiers carried by 'contingent statements' allow variation of conditions to be introduced. When we say 'If John jumps [from a stool of 25 cm high measured from the floor beneath on which the stool stands] then [it is unlikely that] Mary cries'. Variation of the 'height of the stool' in the antecedent may change the 'likelihood' of Mary crying.

Further to the brief discussion in section 1.1., there is a very large number of *'representations'* produced by the large number of intellectual efforts a sample of which is shown in the diagram of Figure 2.1. They are available ranging from precise, mathematical models describing cases of limited generality such as, for example, work out the 'the time required to reach the railway station from home by a slowly walking person' to those of great generality such as, for example, Newton's second law of motion. Symbolic models for representation are also widely available in a great variety such as natural language, gestures, drawings etc, for every day communication and for generating the large number of speculative and the kind of 'ad hoc' efforts in current 'systems thinking' as discussed in CHAPTER 2.

However, *'explanatory'* and *'conditional'* structures go beyond *'representations'* which are employed by the former. For example, we can say 'The car crashed into the ravine' *because* 'One of its tyres blew' which is an 'explanatory structure' which may or may not be regarded as satisfactory explanation. 'Explanatory structures' can be inverted to become 'conditional structures', thus, we have '*If* one of its tyres blows' *then* 'The car crashes'. We note that a 'blown tyre' implies only that the 'car crashes', it does not imply that the 'car crashes into the ravine' which would need much more precisely described conditions [Hempel, Oppenheim, 1948, Hospers, 1978].

Here we are interested in 'conditional structures' which are of great intellectual and practical value since they may be seen to have greater 'cognitive value' than 'representation' because they

1. Imply *causality* or a kind of deductive scheme which suggest a possibility of 'reasoning',
2. Have the mechanism for investigation of certainty of occurrence of 'outcomes', and
3. Have the **2**[nd] **advantage** of the 'conditional structure' which is that it can be transformed into a *predictive structure*'.

For example, we can say 'If one of its tyres blows then the car will crash' which means that a 'blown tyre' can cause the 'car crash' unless the 'driver's skill prevents the crash'.

We can generalise these considerations as follows:

456. --- 'Representations using 'contingent statements' or elcons which offer the possibility of transformation into 'conditional structures', may be seen to be *non – speculative* and can lead to expression in operational terms. Producing this kind of representations is a desirable direction to take for creative, inventive and inspirational, intellectual efforts. The great majority of scientific, artistic and engineering work is of this kind as demonstrated to a limited extent in the diagram in Figure 2.1.' ---

C. The *generality* of the 'systemic or structural view' of parts of the world as summed up by the 1st hypothesis in section 1.3., tells us that any part of the world can be seen in terms of its 'structure' [concrete, symbolic, abstract, imaginary] which, thus, includes 'symbolic models'. The term 'structure' implies that a part of the world is seen to consist of more than 'one element', it is a *complex* entity or we can say that any structure is understood to consist of 'elcons' of a kind such as: Carrying quantifiable adjectival and adverbial qualifiers or qualitative qualifiers. Accordingly, when constructing an intellectual structure or a symbolic model we need to search for *elcons that* *reflect our beliefs in an aspect of part of the world of interest* as indicated in Figure 4.3. and discussed in the 1nd criterion in section 1.3. irrespective of whether the 'subject of interest' is a

X. Single object as practiced in 'conventional science of physics', or
Y. Multiple objects as practiced in 'systems science' [Korn, 2018].

End of **Remarks**

Notion of interrelations

So far we have discussed various aspects of 'objects or agents', their representations or symbolic models in natural language as 'noun phrases' and their 'qualifiers'. We have introduced 'case grammar' in section 3.2. which describes their 'functions in sentences' [Fillmore, 1968, Burton, 1984]. 'Objects or agents' create 'static or dynamic events' when they engage in 'static or dynamic activities' which involves *self* or at least *one other object* or agent or part of the world. Involvement of 'self' or 'at least one other object' implies the existence of *interrelations* to itself or between objects or agents which are represented in natural language by 'stative and dynamic verbs' and their 'adverbial qualifiers'. Thus, the main job of verbs is to connect the 'subject' with the 'predicate' in a sentence.

There are two kinds of *interrelations*:

I. Relations
This term describes *static states* or 'static event' and is designated by 'stative verbs'. The function of a 'stative verb' is to tell us what the subject of a sentence is or about its 'being' or 'existence'. For example, 'The business seems profitable' which is a '1 – place sentence' because the verb 'to seem' attracts one noun phrase or 'The cork floats on the water' which is a '2 – place sentence' because the verb 'to float' attracts two noun phrases or 'The guest noticed the dish of spaghetti on the table in front of h/her' which is a '3 – place sentence' because the verb 'to notice' attracts three noun phrases. Also, the *passive voice* of dynamic verbs can be used to convey 'static states' as in = 'The two plates are stuck or welded or bolted together' or 'These two friends are very close'.

The concept of 'relation' between 'objects or agents' or self [described by 1 – place sentences] can refer to: Space [left, above…], kinship [father of …], connection [and, or…].

II. Interactions

The term 'interaction' refers to creation of *dynamic states* and is modelled by 'dynamic verbs'. The function of a 'dynamic verb' is to tell us what the subject of a sentence 'does' or describe its 'action' or activity forming a 'dynamic event'. For example, 'Fish swim' which is a '1 – place sentence' because the verb 'to swim' attracts one noun phrase or 'The detective found two witnesses' which is a '2 – place sentence' because the verb 'to find' attracts two nouns.

Interactions can bring about 'changes of physical or mental state [intellectual or emotional]'. The notion of 'interaction' between 'objects or agents' or self [described by 1 – place sentences] can refer to:

1. *Material objects* carrying the appropriate *energy*. Material object, the carrier or medium of energy means energy flow or 'physical power' such as:

Interactions of this kind occur in the inanimate as well as in the animate sphere of existence. They are described as --- Mechanical [earthquake, change of momentum of a large mass, compressed or expanded, elastic object like a spring, friction force], electrical [copper wire wound in a coil carrying current], fluid [waterfall, pipe carrying oil at high pressure], thermal [warm air carried by wind, air in an oven] [Korn, 2012], chemical [burning hydrogen], nuclear [fission], crude oil [burning], coal [burning].

In addition, we recognise the exercise of *skilled, physical power* which involves 'purposive activity' as in: 'Man digs a trench on the side of the road [in accordance with requirements by the council]' where the verb 'to dig' designates skilled, physical power] [Korn, 2009, 2018, Nise, 2008].

Kinds of interaction created by *chance*: Wind, sea, volcanic power, earthquake, oxygen in air when breathed in, floods etc.

2. *Material objects* carrying the appropriate *material* possessing 'qualities and quantities' which can contribute to change of 'physical states' possibly leading to change of 'mental state'. Here we can suggest a generalisation:

HXJ. --- *Material interaction*, in fact '*any kind of interaction*' consists of THREE parts:

A. The part which contains the *quality* and *quantity* of the substance,
B. The part which acts as the *material carrier* of the former, and
C. The means which is used for delivering the *material*. ---

Part A. and B. are a matter for *physics* or 'material science' or 'chemistry', Part C. is a matter for 'systems' or *action* and the whole is modelled by *dynamic verbs* qualified by adverbs as part of 1 – and 2 – place sentences. The whole can be seen as a *product [3]* which, when delivered, can exert interaction.

For example, we can have: 'Paint with 'colour' [A., B.] which when applied [C.] to the walls of a room changes its physical state which when observed by the inhabitant of the room, can cause satisfaction or not'. Another example is provided by a drink such as 'rum', the material object with distinctive 'taste and alcohol content' which is its quality [A. and B.] when consumed [C.] can exert the desired 'interaction' or affect the physical and mental states of its consumer. Also, there is movement of people, equipment, food, drink, cloths, raw materials and so on with similar effect when processed or consumed [Forrester, 1969].

Material interaction also covers the notion of *use* such as a 'car', 'writing desk', 'bed' and so on which generate physical as well as mental change of state. For example, 'wearing a pair of comfortable shoes' creates physical and mental satisfaction.

3. *Material objects* carrying *influence* which they can exert on living things to provoke, or not, 'action' such as

'Soldiers having listened to the general, throw themselves into the battle', or
'The child smelt cooked food in the air and h/she felt hungry' or
'The eagle saw the prey on the ground so he dived to catch it'.

The manner in which *influence* is exerted can be divided into:

a. Information

The idea of information has a practically unlimited application from 'The mother shouted to her son 'Come in at once to have your dinner" to calculating the measure of and definition of 'information' by 'logarithmic functions' [Hartley, 1928, Shannon, Weaver, 1964, Korn, 2009, 2010]. In this book by 'information' we understand symbolic, linguistic or any other structures [such as a road sign or smoke signals or gestures or any other manifestation of a 'material object' to which *meaning* is assigned for *interpretation*]. Or these structures are intended to carry encoded 'meaning', calculating the 'quantity of information' is of no interest although this has been attempted in [Korn, 2009]. The sentence above is an example. This understanding of 'information' fits into linguistic modelling, the language of 'systems thinking' [Korn, 2010, 2013, 2016].

Accordingly, 'information' consists of a 'sender', a living thing, the function of which is to generate the 'meaningful content' of information, to encode it in a 'medium or material object' or the symbolic model and to transmit it to a 'receiver' which can then 'decode' it and act on it or ignore it in accordance with h/her *interpretation* or *understanding* or *misunderstanding*. With reference to the example above, the 'sender' is the 'subject [mother]' of the complex sentence [Burton, 1984], the 'information' is represented by the 'subordinate clause [Come in....]' the transmission of which is signalled by 'special, dynamic *verbs* [shouted]' such as 'to note, to announce, to listen and so on' [Korn, 2009].

The term 'information' refers to a statement or a phrase with 'informative content' made *directly* 'to the point, there is usually no argument regarding a state of affairs or an event of interest' only subject to 'interpretation' by the 'receiver'. For example, 'The gardener says to the owner of the lawn: 'That grass is infected by moss" which is a factual statement, there is little room, if any, for interpretation. If there is interpretation, perhaps leading to 'speculation' then we are dealing with 'inference'.

b. Impressions and inferences

Like 'information' 'inference' is created by people, for people 'intentionally or purposively' or arising by 'chance' for producing *awareness*, to be ignored, to be interpreted and to be converted into action. Like other inputs, inferences carried by a 'medium' can be picked up by anyone by means of h/her 'sense organs' to be transmitted to the brain/mind. Information can be produced by non – human creatures such as when a 'Deer notifies other deer so 'He deposits urine at specific points in the landscape to mark what he regards as the boundary of his territory'' which is 'information' as long as the other deer recognise or know the 'meaning' of this kind of signal.

Inferences induced by 'sensations' which is noticed by self or produced by individuals for others through any kind of 'material effect' impinging on the senses, their availability is limitless. The results of such *effect*:

1. When appeal *directly* to a state of affairs is called *impression*,
2. When does not appeal *directly* to a state of affairs or an event which is of interest, the results must be interpreted and then *inferred*. Accordingly,

'**If** there is a statement resulting from observation regarding a state of affairs or an event **and** it is subjected to *interpretation* […it means…] directly or followed by *inference*, **then** the statement can be ignored or followed by 'action''.

For example, we can say 'This dish smells delicious' which is an 'impression'. Impressions occur frequently: Any direct input to the senses other than 'information' is 'impression'.

Inferences can appeal to states of mind such as:

1. Reason --- intentionally created or occurs by chance,
2. Emotions --- intentionally created or occur by chance.

For example, we can have under

'Reason --- intentional':
Sensation … 'The president marched a large contingent of well equipped troops along the boarder of the neighbouring country'.
Interpretation … 'The president is capable of conquering another country'.
Inference … 'Members of the government of the country overseas thought this action was a prelude for invasion'.

'Reason --- by chance':
Sensation … 'An old lady fell down in the middle of the pavement'.
Interpretation … 'A passer by thought she fainted'.
Inference … 'A passer by called the ambulance'.

'Emotions --- intentional':
Sensation … 'The president marched a large contingent of well equipped troops along the boarder of the neighbouring country'.
Interpretation … 'People in the neighbouring country felt threatened'.
Inference … 'Seeing this as a hostile action, people in the neighbouring country became upset and organised mass demonstrations'.

Sensation … 'The ruler punished his best friend'.
Interpretation … 'People thought if he can do this to his best friend he can do it to anybody'.
Inference … 'People thought we had better be scared of him'.

'Emotions --- by chance':
Sensation … 'An old lady fell down in the middle of the pavement'.
Interpretation … 'A passer by seeing this became upset'.
Inference … 'A passer by started crying and panicked'.

At this point we introduce a generalisation:

500. --- 'All kinds of *interrelations* can deliver 'factual and/or emotional content' depending on the intention of the sender and the interpretation by the receiver'. ---

Note: Any object or agent which behaves the way suggested by generalisations **HXJ.** and **500.** is called *product [3]* as shown in Figure 3.1. The 'elementary *product* as part of elementary constituent' or 'affected object' discussed in section 1.3. *once has been constructed*, needs to be *stimulated* to become effective. Energy, information and inference are carried as *adverbial qualifiers* of a dynamic verb as the 'stimulant' to be acquired by the 'affected object' as part of an 'acquired property' in the course of changing its state before it becomes effective. This 'Note' will be put into effect when the construction of semantic diagrams is considered.

Remarks

The Remarks relate to 'Interrelations'.

1. Both 'Relations' and 'Interactions' are exerted by *material effects* to impinge on the sense organs to be ignored or turned into action as implied by contour 1 in Figure 2.1. or turned into symbolic models as suggested by contour 2. The possibility of this effect occurring and its variety are practically limitless so, for this reason, processed, natural language with its also practically limitless variability and expressive power, is a suitable symbolic model for this kind of effect.
2. Both, information and inference, operate by arousing *awareness* in living things.
3. The key factor that the brain/mind is capable of doing is *interpretation* which through prejudice, bias, emotions, preferences, strongly affects subsequent action [mental – forming views and attitudes or physical – fight or flight].
4. We note that it is the 'adjectival and adverbial qualifiers or properties' of nouns and verbs which allow to express variability to regulate *specificity* of effects.

Production of symbolic models showing interrelations through 'physical power' is well developed in conventional science and in network theory of engineering systems and can be modelled in 'systems theory' as well [Korn, 2009, 2020b]. Creation of a comprehensive symbolic model for 'representational, conditional structures' using 'influence' which has been the 'problematic issue' and which the proposed 'systems theory' through its *linguistic modelling* can attempt to resolve.

End of **Remarks**

The table in Figure 4.4. shows a summary of functions which grammatical and systemic terms have in sentences which relate them into a single notion. This also further justifies the use of processed, natural language for modelling scenarios.

Constituents	Function in a sentence	Relationship to a part of the world
Nouns	Subject, Direct and indirect objects	Topic or chosen or initiating object Affected objects
Verbs	Stative verb – being Dynamic verb – action	Relations Interactions
Adjectives	Qualifiers of nouns Adjectival phrases	Properties of objects, agents
Adverbs	Qualifiers of verbs Adverbial phrases	Properties of interrelations
Conjunctions	Joining words, clauses to create arguments, symbolic logic	Relations, complex scenarios

Figure 4.4. The role of grammatical and systemic terms in sentences

4.3 Implementation of Part A. of the problem solving scheme in Figure 3.1

The motivation behind development of the 'problem solving scheme' in Figure 3.1. has been provided by identifying the: The 'problematic issues' as described in CHAPTER 2. which have led to the development of a 'systems theory' to integrate the mental process of identification and resolution of 'problematic issues' with the 'systems or structures thinking' as suggested by the 2nd hypothesis in section 3.1. The function of 'systems or structures' is to generate the means for attempting to solve the problems. In this section we are concerned with consideration of Part A. of the 'scheme'.

The empirical background and the basis of a 'systems theory' have been described in CHAPTER 3., in sections 4.1. and 4.2. we propounded the fundamental mental processes behind construction of symbolic structures. All this discussion helps generating 'elementary constituents [elcons]' and implementing 'model and story languages'. We now begin to develop the details of application of **Part A.** of the scheme in Figure 3.1. which means we are going to attempt resolving 'problematic issues'. Using the 'scheme', resolution may not always be possible but it provides the interested parties with a methodical framework which can help perhaps even in case of 'wicked problems' [Rittel, Webber, 1973].

We need to clarify a number of issues which are directly required for implementing the 'scheme' and is proposed to be done by summarising these issues as seen below:

789. --- **I.** 'A change of state or that of a property can only take place as a result of 'interaction' or stored energy called 'spontaneous process' [Korn, 2012],

II. One property can be changed by one interaction at a time,

III. A change of state must be consistent i.e. the final state must be realisable from the initial state by the same 'structure or system'. For example, a *warm* room is achievable starting with a *cold* room but not from a small room,

IV. The function of an object or agent called 'product [3]' is to generate interaction so each interaction requires one product,

V. An object or agent acquires the ability to generate interaction as a result of having been constructed by another object or agent called 'User/Producer [2]' in Figure 3.1. by its adding 'properties' to the former *one at a time* until it is judged to be capable of generating an interaction,

VI. By the term 'interaction' is meant a 'means by which one entity affects another or self' as described in section 4.2.' ---

General considerations applicable throughout implementation of Part A.

In section 3.1. the '3rd hypothesis' suggests that the idea of 'problem solving' is a particular case of the notion of 'change of equilibrium states' which is shown in the diagram of Figure 3.1. with reference to OPI [object with problematic issue] at contour 5 to OPI at contour 6. However, to be specific a 'state' acquires meaning when it is expressed in terms of 'properties' as introduced in sections 3.2. and 4.1. which are accessible to imagination or visualisation and may lead to 'operational terms'.

Identification and description of OPI is the *first step* in problem solving since without OPI there is no problem in the brain/mind. The subjectively perceived difficulties are outlined as follows:

1. Finding an OPI may not be easy. In order to overcome this hurdle the idea of 'rich picture' was invented [Checkland, 1982]. For the same purpose, here we use a 'story or narrative' in natural language because it is felt that 'The 'selection of the wording' employed by the observer of a scenario carrying one or more 'problematic issues' is likely to be such as 'to name directly the 'problematic issue' or to 'hint' that there is one and to give a description'.

2. Agreement that there is a 'problem' and its description i.e. the one identified in 1. and described by its 'wording', by those involved may not be possible to procure. Stakeholders with financial, environmental, national interests can be involved, people bearing prestige, pride, prejudice, dignity, vanity, love, preferences and so on, may dispute existence and description of a 'problematic situation'.

3. Assuming that there is a 'problematic issue' recognised by the parties involved, any effort towards its resolution can be hindered or prevented by feelings of revenge, hostility, envy, jealousy and so on.

Details of the implementation of Part A. of the scheme given in 'steps'

1st STEP

Having read and digested the 'story' of a 'problematic situation', the *observer* or *investigator* exercises 'perception, imagination, inspiration or methodical thinking' to obtain consensus of all interested parties regarding identification of the object or agent carrying the 'problem' and the subjective beliefs of what is 'wrong', 'undesirable', 'harmful' and so on.

NOTE: Identification of terms such as OPI [5] in Figure 3.1. is based on consideration of the *meaning* of the wording of the text of the story. This is followed by the *observer* or *investigator* stating in one or more 'contingent statements'

'"To identify the Object with 'Problematic Issue' or the 'Initial state [IS] of OPI [5]"'.

2nd STEP

Having investigated the problematic situation involving the 'User/consumer', the *observer* states

"'The expectations as the 'Initial state [IS] of User/consumer [7]'""

which are formulated by an individual or group of individuals based on what they regard as 'acceptable resolution' of the 'problematic issue' or OPI [5].

3rd STEP
The *observer, investigator* produces, invents a *choice* of

"'The possible, desirable, consistent 'Final state(s) [FS] of OPI [6]'"",

4rd STEP
Investigating how close the 'Final state [FS] of OPI[6]' comes to 'IS of User/consumer [7]' so as to allow the

""Final state [FS] of User/consumer [8]' to happen"",

If the *observer* is not satisfied then the 3rd STEP is repeated until h/sh is.

Remark

At this stage OPI and User/consumer in contours 6 and 8 are *THEORETICALLY* in acceptable states.

End of **Remarks**

5th STEP
The potential 'products [3]' i.e. objects or agents which appear to the *observer* to be capable of converting the 1st STEP to 3rd STEP are found assuming there is a STORE of products in existence, or invented if not found in the STORE. Suitability of any of the variety of 'products [3]' is recognised by 'perceiving' its ability to exert the *interaction* seen to be REQUIRED to accomplish the change of state from the 1st STEP to 3rd STEP.

6th STEP
Further to point 2. in 'General considerations....' above, the *observer* needs to suggest
"The 'pertinent or static properties or characteristics'" of = = =

1. OPI and User/consumer, and

2. Objects or agents and/or circumstances in the *surrounding* which are judged to be 'relevant to the 'problem situation'' such as environmental objects and others with interest in the 'problematic issue'.

Remark X

The *observer* now has:

X. A selection of products seen to be capable of exerting the appropriate *interaction*, and

Y. The 'static characteristics' expressed by 'contingent statements' including *properties* of

1. OPI [5] [**O**],

2. User/consumer [7] [**U**], and

3. Objects, agents or processes perceived as relevant but external to Part A. and B. [**E**]. They can affect any constituents of the scheme and can be affected by any of them.

IF the **5**[th] **STEP** fails then the 'product [3]' has to be invented, designed, manufactured and assembled and the 'Utilising system' has to change to 'Producing system' as discussed in section 3.2.

End of **Remark X**

7th **STEP**

In this STEP the *observer* selects a 'product [3]' by naming its designation on the basis of 'information' summarised in the Remark X above.

To arrive at a suitable 'product [3]' the *observer* needs 'to match and to select' objects using the 'information' in Remark X above aided by the Entailment Relation [ER] and the Object Selector Matrix [OSM] shown in Figures 4.5. and 4.6. [Saeed, 1998, Korn, 2020a].

It is the 'meaning of the terms' and their interpretation in the statements which decides if there is the desired relation between the two sets of properties in points A. and C. in Figure 4.5. For example, 'The lady has just had her hair done and it is raining [A], she does not want her hair do to be spoilt [B],

A. There is a **1ˢᵗ set** of qualifiers carried by 'contingent statements' attached to objects O, U and E in Remark X, and

B. There is a sentence or a phrase of commitment to fit, to match or to satisfy or to the contrary, fulfilment of which,

C. REQUIRES that there be a **2ⁿᵈ set** of qualifiers carried by 'contingent statements' which fit or match or satisfy those in point A. and are designated a, b, c, ...

Figure 4.5. The notion of entailment [ER]

	2ⁿᵈ set of qualifiers			
	a.	b.	c.	and so on ....
objects or agents carrying,	1	0	0	
or not, the qualifiers	1	0	0	
---	0	1	1	
---	1	1	1	

Figure 4.6. Diagram of Object Selector Matrix [OSM]

requires or entails that she carries a waterproof appliance such as an umbrella or any other implement to protect her hair from rain [C]'.

In ER once the second group of qualifiers has been obtained, an object or agent i.e. 'product [3]' presumed to carry these qualifiers needs to be found. This can be helped by OSM which is constructed as shown in Figure 4.6. The top horizontal line carries the qualifiers from point C. in Figure 4.5. in ER, the vertical line shows the selected objects or agents in the 5ᵗʰ STEP and the numeral '1' is inserted against that object or agent which is presumed to have that qualifier, '0' which has not. The object carrying the largest number of '1's is selected.

The practice of ER and OSM takes place at a notional or actual **MARKET** at contour 4.

The *observer* now has

1. After the 4th STEP, OPI and User/consumer are theoretically in 'acceptable states' i.e.

At contour 6: OPI [6] is in --- Final state [FS], and

At contour 8: User /consumer [8] is in --- Satisfied [or not] and observed by the Brain/mind at contour 1 and compared with 'what is thought to be desirable' stored by Brain/mind [1],

2. The designation of 'product [3]' which is capable of exerting the required *'interaction'* in a Utilising system,

3. The qualifiers of 'product [3]', a, b, c,..., which *match* the characteristics of O, U and E.

Points *2.* and *3.* are the **PRODUCT design parameters.** i.e. 'product [3]' must be *selected* or *designed, fabricated* or *manufactured* or *constructed* so as to exhibit these 'parameters'.

The considerations so far have *completed* Part A. of the scheme in Figure 3.1. which is shown as a diagram in Figure 4.7.

Remark 1.

The considerations also have

A. Established 'objects or agents' in contours 1, 4, 5, 6, 7, 8, and
B. Resulted in stating the 'product design parameters' for 'product [3]', and

To satisfy the 'Product design parameters':

I. As a 'Utilising system', the User/Producer [2], when chosen by the *observer* or available already, need to have *properties and the 'objects or agents' to carry them*, which enable it:

1. to drive, position, process, handle, treat, control the *recognised* 'product [3]' and/or its component parts so that, in it/their turn, it/they can produce the correct kind and quantity of *interaction* which can bring about the change of state in OPI [5],

2. to be able to accommodate the properties a, b, c, ... called the *accommodating properties*. For example, 'A contingent statement with property a. is: 'The lady has a new hairdo" and 'A contingent statement with accommodating property is: 'She operates the waterproof umbrella 'to protect the new hairdo",

3. to cope with *external conditions* by generating *additional properties.* For example, 'A statement with external condition is: 'In a coal mine the atmosphere is dusty" and 'A statement accommodating property is: 'The miners wear suitable mask",

4. to generate *'objects or agents' with properties to assemble, deliver and sell* the 'product [3]'.

The conditions in points 2., 3. and 4. arise from outside the scheme in Figure 3.1. but they are included in the 'story' of a scenario or the need for them to turn up in the course of implementing Part A. and/or B.

II. As a 'Producing system', the User/Producer [2] must be able *to design, fabricate, manufacture, assemble* product [3] so as to satisfy Points **2.** and **3.** followed by *delivery* to MARKET [4] for eventual sale or give away the 'product [3]'.

In other words, a Producing system needs to be set up and to operate so as to produce the product [3] which is capable of changing states and fits into its surroundings, it needs to be an *adaptive system.*

Utilising and Producing systems are particular cases of the scheme in Figure 3.1. discussed in section 3.1. and having the capability

Utilising systems = Point *I.*, and   **exp 4.3.**
Producing systems = Point *II.*

which are the **SYSTEMS *design parameters*.** Any additional components like waste removal, supply of food, accountancy, management, personnel department etc arise from needs of operation.

We further comment that

a. 'Product and Systems design parameters' are those **properties** of products and systems which they must have in order to

1. Fit into the scheme of problem solving in Figure 3.1. i.e.

For a Product [3]: Exert the appropriate interaction and matching the characteristics of O, U and E object or agents, and

For a User/Producer [2]: Drive the selected product [3] in Utilising systems, and Manufacture and deliver product [3] in Producing systems.

2. Serve as a guide in ensuring that the *detailed design* of product and system or structure' is such as to lead to possession of these 'properties' by product [3] and User/Producer [2].

Product Design Parameters must be catered for because without them no 'change of state OPI [5] to [6] can take place i.e. no problem solving exists. Practicing Part A. requires much creative and joint efforts by all parties involved in attempting to solve a problem. Success is by no means guaranteed. In particular

1. There is a possibility that a suitable 'product [3]' cannot be found,
2. There may be a single 'product [3]' so there is no choice, and
3. The IS and FS of OPI [5] do not admit a suitable 'product [3]' i.e. wicked problems.

End of **Remark 1 &&&**

To facilitate understanding, we present the process of carrying out the '7 STEPS' as a 'story' which perhaps helps to appreciate its application. The 'story' is as follows:

'The *observer* or *investigator* who can be the 'brain/mind [1]' in Figure 3.1. or a 'committee' or any 'individual' or a general in the army and so on, having composed and studied the 'story' of a 'problematic situation' as suggested in the 1st STEP, identified an OPI [5] or the object with a 'problematic issue' which is its 'undesirable, initial state, IS'. There is another identifiable object in the scenario with *expectations* of a satisfactory change of state of OPI [6] called User/consumer [7] which is its 'initial state, IS'. The observer then suggests a 'desirable, final state, FS' or OPI [6] which the User/consumer [7] compares with h/her 'expectations' and accepts or not as a 'favourable outcome' to become a satisfied, User/consumer [8]. If the 'outcome' is not favourable the 3rd STEP would have to be repeated

The *observer* follows this development by finding products [3] from h/her

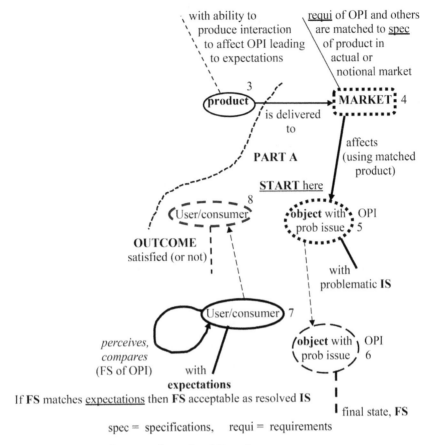

with ability to
produce interaction
to affect OPI leading
to expectations

requi of OPI and others
are matched to spec
of product in
actual or
notional market

3

product

is delivered
to

MARKET 4

affects
(using matched
product)

PART A

START here

8

User/consumer

object with OPI
prob issue 5

OUTCOME
satisfied (or not)

with
problematic **IS**

User/consumer 7

perceives,
compares
(FS of OPI)

with

object with OPI
prob issue 6

expectations

If **FS** matches expectations then **FS** acceptable as resolved **IS**

final state, **FS**

spec = specifications,   requi = requirements

Figure 4.7. Semantic diagram of completed Part A.

store of knowledge of components selecting those which appeared to have the capability of exerting the kind of 'interaction' suitable to accomplish the 'change of state' of OPI [5] to [6]. H/she also investigated and found the:

1. Pertinent, static properties of OPI and User/consumer, and
2. Those of objects or agents which appeared to have interest in the scenario but seen as external to it.

The observer then selected the product [3] using ER and OSM which seemed to exhibit features which matched the properties specified in points 1. and 2.

The mental process described has identified the:

1. Acceptable states of OPI and User/consumer,
2. Designation of and the ability to exert the right kind of interaction by the product [3],
3. Product design parameters

which has completed the application of Part A.

A simple **example** is given to demonstrate the use of the *terms* in Part A.:

The idea is to go through the STEPS in concrete terms as presented before in general terms.

1st STEP
The 'story' of the 'problematic situation' is as follows = 'The basket of fruit is found downstairs by the housewife who did not like it being there'.

Following the NOTE in the 1st STEP, we can say from the 'story' that it is the 'position of the basket' that seems to present a problem to affect the state of mind of the 'housewife', it is the source of the problem. Thus, the 'basket' is the object with 'problematic issue', OPI [5].

IS of OPI [5] = basket is downstairs [problematic issue],

2nd STEP
Expectation of the 'housewife' who is the User/consumer is

IS of User/consumer [7] (housewife) = to be happy by seeing the basket upstairs,

3rd STEP
The 'desirable and possible final states' of OPI [5] which is

FS (s) of OPI [6] = basket is outside, upstairs, in the cellar, all are consistent possibilities,

4th STEP
The FS of OPI [6] closest to 'expectation of housewife' is = 'basket is upstairs' selection of which ensures that

FS of User/consumer [8] (housewife) is 'satisfied'

5th STEP

The potential 'products [3]' which can exert the 'interaction' to 'change the state of OPI' i.e. 'Carries basket from downstairs to upstairs', are: 'housewife, husband, 10 year old son'. They are expected to be able to exert the 'Same interaction' = 'to carry [the basket from one position to another]

6th STEP

Pertinent objects and pertinent, static properties:

OPI [O] ---

    basket is heavy, weighs 26 kgf

    basket carries a sticky substance which can leak

    basket is circular, 0.5 m in diameter

User/consumer [U] ---

    expects basket to be upstairs in 25 s time

External objects or agents [E] --- none

7th STEP

We now have:

From the 5th STEP = A selection of products [3] all of which can exert the required 'interaction',

From the 6th STEP = The characteristics or properties of objects or agents O, U, E

Using the selection of products [3] and the characteristics, the Entailment Relation, ER, in Figure 4.5. gives

A. The *basket* which: 1. weighs 26 kgf, 2. sticky, 3. 0.5 m diameter,
   User/con which: 4. expects basket upstairs in 25 s

B. There is to be a 'product [3]' with properties which can cope with those in A.

C. REQUIRES properties of 'product [3]' which match those in A. and are:
   a. strong enough, b. wears apron, c. has long arms, d. powerful enough.

From OSM, the 'product [3]' which scores the highest number of '1' is the 'husband' so it is selected. Accordingly, 'husband', 'product [3]', has the '*product design parameters*', **2.** and **3.**:

Interaction = Able to carry basket upstairs,

Static properties = a. strong enough, b. wears apron, c. has long arms, d. powerful enough.

The Object Selector Matrix, OSM, from Figure 4.6. gives:

list of 'products [3]'	qualifiers of 'product [3]'			
	a.	b.	c.	d.
housewife	0	1	1	0
husband	1	1	1	1
10 year old son	0	1	0	0

Remark

Part A. of the scheme diagrammed in Figure 3.1. deals with the statement and elaboration of the 'problematic issue' based on elucidating the 'meaning' of terms in a 'story' of a scenario presented in natural language. It is the elucidation of a current, *equilibrium* state of affairs as discussed in section 3.1. unbalanced by an agent who for whatever reason or no reason considers this state *unsatisfactory* and as such needing a change. This idea is elaborated into its elements in this section.

The results of elaboration are arrived at by constructive, imaginative, inventive, collective discussion by individuals having an interest in the problem situation although the material presented in this section does not fully reflect this creative approach. It is intended to develop the mechanism of organised thinking process. The result of this process is the 'product and systems design parameters' which is intended as the *guide* of how to construct the details of Part B. based on *linguistic modelling*. This part consisting of product [3] and User/Producer [2] operate as the agent the function of which to implement the new *equilibrium state* worked out by the creative thinking process exercised in Part A. Accordingly, the basic aim of the proposed 'system theory' is realised which is 'to act as a symbolic model for integrated representation of problem solving and systems and product design'.

End of **Remark &&&**

CHAPTER 5

LINGUISTIC MODELLING PART OF 'SYSTEMS THEORY'

The aim of CHAPTER 5

--- In section 3.1. we put forward three hypotheses or axioms which underlie the subject matter of 'systems theory' and in section 3.2. the unified scheme of 'production, product, system or structure' and its role as a 'means of resolution' in 'problem solving' in Figure 3.1. was described. In CHAPTER 4. the connection between the grammatical terms of natural language and their meaning in 'systems thinking' is discussed followed by describing the details of the creative part of 'problem solving' leading to the statement of 'product and systems design parameters'.

In order 'to select, create or design' and to produce a *prototype*, the product [3] and User/Producer [2] in Figure 3.1. need to be modelled. The model used in 'systems theory' is processed natural language or *linguistic modelling*.

Also, to conform to accepted scientific practice

Conventional science of physics adopted the following pattern of operation

GENERAL PRINCIPLES + VARIETY OF MATHEMATICAL MODELS

exp.5.1.

depending on the discipline. For example, Newton's 1st and 2nd laws can be written as

'A body remains stationary or maintains its steady motion along a straight line until a force acts on it' and 'Force equals mass times acceleration'.

Systems science follows this pattern by proposing [Korn, 2018]

Accordingly having introduced the 'general principles' or hypotheses, the aim of CHAPTER 5. is to describe 'linguistic modelling' using the content of past publications with modifications due to recent developments. ---

5.1 General features of 1 – and 2 – place sentences

We have already introduced 1 – and 2 – place, simple sentences in section 1.3. as the likely candidates for elcons in 'linguistic modelling' or the minimal, linguistic structural units with complete sense which means: Removing the 'subject' or 'verb' element of the sentence results in 'incomplete sense'. Here we describe the development of the *features* of these sentences which make them *generally* applicable to modelling 'systems or structures' functioning as 'elementary constituents, elcons'. The main feature is that natural language due to its *general* applicability is suitable for modelling the empirical perception of the *general* structural or systemic aspect of parts of the world or the product of imagination.

FIRST feature
The basis of 1 – and 2 – place sentences is the *contingent statement* introduced in section 4.1.

Accordingly, we have

'Contingent statements' can refer to
A. *Static states such as description or being or existence or capability using STATIVE verbs*
For example, 'This book 'costs' £20 in the bookshop', 'The frog 'is' still alive after having been bitten by a snake', 'John 'understands' Japanese which is a difficult language'.
B. *Dynamic states such as physical or mental activity using DYNAMIC verbs*
For example, 'The hungry frog 'swallowed' the caterpillar in one go', 'John got angry and 'hit' his best friend'.

Furthermore, both 'static' and 'dynamic statements' can be

'*Context – free*', or

'*Context – dependent*'.

To maintain the 'subject – predicate' construction, the *minimum* content of a 'context – free sentence' is: 'The subject and the verb' with not necessarily reflecting 'complete thought'. The content of a 'context – dependent sentence' is theoretically limitless and is constructed until 'complete thought' will have been achieved i.e. they can be 'simple' or 'complex'.

Thus, we see that 'context – dependency' is achieved by adding to a 'context – free sentence'

1. Adjectival and/or adverbial qualifiers,

2. 'Cases' from 'case grammar' as referred to in section 3.2. [Fillmore, 1968].

For example, Context – free = 'Book costs', 'Frog swallowed', Context – dependent = 'The 'hardbound' book costs 'much money'', 'The 'hungry' frog swallowed the caterpillar'.

So far in this section we have summarised the topics which we have touched on previously, they are likely to cover the 'declarative part' of speech. At this stage, we are not interested in 'imperative and other moods' and we use 'dynamic verbs' in past tense. However, we propose the generalisation

101. --- 'Dynamic verbs in a sentence imply the representation of impression of *flow* of a physical or mental process which, by its very nature of being termed 'flow', must be impelled by a factor called ***propensity*** or 'favourable tendency' of any of the vast variety generated by 'purpose' or 'chance' associated with animate or inanimate entities [Anon., 1994]. Stative verbs have no such facility'. ---

'Generalisation **101.**' leads to the

I. Need to search for the means that generate 'propensity'. When formulating sentences these are given by 'adjectival qualifiers' of noun phrases, in particular those which qualify the 'subject' of the sentence. The 'qualifiers' are not always explicitly visible, their use is implied by the 'context' or scenario described by the sentence,

II. Division of 'objects or agents' into those performing the functions of *initiators* and *affected* objects. The functions can be detected by considering the cases given by 'case grammar'. Usually the 'subject of the sentence' plays the part of 'initiator',

III. Recognition that 'linguistic modelling' fits into the general framework of viewing **processes** taking place in parts of the world as 'flows' and 'propensities'. This view prevails in 'Network analysis of engineering systems' which uses the concepts of *through* and *across variables* which correspond to the idea of 'flows' and 'propensities'. Here we have:

Propensity or across variables = voltage, velocity, pressure, temperature
Flow or through variables = current, force, flow rate, entropy flow [Korn, 2012].

We can say: 'Voltage difference across a piece of copper wire drives the current', 'Maintenance of difference in speed across a flat, rough surface requires force', 'The gradient in the terrain makes the water flow', 'Difference of temperature between the inside and outside the wall makes the entropy [heat] flow'.

SECOND feature

Scenarios are described by *declarative sentences* in natural language or in any other symbolic model best suited to convey thought of the 'thought generator'. For example, we can have all the 'works of art', 'road maps', 'map of railway networks', 'road signs', a 'gesture' and so on. In the current work, we are concerned with producing 'stories' or 'narratives' in natural language as the *primary model* constructed of 'declarative sentences'. When a 'story' has 'linguistic complexities or complex sentences' such as 'The bandits robbed the bank because they wanted a high level of lifestyle', this kind of sentences need to be transformed by *meaning preserving, linguistic transformations* into simple sentences [Korn, 2009].

However, there are advantages in the 'transformation' of a 'story' into 'conditional, linguistic structures' which is proposed here. A 'conditional structure'

1. Makes dependence of a state of affairs explicit on another i.e. propensity,
2. Expresses the dependence of the occurrence of a future state of affairs on proposed conditions,

3. Shows the conditions of validity or truth of a hypothesis.

The **FIRST** and **SECOND** features are now applied to 'linguistic modelling' of elcons.

2 – and 1 – place sentences are 'contingent statements' consisting of linguistic
    elements of:
2 – place: Two noun phrases [initiator and affected objects]
    Dynamic verb designating interaction
    Adjectival and adverbial qualifiers
1 – place: One noun phrase [combined initiator and affected object]
    Dynamic verb designating interaction
    Adjectival and adverbial qualifiers.

We introduce the diagrammatic representation of 2 – and 1 – place sentences which are called
2 – tuple or ordered pair or *1 – tuple or singleton or reduced ordered pair* respectively shown in Figure 5.1. [Lipschutz, 1982]. This type of diagram is called *semantic diagram* or 'linguistic network'. The diagram is constructed by placing the name of an 'object or agent' or the 'subject' of the sentence or the initiator of action in a contour and the directed line attached to another contour together designate the 'predicate'.

So far we have established: The FIRST and SECOND features and the diagrammatic representation of 2 – and 1 – place sentences which fit into the structural or 'network' view of 'engineering systems' as briefly recalled above. Now we consider a 'story' of a scenario to see how to animate or how change or event enters, 'linguistic modelling' although there is not suitable software to carry this out.

The 'story': 'Two men, each wearing a hat and walking along the street, helped an elderly lady to push a large car which seemed to have broken down, slowly from the street into a garage all this taking place early afternoon'.

The 'story' can be broken down into the statements:
1. There are two men
2. The men are walking along the street

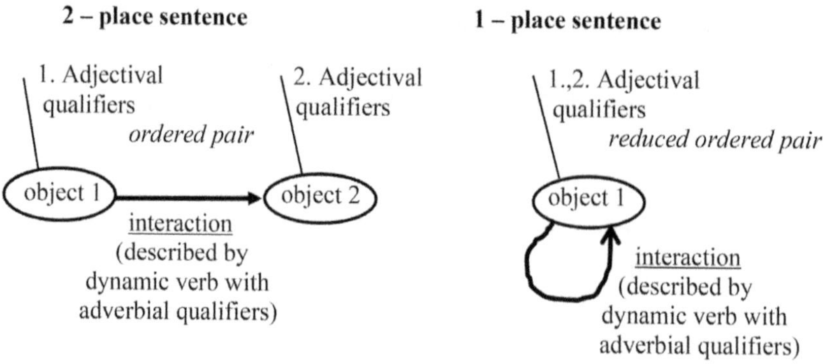

2 – place sentence　　　　　　　**1 – place sentence**

Figure 5.1. General diagrams of 2 – and 1 – place sentences

3. Each man is wearing a hat
4. *The men helped the lady*
5. The lady is elderly
6. The lady needs help
7. The car is large
8. The car is broken down
9. The car is in the street
10. *The lady, helped by men, pushes the car slowly into the garage in the early afternoon.*

On the basis of the description which may be due to an eyewitness, we identify three theoretical entities called 'objects or agents' for the moment. They are = The men, the lady and the car. Grammatically they are the 'subject' part of the statements and they
Take part in the events, and
Statements are made about them.

We can separate out the statements which stand for 'adjectival phrases' and describe 'conditions' prevailing in the scenario, referred to as

'Conditions' = 1, 2, 3, 5, 6, 7, 8, 9, and
'Events' = 4, 10.

The former refer to the 'state of the objects or agents' shown diagrammatically in Figure 5.2. and are 'stative statements'.

Figure 5.2. *Semantic diagram of the static scenario*

We note that in Figure 5.2. the situation is 'static', no 'change of state' takes place but from the 'meaning' conveyed in the 'story' we can say that:

'Men' are *initiators of action*, 'car' is affected *object*. The 'lady' is an 'affected' agent in relation to 'men' and becomes an 'initiator' as far as the 'car' is concerned.

In Figure 5.2. the contours with 'objects or agents' are separated and neither of them is capable of changing its own state as far as this scenario is concerned. This statement can be generalised into saying that

102. --- 'Nothing can change by itself, an agent is required for the change of state of equilibrium of the *affected object*.' ---

which is an alternative statement of Newton's 1st law of motion.

In order to effect a specified change of state, 'objects or agents' must enter into *interactions* made explicit by statements 4. and 10. and considered in section 4.2. This development is shown diagrammatically in Figure 5.3.

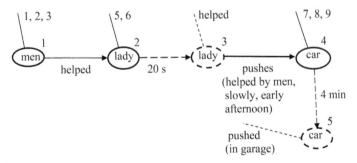

Figure 5.3. *Semantic diagram of the dynamic scenario*

The notation in Figure 5.3. is as follows:

A. 'Interaction' is designated by continuous, directed lines connecting contours. The thicker line from 'lady to car' designates 'material object carrying energy or physical, skilled power', the thinner line connecting 'men to lady' designates 'material object carrying information'. This form of influence is 'information' because expanded, it says: 'Men offer their help to the lady to push her car from the street to the garage' which is a direct influence, no inference is involved.

B. The dotted, directed line connecting contours 2 to 3 and 4 to 5, designate 'changes of state' *in time* which is marked along the lines. The dotted lines attached to dotted contours designate 'acquired properties' of the changed states as marked.

C. The dotted line attached to a contour at the end of a dotted, directed line means an 'acquired property' which is the qualified, past participle of the dynamic verb designating the interaction which has produced the 'change of state'.

Remark

Figure 5.3. shows the complete semantic diagram representation of the story of the scenario. However, both the FIRST and SECOND features are not yet incorporated, there is no 'propensity' which would drive or motivate the 'men' to initiate the events and there is no way to derive the 'conditional forms of predicate logic'.

It is the "men's' desire to help' could serve as *propensity* or favourable inclination to initiate events in this scenario and to begin deriving the 'conditional forms' which would enable the propagation of events towards 'changes of states' .

Figure 5.3. shows the diagrammatic representation of *generalisation* **500.** *in section 4.2.* or the 'material interaction' in this case i.e. 'to help means: to push [carrier] the car [material object]'. The continuous, directed line represents the 'dynamic verb' qualified by 'adverbials' and the changing object carries the 'quality and quantity' which is the 'car', the product [3] that once 'in the garage' affects the 'lady' who is then satisfied. The dotted, directed lines designate the *change of equilibrium states*', for example, 'The helpless lady becomes helped in

20 seconds' with the 'final state', helped, designated by dotted line attached to a contour.

End of **Remark**

If we accept the generalisation that

103. --- '*Propensity* or favourable inclination is any 'condition' of mind or body, animate or inanimate, which is perceived as the *initiator* of events or changes of state by an 'observer' who is engaged in producing a symbolic model. Such a condition is designated by a qualifier or 'adjectival phrase' as part of a 'contingent statement' and is designated by continuous, lines attached to contours and is captured by the 'predicate logic implication or conditional' as follows:

'**IF** object 1. has the *appropriate* qualifier **AND** supplemented by adjectival qualifiers facilitating or hindering the production of interaction **THEN** a qualified interaction from object 1. to 2. can be generated,
IF a qualified interaction from object 1. to 2. can be generated **AND** object 2. has adjectival qualifiers facilitating or hindering change **THEN** there is a change of state of object 2.' ---

Generalisation **103.** can be rephrased in a continuous fashion as follows:

'There is an object 1. with propensity or favourable inclination supplemented by conditions to facilitate or hinder the production of interaction then an interaction or flow qualified by adverbial phrases, is produced.

This interaction affects another object 2. qualified by conditions to facilitate or hinder change, results in a change of state of object 2. exhibiting an *acquired condition* or *property*. This property is qualified by the past participle of the dynamic verb designating the interaction'.

Remark

We note that generalisation **103.** captures both, the FIRST and SECOND features.

End of **Remark**

The example with a 2 – place sentence as a 'story', illustrates generalisation **103.** 'The [angry] boy kicked [with a great deal of force and with healthy feet] the ball [which is well inflated]'. The diagrammatic representation is depicted in Figure 5.4.

The conditional statements which follow from the generalisation **103.** and from Figure 5.4. are

$$dp(1,1) \land ip(1,1) \rightarrow in(1,2)$$
$$in(1,2) \land ep(2,2) \text{ and } cp(2,2) \rightarrow ap(3,3)$$

exp 5.3.

Exp 5.3. are expressed in the notation of 'linguistic modelling' [Korn, 2009] which are

dp – driving property or *propensity*
ip – initiating object property
ep – affected object property
ap – acquired property
cp – calculating property
in – interaction

The first numeral in brackets refers to the object which is qualified, the second numeral refers to the same object which occurs at another place in the semantic diagram or 'dynamic, linguistic network' [Korn, 2009].

The abbreviations of the properties are explained as follows:

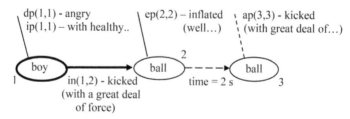

Figure 5.4. Semantic diagram of the 'boy – ball' scenario

'Driving property' [dp] is part of a contingent statement signifies the *propensity* or favourable inclination of an 'object or agent', the 'subject' of the sentence, the 'agentive case', the *initiator* of the cause of an event or action to occur by **chance** or in accordance with **purpose**. A 'dp' property motivates the cause of the event as suggested in 'generalisation **101**.' in section 5.1. such as in 'The continental shelves are out of balance [dp] resulting in earthquake which can be followed by eruption of the volcano' or 'There is a voltage of 110 V across the switch [dp] which causes the current to flow when the switch is closed'.

'Initiating object property' [ip] is part of a contingent statement which is assigned to an 'initiator object or agent' to facilitate or hinder the action of that 'object or agent' to cause an event. For example, 'The job of the post man [dp] with good eyesight [ip], is to sort letters according to their address'.

'Affected object property' [ep] is part of a contingent statement assigned to an 'object or agent' which is seen to be affected by the initiating object so as 'to change its state'. This property acts so as to facilitate or hinder the 'change of state' of an 'object or agent' which can be any of the 'cases' in a sentence but most often it is the 'dative case' as considered in section 3.2. [Fillmore, 1968].

'Acquired property' [ap] is part of a contingent statement seen as the result of a 'change of state'. An 'acquired property' is expressed by the 'past participle of the dynamic verb seen as causing the change qualified by adverbial qualifiers'.

'Calculating property' [cp] is part of a contingent statement which can be added to Driving property or Initiating or Affected object property with a view to modify any of these properties. A 'calculating property' usually refers to a condition internal or external to the scenario and can improve or worsen the chance of occurrence of an 'acquired property'. For example, in 'The snow melt on the side of the mountain helped by the warm sunshine'.

'Interaction' [in] designated by a 'dynamic verb' is part of a contingent statement refers to an action or the *cause* of an event or 'change of state' of an 'object or agent'.

'Adverbial phrases' which are used to modify the *meaning* of verbs i.e. interactions, adjectives and other adverbs in a sentence. For example, 'The [very] long goods train arrived [punctually, at the station]'. The function of adverbs is to answer the questions: 'How (in what manner, by what means, in what way), How much (to what degree), When (at what time), Where (in which place), Why (what cause) [Burton, 1984].

Exp 5.3. reads in words

IF the boy is angry AND has healthy feet THEN the boy kicked the ball with a great deal of force
IF the boy kicked the ball with a great deal of force AND the ball is inflated well and the ground is hard [cp(2,2)] THEN the ball becomes kicked with a great deal of force in 2 s.

The conditionals in exp 5.3. can be reversed which produces a **predictive expression** i.e.

in(1,2) IF [dp(1,1) $\wedge$ ip(1,1)]
ap(3,3) IF [in(1,2) $\wedge$ ep(2,2) and cp(2,2)]   **exp 5.4.**

where the first term in the first expression is 'interaction or event' and first term in the second expression is 'acquired property or condition'. Exp 5.4. reads ===

'The boy will kick the ball with a (great deal of force)' *occurs*
IF ['The boy is ((angry))'] AND ['The boy has (healthy feet)']

'The ball 'becomes' kicked with a (great deal of force)' *occurs*
IF ['The boy kicks the ball with a (great deal of force)'] AND ['The ball is (well inflated)' and 'The ground is hard']

The qualifier in the double, round brackets functions as the *propensity*

Remark

Exp 5.4. shows
1. 'The conditions' on which the occurrence of an 'event' and that of an 'acquired property or change of state' depends, and
2. A sequential feature since the occurrence of the 'change of state' in the

second expression depends on the 'interaction' taking place in the first expression.

3. The possibility of attaching mathematical models or numerical measures to the qualifiers enclosed in round brackets which make the continuity or sequence from the first to the second expression 'uncertain' which can be counterbalanced by the presence of 'cp(x,y)' properties.

To show the applicability of 'linguistic modelling' at this stage to 'engineering systems', we use a simple example to apply the verbal version of exp 5.4. as follows:

'The (electric) current will flow in a (copper) wire'
IF ['There is a ((20 V potential)) difference across the (copper) wire'] AND ['The (copper) wire is a (good conductor with resistance 'R')']

which is the verbal version of Ohm's law, 'potential difference = R times current'.

End of **Remark**

A further development of sematic diagram representation of sentences is the possibility of introduction of ***purposive activity*** [Nise, 2008, Korn, 2009, 2012].

To take into account such activity a declarative sentence needs to be modified by introducing a 'purpose' or a 'final state' of an 'object or agent' to be achieved which is compared with the current or 'initial state' of the same object. The difference is to act as the *propensity* in the scenario. Applying this description to the previous example, we obtain Figure 5.5.

Introduction to the application of 'linguistic modelling'

This is considered again more fully but is introduced here to demonstrate the 'propagation of state' designated by the 'acquired property' in exp 5.4.

The 'story' of the scenario is: 'The boy with healthy feet and good eyes, wanted to break the window because he was angry so he kicked the well inflated, streamlined ball with a great deal of force. The ball then moved at a speed in direction of the window which he observed.'

The STAGES of 'linguistic modelling' are ===

A. Homogeneous language of context – free, 1 – and 2 – place sentences derived from the story by *meaning – preserving, linguistic transformations* [in this case, there is no need since all sentences are already in this form]

The boy [1] kicked the ball [2] [2 – place sentence]
The ball moved [1 – place sentence]
The ball was observed by the boy [2 – place sentence]

which stand for the 'interactions' in the 'story'.

B. Semantic diagram

Shown in Figure 5.5.

C. Adjectival qualifiers with grading or other modifiers [such as certainty factors [Durkin, 1994, Korn, 2009]

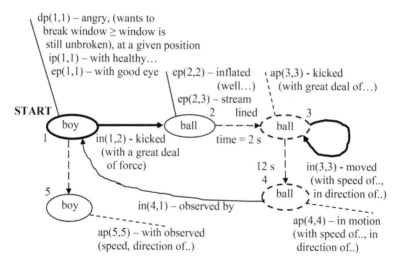

Figure 5.5. Semantic diagram of purposive action

dp(1,1) – boy is angry, wants to break the window compared with still unbroken window

ip(1,1) – with healthy feet…

ep(1,1) – with good eyes

ep(2,2) – well inflated

ep(2,3) – streamlined

D. Interactions with adverbial qualifiers

in(1,2) – Boy kicked the ball [with a great deal of force]

in(3,3) – Ball moved [with speed of …, in direction of …]

in(4,1) – Ball was observed by the boy

E. Logic sequences or topology of the scenario with graded adjectives and adverbials

Derivation of the 'logic sequences' is aided by *causal chains*. A 'causal chain' is found by starting at a contour in the semantic diagram which no longer changes and proceeding against the arrows of the directed lines until there is no more such lines. With reference to Figure 5.5.

The First causal chain = 4, 3, 2, 1 and The Second causal chain = 5, 1

For the First causal chain

in(1,2) IF[dp(1,1) ∧ ip(1,1)]

ap(3,3) IF[in(1,2) ∧ ep(2,2)]

in(3,3) IF[ap(3,3)]

ap(4,4) IF[in(3,3) ∧ ep(2,3)]

For the Second causal chain

in(4,1) IF[ap(4,4)]

ap(5,5) IF[in(4,1) ∧ ep(1,1)]

which show the 'continuity of events' taking place. However, the events as shown in Figure 5.5. are incomplete because after 'having observed' the state of the 'window' further events of 'comparison' are not depicted.

Remarks

Availability of semantic diagram interpretation of a 'story of a scenario' and its expression in terms of predicate logic sequences such as exp. 5.3., 5.4. and STAGE E. of 'linguistic modelling' opens the way:

1. To introducing methods to make the verbal expressions more specific. For example, we can have mathematical models such as Newton's 2nd law in 'kicked with a great deal of force which can be further expressed as 'force = mass times acceleration', certainty factors [Durkin,1994], graded adjectives [Korn, 2009] and so on,
2. To substituting objects thought to be more effective, preferred due to interest or being a protégé and so on,
3. To exploring or to *evaluating* the effectiveness of an 'agent or object' through its adjectival qualifiers and interaction through its adverbial qualifiers to fulfil its function which is a possibility due to the explicit representations of 'conditions' inherent in exp.5.4., for example.

The semantic diagram in Figure 5.5. is *superficial* in the sense that more details are needed to carry out the 'objective' of 'breaking the window'. However, at this stage, the intention was to introduce 'linguistic modelling' of 'purposive activity' and the idea of demonstrating the 'continuity of events'. Such continuity may be 'facilitating or hindering' by 'grading' properties of initiating and affected objects and introducing cuff off points [Korn, 2009]. This kind of exercise is demonstrated later.

4. The intention of using 'linguistic modelling' is *to transform* a 'story' or 'narrative' or 'text' expressed in 'declarative sentences' into *'conditional statements'* which show the conditions on which the existence states or occurrence the events, depend. This kind of expression enables to expose the 'conditional statements' to *test*.

End of **Remarks**

The second kind of 'elementary constituent' is the '1 – place sentence' such as, for example, 'Having a sharp razor the man with good vision shaves himself'. The semantic diagram is shown in Figure 5.6. The derivation of logic sequence is the same as for a '2 – place sentence', the difference is that in a '1 – place sentence' object 2 coalesces into object 1. The verbal equivalent from Figure 5.6. is given as follows:

'Man shaves himself (closely)'
IF ['There is a difference between 'the man wanted to have a close shave' and 'he has no close shave yet']
'Man 'becomes' (closely) shaved'
IF ['Man shaves himself (closely)'] AND ['Man has a sharp razor']
'Man is shaved (closely) is checked by man'
IF [Man 'becomes' (closely) shaved [or not]]
'Man (aware of) being closely shaved [or not]
IF ['Man is shaved (closely) is checked by man'] AND ['Man has good vision']

5.2 Introduction to construction of aggregates using 'ordered pairs'

In section 5.1. we discussed the generality of 1 – and 2 – place sentences or elcons, their representation as semantic diagrams or 'dynamic, linguistic network' and we introduced the scheme of 'linguistic modelling' using

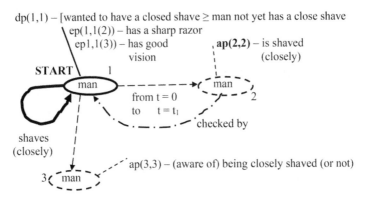

Figure 5.6. Semantic diagram of a '1 – place sentence' with feedback

an example of 'purposive activity'. The intention in this section is to show how more complex instances of Part B. of the scheme in Figure 3.1. can be represented in terms of 'linguistic modelling'. However, Part B. consists of a User/Producer [2] and a product [3] where both can be represented as 'dynamic, linguistic networks' but product [3] can also by modelled as 'static, linguistic networks'.

The reason for this is that a product [3] as a general proposition can be understood as follows

104. --- 'Product [3] is constructed of 'acquired properties, 'ap'' which form a *continuous* i.e. *non-disjointed* static, linguistic network induced by 'interaction' which is designated by a 'dynamic verb with adverbial qualifiers'. A disjointed, static, linguistic network cannot produce a *'single interaction'* for the accomplishment of a single 'change of state''. ---

Accordingly, we need to learn how to construct 'static, linguistic networks. The 'elcons' as 'dynamic, linguistic networks' can be seen as *ordered pairs*, thus, the *'elements'* of 'static, linguistic networks' are also seen as *ordered pairs* which are the basic elements of *static structures*. They are now introduced using the writing from [Korn, 2009, 2013, 2016] with slight modifications.

An 'ordered pair' is a set with two elements such as {2, 9} or {Mexico is under the USA}, a 'reduced order pair' consists of one element with a self – connection as in {Lovely girl}. In an ordered pair one is designated as the first element and the other as the second element. Such ordered pair is written (a, b), where 'a' is the first element and 'b' is the second element. Two ordered pairs (a, b) and (c, d) are equal if and only if 'a = c' and 'b = d' [Lipschutz, 1982].

Assuming we have two arbitrary sets A and B. The set of all ordered pairs (a, b) where 'a' is a member of set A or (a $\in$ A) and 'b' is a member of set B or (b $\in$ B) can be formed into a product called Cartesian product of A and B. This product is expressed by

$$A \times B = \{(a, b) \mid a \in A, b \in B \} \qquad \text{5.5.}$$

where the symbol '|' means 'such that'. So eq.5.5. reads 'the product of sets

'A' and 'B' such that the element 'a' is a member of set 'A' and element 'b' is a member of set 'B', is given by the set of all ordered pairs (a, b). If A = B i.e. we form the product of the same two sets then 'B' in eq.5.5. is replaced by 'A'. The product in eq.5.5. can have any number of terms: A × B × C... and so on.

For example, we let A = {1, 2, 3} and B = {a, b} then

$$A \times B = \{(1, a), (1, b),$$
$$(2, a), (2, b), \qquad \qquad \textbf{5.6.}$$
$$(3, a), (3, b)\}$$

The elements in an ordered pair can be free standing or unrelated but there can be relations between them as in simple '2 – place sentences'. For example, in 'goats eat grass' 'a = goats', 'b = grass' and 'eat' is the 'relation' or 'relation indicator' between them. Or we say that two countries are 'adjacent' when they 'share part of their boundaries'. Then 'is adjacent to' is a relation indicator between the countries of the earth. Thus,

(Canada, US) are part of the set of relations, R, but (Peru, US) are not.

Accordingly, we can say that the binary relation, R, from A to B assigns to each ordered pair (a, b) in A × B exactly one of the following statements:

i. 'a is related to b' or 'a R b',   ii. 'a is not related b' or 'a notR b'

For example, we let A = {1, 2, 3} and R = {(1, 2), (3, 2)} then R is a relation on A since R is a subset of A × A. We form the product to obtain

$$A \times A = \{(1, 1), (1, 2), (1, 3)$$
$$(2, 1), (2, 2), (2, 3) \qquad \qquad \textbf{5.7.}$$
$$(3, 1), (3, 2), (3, 3)\}$$

from which the second and eighth ordered pairs are members of the set R or R is the subset of the product in eq.5.7. All the other terms are 'notR'. We also note that the ordered pairs in brackets indicate relations between the two elements without explicitly stating the relations themselves. So whether the elements are related or not is arbitrary which means that members of the set R vary:

number of ordered pairs in set 'R' = from 0 to number of ordered pairs in the product, or

5.8.

number of ordered pairs in set 'notR' = from number of ordered pairs in the product to 0

In eq.5.5.

number of ordered pairs in A × B =
(number of elements in A) x (number of elements in B)   **5.9.**

since each element in A pairs with that in B. When A = B then the number of ordered pairs is A^2. For example, in eq.5.6. the number of ordered pairs is 6 since the number of elements in A is 3, in B it is 2 so 3 x 2 = 6.

To show how designations of relations explicitly enter into ordered pairs we look at two sentences: 'milk (is given by) cows' and 'eggs (are laid by) hens' in which the passive voice of dynamic verbs 'give' and 'lay', designates relations in brackets indicating static activity. We have four objects which we regard as elements of set A and to which we assign numerals as follows: milk = 1, cows = 2, eggs = 3, hens = 4. Using a simplified notation omitting all brackets since we know we are dealing with sets in curly brackets and with ordered pairs in round brackets, we construct the product set following eqs.5.5. to obtain

1, 1	1, 2	1, 3	1, 4	
2, 1	2, 2	2, 3	2, 4	**5.10.**
3, 1	3, 2	3, 3	3, 4	
4, 1	4, 2	4, 3	4, 4	

from which as indicated by the sentences we have R = {(1, 2) and (3, 4)}, a subset of set of eq.5.10. or in words R = {(1 (is given by) 2) and (3 (are laid by) 4)}. Also, from eqs.5.8. and 5.9. R = 2 and notR = 14 since number of elements in A = 4 and from eq.5.9. the number of ordered pairs = 16.

We note that we have recovered the two sentences from the set or array of eq.5.10. but nothing else since we have allowed no other relations between the four objects. We make two modifications:

1. We allow the first object in the sentences, the subject of the sentence, or the first element in an ordered pair to enter into relations with the second object or the second element in the ordered pairs but not vice versa. We rewrite the array of eq.5.10. by inserting the relations where appropriate

1, 1	1, 2	1, 3	1, 4
milk is given by milk	milk is given by cows	milk is given by eggs	milk is given by hens
2, 1	2, 2	2, 3	2, 4
----------------	--- -------------	----------------	--------------
			5.11.
3, 1	3, 2	3, 3	3, 4
eggs are laid by milk	eggs are laid by cows	eggs are laid by eggs	eggs are laid by hens
4, 1	4, 2	4, 3	4, 4
----------------	----------------	----------------	--------------

in which from eq.5.8. R = 8 and not R = 8.

In the array of eq.5.11. the second term in the first row, (1, 2), and the fourth term in the third row, (3, 4), are the original sentences, the ordered pairs (1, 1) and (3, 3) make no sense: something cannot be reproduced purely by itself. However, a few of the other terms 'make sense' syntactically and semantically although they are empirically impossible. Terms (1, 4) and (3, 2) make suggestions which may sound surprising. A point which could be interpreted in favour of the analysis so far is that it has suggested new kinds of regularity which may be considered unexpected and have not happened yet. It is unlikely to happen in the literal sense but could spark a new idea or a new direction of investigation.

2. Let us now expand the example by assuming that each of the four objects can be assigned one relation only which is selected from a number of empirically and technically feasible ones based on our semantic knowledge of the terms in a specific context. For example, 'milk (is given by) is one of other feasible relations like 'milk (is drunk by)', 'milk (is white)', 'milk (is taken by machine from)'.

We can then have: milk = 1 (is given by), cows = 2 (are fed with), eggs =

3 (are laid by), hens = 4 (are eaten by). This can be interpreted as a 'heap' of objects each with a relation attached floating freely about 'eager' to join another object within the heap like atoms or molecules with free valences. For the moment we assume that the heap is closed , it contains four objects which can form an aggregate among themselves and which following eq.5.5. or 5.7., becomes **exp 5.12.**

Again, in the array of exp 5.12. we can observe a number of interesting ordered pairs with relations between the elements. Ordered pairs (1, 2) and (3, 4) return the original starting sentences, (2, 1), (2, 3) suggest a possible new fodder for 'cows' and (1, 4), (3, 2) makes the suggestions as before.

1, 1	1, 2	1, 3	1, 4
milk is given by milk	milk is given by cows	milk is given by eggs	milk is given by hens
2, 1	2, 2	2, 3	2, 4
cows are fed with milk	cows are fed with cows	cows are fed with eggs	cows are fed with hens
			5.12.
3, 1	3, 2	3, 3	3, 4
eggs are laid by milk	eggs are laid by cows	eggs are laid by eggs	eggs are laid by hens
4, 1	4, 2	4, 3	4, 4
hens are eaten by milk	hens are eaten by cows	hens are eaten by eggs	hens are eaten by hens

in which R = 16 and notR = 0 from eqs.5.8.

An alternative way of handling elements and relations within an ordered pair is to consider the elements and their relations as three objects leading to 'three-tuples' like (a r1 b) where we have omitted the commas for simplicity's sake. Let us see how three-tuples are obtained when we have three sets instead of two as in **exp 5.5.** and **5.7.** In general, the number of members of a set can be any. Here we assume that each set has three members.

$$A = \{t\ l\ c\}\ R = \{r1\ r2\ r3\}\ A = \{t\ l\ c\} \qquad\qquad 5.13.$$

Forming the product

$$
A \times R \times A =
\begin{array}{lll}
t\ r1\ t & t\ r1\ l & t\ r1\ c \\
t\ r2\ t & t\ r2\ l & t\ r2\ c \\
t\ r3\ t & t\ r3\ l & t\ r3\ c \\
l\ r1\ t & l\ r1\ l & l\ r1\ c \\
l\ r2\ t & l\ r2\ l & l\ r2\ c
\end{array}
$$

$$5.14.$$

$$
\begin{array}{lll}
1\,r3\,t & 1\,r3\,1 & 1\,r3\,c \\
c\,r1\,t & c\,r1\,1 & c\,r1\,c \\
c\,r2\,t & c\,r2\,1 & c\,r2\,c \\
c\,r3\,t & c\,r3\,1 & c\,r3\,c
\end{array}
$$

in which the number of ordered pairs is = A times R times A terms which comes to 27.

Instead of allowing each first element to have any relation from the available choice, we allow each first element in the three-tuples to have just one relation i.e. 't r1', 'l r2' and 'c r3' then the relation subset of eq.5.14. becomes

$$
\begin{array}{lll}
t\,r1\,t & t\,r1\,1 & t\,r1\,c \\
1\,r2\,t & 1\,r2\,1 & 1\,r2\,c \\
c\,r3\,t & c\,r3\,1 & c\,r3\,c
\end{array}
\qquad \textbf{5.15}
$$

in which the number of term are A^2 i.e. 9.

Eq.5.15. corresponds to the 'milk, cows, eggs' example in which we have also disallowed the variation of relations of the first elements of the three-tuples.

Remarks

We have outlined how to use Cartesian products for forming sets of ordered pairs in which the two elements are related. The method leads to the formation of sets of expected, new or nonsensical ordered pairs constructed from simple 2 – place sentences, one or more of which may prompt a new idea which could be worth exploring. This judgement is based on our understanding of the semantic content of such sentences.

The notion of 'heap' of objects has been introduced in which objects can be imagined 'to float around' in a random manner unattached and waiting to combine into aggregates of ordered pairs with relations which in turn can be arranged into sets or arrays as shown by eq.5.5. If we can say that 'Nothing can exist on its own', conversely, everything enters into relation with something else then the reasoning scheme which we have introduced here demonstrates this remark in precise details. Exploring the variation of distribution of relations themselves that objects can have is left for **future research**.

End of **Remark**

So far we have outlined an aspect of the 'mathematics of relations' which appears to be suitable for constructing a *reasoning scheme* showing how unexpected pairs of related objects can emerge from combining objects through relations in various ways. We now take this matter further to show how 'ordered pairs' can be *aggregated in different ways* to form complexities or wholes.

We have shown how 2 – place sentences can be seen as *ordered pairs* with relations between elements. We now use this type of sentences only for the construction of arrays, or sets, of ordered pairs such as eq.5.12. Ordered pairs as 2 – place sentences are distributed off diagonal, one-place sentences or 'reduced ordered pairs' with one element missing, occupy spaces along the main diagonal of an array.

In general, a series of 2 – place sentences can be written as

$$n_i\,(adj_{ix})\,rel_i\,(adv_{iy})\,n_j\,(adj_{jz}) \hspace{4cm} \textbf{5.16.}$$

where 'adj' – are adjectival qualifiers of nouns 'n' which can include adverbial like in 'very good', 'adv' – are adverbial qualifiers of relations. These are parts of 'contingent statements' which locate a sentence element, a noun phrase, at a point in its *space of meaning* and selected so as to be relevant to the nouns and relations. Without such properties a sentence is **context – free**, its truth value cannot be ascertained [Magee, 1985]. In a 1 – place sentence the subscript 'j' attached to 'n' is zero.

For each 'i', specifying a noun, we can have a number of adjectival qualifiers

$$for\ i = 1\ x = 1, 2,\dots X(1)$$
$$i = 2\ x = 1, 2,\dots X(2)\ and\ so\ on$$

where 'X' is a positive integer and can be further expanded into properties 'pk', 'pm and 'pn' [Korn, 2009].

Subscript 'j' can be similarly expanded. Each noun as the subject of the sentence has a relation attached to it as in eq.5.12., therefore, the 'rel' carries subscript 'i' as well with a number of adverbial qualifiers, $y = 1, 2,.... Y$.

For example, in order to illustrate the use of the notation we can write a 2 – place sentence 'The well camouflaged, fast moving **rabbit escaped** quickly **from** the blood **hounds** which were chasing him' with bold print indicating a context – free sentence,

$$\text{for } i = 1 \quad x\,(1, 2) = \text{well camouflaged, fast moving}$$
$$j = 1 \quad z\,(1, 2) = \text{blood, chasing}$$
$$\text{rel}_i = 1 \; y\,(1) = \text{quickly}$$

In order to arrive at a set of the form of eq.5.16. we assume that we have a set 'A' of qualified objects 'ni', not yet related to others but to which we attach relation indicators 'reli'. The objects are randomly distributed in a heap or group as follows

$$A = \{(n_i\,(adj_{ix}))\,(rel_i\,(adv_{iy}))\} \qquad\qquad \textbf{5.17.}$$

each member of this set is called 'a' as indicated in eq.5.5. To each object 'n' we have attached a qualified relation or relation indicator which designates the static relationship that the object is judged to be capable of entering into. The relation itself depends on the scenario in which the object finds itself. For example, we can say 'rock (is thrown)', 'rock (is used as a weight)' or 'rock (is picked up)'.

Another set 'B' with members 'b' as indicated in eq.5.5. is formed as shown by

$$B = \{(n_i\,(adj_{ix}))\} \qquad\qquad \textbf{5.18.}$$

with objects as in set A except without relations, they are the 'receivers of relations'. The two sets enter into a product set as given by eq.5.5.

Each unrelated object represented in eq.5.17. as 'i = a' enters into relationship with itself and with others in the same heap as given by eq.5.18. but now designated by the subscript 'k = b' instead of 'i' in the same group to form ordered pairs arranged in accordance with eq.5.5. as shown by eq.5.19.

$$A \times B = \{(n_{ik} \, (adj_{ix})) \, (rel_i \, (adv_{iy}))\}$$
5.19.

or without qualifiers

$$A \times B = \{n_{ik} \, rel_i\}$$
5.20.

for i = 1   k = 1, 2, 3.... K
  i = 2   k = 1, 2, 3.... K
  i = 3   k = 1, 2, 3....K and so on

....

  i = K   k = 1, 2, 3....K

Here the subscripts 'i' and 'k' indicate the vertical and horizontal expansions leading to a square array which represents eq.5.20. with the number of ordered pairs given by eq.5.9. or by n^2.

We bear in mind that each term in the set of eq.5.20. stands for an ordered pair

$$\text{ordered pairs} = (n_i \, rel_i, \, n_k)$$
5.21.

For example, we let: i = k = 4 and x = y = 0, i.e. we consider context-free sentences and for simplicity's sake we omit 'rel' in eq.5.21. so we construct a particular case of the set or array of eq.5.21. by letting i = 1, for the first row, which is expanded horizontally when k = 1, 2, 3, 4, followed by i = 2, for the second row which is to be expanded again and so on. The result is

$$
\begin{array}{cccc}
n_{11} & n_{12} & n_{13} & n_{14} \\
n_{21} & n_{22} & n_{23} & n_{24} \\
n_{31} & n_{32} & n_{33} & n_{34} \\
n_{41} & n_{42} & n_{43} & n_{44}
\end{array}
$$
5.22.

in which each term is an abbreviated form of eq.5.21. such as 'n_{23}' = $(n_2 \, rel_2 \, n_3)$. We shall use this abbreviated form for the sake of convenience.

Each term in eqs.5.19., 5.20., 5.21., 5.22. is an ordered pair. For example, the sentence or the 'story'
'Top of the table is supported by legs which stand on the carpet' is expressed following eq.5.21. as:

$i = 1$ = 'top (is supported by)', $i = 2$ = 'legs (stand on)' and $i = 3$ = 'carpet (is)' which refers to identity of an *object without active part* but acts as support. Using eq.5.21. we have

n_{11}	n_{12}	n_{13}	
0	top is supported by legs	top is supported by carp	
n_{21}	n_{22}	n_{23}	
legs stand on top	0	legs stand on carp	**5.23.**
n_{31}	n_{32}	n_{33}	
carp is top	carp is legs	carp is carp	

In eq.5.23. one selected term in each row is part of the complete sentence. We have in the 1st row 'top is supported by legs, (n_{12})' , in the 2nd row 'legs stand on carpet, (n_{23})' and in the 3rd row 'carpet is carpet, (n_{33})'. The three relations together forming an aggregate which may be described as: 'Table top supporting arrangement', the 'emergent property' of the whole bounded by the conjunction, or 'simultaneous presence', of the three ordered pairs with relation which is called the *conceptual boundary* of the whole or just whole. The emergent property can be labelled by the noun phrase, 'table'.

However, the array offers a choice of groups of ordered pairs or there is a choice of aggregates as the possibility of variation was already mentioned in connection with eq.5.12. For example, we have in the 1st row 'top is supported by the carpet, (n_{13})', in the 2nd row 'legs stand on top, (n_{21})', and in the 3rd row 'carpet is carpet, (n_{33})'. This aggregate also makes sense, we can name it 'upside down table' as its emergent property but we cannot assign a label to it since natural language does not recognise this object as one that occurs regularly and merits assignment of a 'noun phrase'. For the moment, we include the third term 'carpet is carpet' for completeness but we shall return to this subject later when we define precisely the selection of terms in aggregates or bounded wholes.

We have discussed how we can construct sets or arrays of ordered pairs with relations as shown by eqs.5.21., 5.22. from which we can select a number of ordered pairs somewhat intuitively at this stage. This is a subset of A × B forming the conceptual boundary of a whole carrying an emergent property or not or a new concept labelled by a word depending on whether we can identify or name such property. We have seen that a number of subsets can be generated leading to a number of wholes or aggregates or variation of wholes. Each conceptual boundary consists of a number of ordered pairs which are simultaneously present therein. This statement can be expressed as

$$
\text{simultaneous presence (sp)} = \prod_{i=1}^{i=I} ((n_{i(\text{with any one of } k\,=\,1,2,3...)})(adj_{ix}))(rel_i\,(adv_{iy}))) \qquad \textbf{5.24.}
$$

in which for each 'i' we select a specific 'k' from each row. $\prod$ is the operator which defines the *conceptual boundary* of a whole and indicates that an emergent property may describe a whole which is greater than the 'sum of its parts'. In other words, a whole is not an algebraic sum of parts but an *aggregate of parts with relations.*

Application of eq.5.24. to one of the wholes in eq.5.23. results in

$$
\text{table supporting arrangement} = \prod_{i=1}^{i=3} (n_{12} \times n_{23} \times n_{33}) \qquad \textbf{5.25}
$$

where the sign 'x' means simultaneous occurrence.

Remark &&&

We have introduced a method of how to construct sets of ordered pairs and sets of three-tuples using Cartesian products. These sets, or arrays, serve as sources from which collections of ordered pairs are selected to form wholes as defined by eq.5.24. By stipulating that each object, or first element in a three-tuple, can have one relation only we have restricted our consideration to ordered pairs as in eq.5.21. Further investigation of sets of three-tuples, or allowing an object to enter into more than one relation, will not be undertaken here.

We can conclude that the arrays in eqs.5.21., 5.22. show a variety of possible choices of structures or wholes any of which can be selected [Korn, 2009]. A novel emergent property may be produced by a new structure.

We have demonstrated how a variety of structures can emerge from a single source, or 'heap' of objects with relations attached as in eq.5.19. We now go on to formulate the precise rules for calculating the number of structures that can emerge from a given array or set of ordered pairs.

End of **Remark &&&**

5.3. Representation of arrays by graphs or *'static, linguistic networks'*

We have discussed in section 5.2. that an ordered pair consists of two elements with a relation or 'a R b' where 'a' is the first and 'b' is the second element implying a direction. When 'a = b' the ordered pair is reduced to 'a R a'. Thus, an ordered pair may be represented pictorially as a two – terminal network element similar to an electrical or mechanical network element [Sanford, 1965, Korn, 1995]. Using network terminology [Jung-Ming, 2003] we can regard the elements as 'nodes' or 'vertices' and the relation as the connecting 'link', 'branch' or 'edge'. Thus, an ordered pair may be represented as a network element or graph shown in Figure 5.7.

As we have seen in section 5.2. the notion of ordered pair ties in with that of 1 – 2 place sentences. Thus, the network or directed graph in Fig.5.7. can be used to represent 2 – and 1 – place sentences respectively with nodes or oval shaped contours depicting 'nouns' and the directed lines connecting them representing relations. A node with self-loop indicates a 'reduced ordered pair' or 1 – place sentence.

Figure 5.7. Graph or network representation of ordered pairs

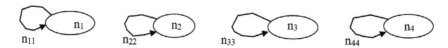

Figure 5.8. Graph of unrelated objects

An array of ordered pairs as eqs.5.19., 5.20., 5.21. is a collection of objects and relationships which can be represented as a graph [Ore, 1962, Korn, 1995]. Using eq.5.22. as a demonstration we construct Figure 5.8. which stands for eq.5.18. i.e. the objects are unrelated.

Each object can enter into relationships with the others in '(n − 1)' ways and with itself making the total number of relations at each node in an undirected graph, equal to 'n'. Thus, Figure 5.8. is modified to in Figure 5.9. with 4 relations at each node.

In Figure 5.9. every connection between the nodes represents a directed line going both ways. We have used the relations such as 'n_{12}, n_{21}' to indicate this. The same terms stand for the ordered pairs in eq.5.21. and in the an array in eq.5.22. The direction is defined by the subscripts: a line leaves a node with the first subscript and enters a node with the second. For example, line 'n_{14}' leaves node 'n_1' and enters node 'n_4'. It is in this sense that we use the 'n' terms in arrays and in graph, they are abbreviations of eq.5.21.

We have seen in section 5.2. that an ordered pair can act as a representation of a 2 − place sentence since both have two objects which, in the latter case, are connected by relations which can be verb phrases. The first element in the ordered pair stands for the subject of the sentence and the second element is a noun in another case [Fillmore, 1968]. A 1 − place sentence like 'the man (shaved)', is represented by a 'reduced ordered pair'. Both are shown in Figure 5.7. We have seen in section 5.2. that ordered pairs in an array are distributed off the main diagonal and reduced ordered pairs are part of the main diagonal or the diagonal elements counted from top left towards the bottom right corner of an array. In graph terms this means that ordered pairs are branches emanating from one node and terminating at another and reduced ordered pairs emanate and terminate at the same node.

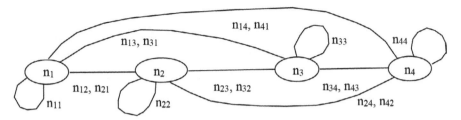

Figure 5.9. Graph of related objects

We can generalise these observation in saying that

105. --- 'Ordered pairs define the structure of a graph or a system, reduced ordered pairs contribute nothing to structure'. ----

The topic of both ordered pairs and reduced ordered pairs are the subject matter of 'systems science' or the 'systems theory' under consideration, the topic of reduced ordered pairs are the subject of 'conventional science of physics'. The latter is interested in making statements about single objects [Korn, 2018]. An ordered pair carries a pair of related objects each with contingent qualifiers, a reduced ordered pair carries one object with contingent qualifiers carried by 'contingent statements'. An ordered pair can be converted into a reduced ordered pair since both can be expressed by statements of the 'subject-predicate' form. Thus, the sentence 'the monitor (is placed on) the desk' may be seen as an ordered pair with the relation in brackets. It may also be seen as a reduced ordered pair if we say 'the monitor (is placed on the desk)' with subject, 'the monitor', and the predicate enclosed in brackets.

We have constructed sets or arrays of ordered pairs as shown by eqs.5.19., 5.20., 5.21., 5.22. and their network or directed graph representation. We now have to consider both, the array and graph so as

To develop the rules for selecting groups of ordered pairs

for formulating conceptual boundaries of wholes as in eq.5.24.:

Rule 1 -- One-place sentences or reduced ordered pairs are located along the *main diagonal of an array* and designated by double subscripts with the same numerals. They are shown as self-loops in a graph and are selected freely to be part of a conceptual boundary as in eq.5.24. since being self-loops, they do not contribute to the structure of a graph and consequently to the structure of the whole which the graph represent. For example, the sentence 'The dog was frightened and bit his keeper' which can be expressed in 'passive voice' as 'The dog was frightened and his keeper was bitten by dog' and, following eq.5.12. can be analysed into:

dog = n1, keeper = n2, and following eq.5.20., is written as

$$
\begin{matrix}
n_{11} & n_{12} \\
n_{21} & n_{22}
\end{matrix}
\qquad\qquad\qquad \textbf{5.26.}
$$

from which we can recover: n_{11} = 'The dog was frightened', n_{21} = 'His keeper was bitten by the dog' and its directed graph is shown in Figure 5.10.

We note in Figure 5.10. that the structure of the scenario is defined by the relation between the two distinct objects, 'dog and keeper', the one-place sentence does not contribute to the structure.

Rule 2 -- A *structure of unrelated objects* can be constructed from reduced ordered pairs distributed along the diagonal of the array in eq.5.22. or 5.23. as shown in Figure 5.8.

Rule 3 -- Only *one ordered pair can be selected from any one row in the array* of eqs.5.19., 5.20., 5.21., 5.22. otherwise the first element would be related to more than one second element. For example, in eq.5.23. we would have 'top is supported by legs AND by carpet'. This kind of relation is not admitted

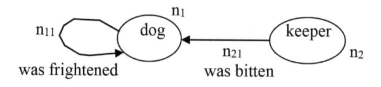

Figure 5.10. Directed graph of 'dog-keeper' example

because it makes the first element, 'top', ambiguous and would no longer be an ordered pair expressing a 'function'. In other words, more than one point in the range of a relation (the second element of the ordered pair) or the vertical or 'y' axis of the Cartesian coordinates, would correspond to one point in the domain (the first element of the ordered pair) or the horizontal or 'x' axis. Alternatively, a function is a relation in which no two of its ordered pairs can have the same first element but different second elements [Lipschutz, 1982].

Selection of one term in a row of an array means in graph terms that only *one branch is allowed to leave a node but a node can have any number of lines entering.* 'Leaving' and 'entering' are defined by the order of subscripts. Selection of one term in a row also obviates the possibility of the same two or more objects having the same relationships with different objects at the same time. Eq.5.23. demonstrates this restriction: 'carp is legs', 'carp is top'. 'Carp' cannot be both at the same time, it must be either, the 3rd law of thought [Hospers, 1978]. In eq. 5.21. entering a node means that any number of terms can exist in a column.

Rule 4 -- The *number of rows available for selection of ordered pairs is 'n – 1'* which is the number of branches in a graph which define a 'tree' (Ore, 1962, Korn, 1995). 'Tree' is defined as a graph which connects all nodes without forming a loop (self-loops are exempted). A 'tree' in a graph defines the *structure of the graph* by connecting all the 'structural elements' i.e. nodes, adding any more connections or branches introduces *redundancy* or superfluousness into a structure One possible tree of the graph depicted in Figure 5.9. is shown in Figure 5.11.

A graph other than a tree involves a loop which can be seen in Figure 5.11. when we insert an additional branch from the graph in Figure 5.9. such as, for example, 'n34'. A loop can be formed

A. Either by a sequence of branches starting and ending at the same node which would lead to a reduced ordered pair or self loop involving a series of relations of one object or node with itself which would make a graph topologically closed as shown below under III. This would also render the whole or totality from which the array and subsequently the graph has been derived, structurally closed or converting it into a 'closed system'.
This means that ---

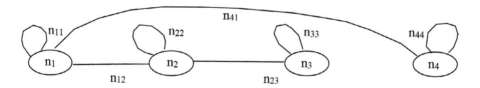

Figure 5.11. Graph showing a tree

I. A tree connects all nodes, thus defines the structure or topology of the graph and subsequently that of the whole,

II. In constructing the conceptual boundary as given by eq.5.24., we select an ordered pair not from all the 'n' rows of an array but from $(n - 1)$ rows,

III. With reference to Figure 5.11. selection of an ordered pair from all the rows would lead to

$n_1(n_{12})\, n_2,\, n_2\,(n_{23})\, n_3,\, n_3\,(n_{34})\, n_4,\, n_4\,(n_{41})\, n_1$. We substitute one expression into the other successively and we again obtain -- $n_1\,(n_{12})\,(n_{23})(n_{34})(n_{41})\, n_1$ which is a self loop.

Another example: If in Figure 5.11. we insert 'n_{43}' the result is a sequence of branches or ordered pairs as follows: $n1\,(n_{14})\, n_4,\, n_2\,(n_{21})\, n_1,\, n_3\,(n_{32})\, n_2,\, n_4\,(n_{43})\, n_3$. We substitute one expression into the other successively to obtain $n_2\,(n_{21})\,(n_{14})\,(n_{43})\,(n_{32})\, n_2$.

B. Or by two branches leaving one node which is not admitted by Rule 3 above.

For example, in Figure 5.11. if we insert 'n_{34}' we have two branches leaving node 'n_3' which is recognised by 'n' having the same first numeral in its subscript. In this case 'n_{32}' and 'n_{34}' as indicated in Figure 5.9.

We can say that the number of tree branches which connect 2 nodes is 1 as shown in Figure 5.10. and 3 nodes are connected by 2 branches without forming a loop. Thus, in general

number of branches in a tree $= n - 1$ **5.27.**

which is one less than the number of rows in eq.5.19., 5.20., 5.21. and defines the possible number of ordered pairs to form a whole or simultaneous presence (sp), or conceptual boundary, as given by eq.5.24. as long as a the *tree does not contravene Rule 3.* If a tree defines a whole by constructing a simultaneous presence (sp) then the number of 'sp' generated from an array as eq.5.19. or 5.20. or 5.21. is given by

$$\text{number of possible sp} = \text{number of trees} \qquad \textbf{5.28.}$$

which is always true for undirected graphs. This point is considered for directed graphs as well in [Korn, 2009].

The number of trees for an **undirected graph** defined as 'structural trees' which can be constructed on 'n' nodes is given by (Ore, 1962)

$$\text{number of structural trees} = n^{(n-2)} \qquad \textbf{5.29.}$$

which, thus, defines the number of wholes that can be generated from an undirected graph. An undirected graph represents the basic structure of the graph so we call the trees obtained from eq.5.29. 'structural trees'.

Let us go back to the example of the 'top of the table' arrangement considered in section 5.2. which resulted in the array of eq.5.23. We can represent the array by the directed graph depicted in Figure 5.12.

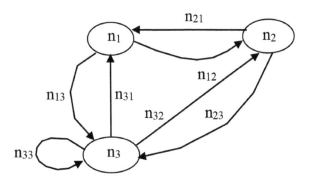

Figure 5.12. Directed graph representation of eq.5.23.

The number of nodes is 3 and the number of trees from eq.5.29. is 3. This is always true for undirected graph and we shall consider its limited applicability for directed graphs as well later. The number of tree branches from eq.5.27. is 2 and the number of 'sp' from eq.5.28., or wholes, that we can have using this simplified consideration from eq.5.28. is 3 which are shown in Figure 5.13. in which the direction of arrows has been chosen to give meaningful 'sp'.

From Figure 5.13a. we can write the equivalent to eq.5.25:

n_{12} = 'top is supported by legs'
n_{23} = 'legs stand on carpet'
n_{33} = 'is carpet'

Also, from b.

n_{21} = 'legs stand on top'
n_{13} = 'top is supported by carpet'
n_{33} = 'is carpet'

Also, from c.

n_{23} = 'legs stand on carpet"
n_{13} = 'top is supported by carpet'
n_{33} = 'is carpet'

We note that the ordered pairs in figures a. and b. in Figure 5.13. can be visualised and form a whole, there is a 'flow' of static activity. However, c. although can be visualised does not form an empirical whole of related

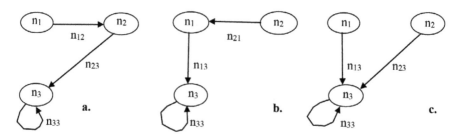

Figure 5.13. Trees from directed graph in Figure 5.12.

objects. We can see the 'legs' standing on the 'carpet' with 'top' somewhere near supported by 'carpet' but the two objects are not related. The problem appears to be that the same object 'carpet' is used by two different other objects, which is impossible. The intention of this example was to demonstrate how we can proceed from a story, the sentence 'Top of the table....' in section 5.2., towards constructing an array and how the array can yield a variety of wholes, two in this case.

This example also draws attention to the fact that, although eq.5.24. is true, not all trees can be used to form empirically possible conceptual boundaries 'sp'.

The increase of possibilities of emergence of different wholes as the number of trees increases as a function of the number of 'nodes', or objects in an array or complexity of an aggregate, is shown by the table

$$n = 1\ 2\ 3\ 4\ 5 \ldots\ldots$$
$$\text{number of trees from eq.5.29.} = 0\ 1\ 3\ 16\ 125 \ldots\ldots$$

which is applicable when the branches in a graph are not directed as in Figure 5.9. or 5.11.

We have discussed in section 5.2. that a whole or totality or entirety is defined by eq.5.24. and the number of *such wholes is equal to the number of trees* that can be generated from a graph constructed from an array such as eq.5.19. The number of trees of an undirected graph is given by eq.5.29. The groups of structural trees of '(n – 1)' branches in each in a digraph can be calculated using the *incidence matrix* of a digraph which is done in [Korn, 2009] in detail, we are going to do it as the need arises. However, the method is demonstrated through an example as shown in Figure 5.14.

First, we need to introduce the notion of 'incidence matrix' derived from a directed graph or digraph [Jung-Ming, 2003]. We may think of a digraph as the pictorial representation of this matrix or this matrix being the mathematical representation of a digraph. We introduce this relationship between mathematical and pictorial representations by means of an example. A digraph is shown in Figure 5.14.

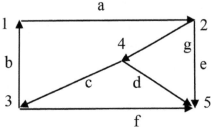

Figure 5.14. Diagram of a digraph

numerals designate nodes,
letters designate branches

In a digraph branches enter and leave nodes. We use the convention that when a branch leaves a node we insert '1' at their intersection in a column and row of the incidence matrix. Conversely, when a branch enters a node we insert '-1' at their intersection. If no leaving or entering takes place, a zero is inserted. Accordingly, we construct the incidence matrix from Figure 5.14. as eq.5.30. The dimension of the incidence matrix is given by 'nodes times branches'.

branches		a	b	c	d	e	f	g
	1	1	-1	0	0	0	0	0
nodes	2	-1	0	0	0	1	0	1
	3	0	1	-1	0	0	1	0
	4	0	0	1	1	0	0	-1
	5	0	0	0	-1	-1	-1	0

5.30.

Here this number is (5 x 7) = 35, the matrix has 35 elements. The rank of an incidence matrix is the number of tree branches or number of groups of branches '(n – 1)'. Since a branch leaves one node and enters another, each column in eq.5.30. has a '1' and a '- 1' or the sum of 'ones' in each column is zero. For example, branch 'e' leaves node '2' and enters node '5'.

We have discussed in section 5.2. that a whole or totality or entirety is defined by eq.5.24. and the number of *such wholes is equal to the number of trees* that can be generated from a graph constructed from an array such as eq.5.19. The number of trees of an undirected graph is given by eq.5.29. We now intend to find how to calculate the number of structural trees and the number of '(n – 1)' groups of branches in a digraph using the incidence matrix such as eq.5.30.

Using the 'propensity argument' in section 5.1., this matrix, eq.5.30., is equivalent to Kirchoff's current or 'through variable' law according to which 'The algebraic sum of currents or through variables [such as force] entering or leaving a *node* is zero' [Boylestad, 1987, Korn, 2012].

However, we can calculate this figure or the number of '(n – 1)' groups branches for the *maximum number of branches* in a digraph. This number in a digraph with 'n' nodes is
'n (n – 1)' since each node connects to all the others or to '(n – 1)' which is repeated 'n' times disregarding self-loops. This number equals the total number of ordered pairs in an array squared as given by eq.5.9. or 'n²' less the number of terms, or self-loops, along the diagonal. The number of branches in a tree is '(n – 1)'. So, the problem is how to calculate the number of combinations of groups of '(n – 1)' branches which can be obtained from 'n (n – 1)'.

This problem can be solved by calculating the number of ways of selecting 'r' different things from 'q' unlike things (Durell, 1959) or calculating the number of combinations of

'q' things taken 'r' at a time =
$$C (q, r) = (q (q – 1) (q – 2)...(q – (r – 1)))/(1 \times 2 \times 3 \times ... r) \qquad \textbf{5.31.}$$

where 'r' are factorials. For example, the question is how many different selections of 2 letters can be made from 4 letters, a, b, c, d. We can write out the selections, each letter can be combined with another 3 times and there are 4 letters so the total number of selections is 12: ab, ac, ad, ba, bc, bd, ca, cb, cd, da, db, dc = 12 but 6 of these are selections with the same letters transposed. Thus, the number of different selections is 6.

Or using eq.5.31. we have with q = 4 and r = 2, C (4, 2) = (4 x 3)/(1 x 2) = 6.

As a matter of interest, we can also find the number of different selections of 3 letters from 4 letters by combining each 3 letters: abc, abd, acd, bcd giving 4 selections. Or from eq.5.31. we have with q = 4 and r = 3, (4 x 3 x 2)/(1 x 2 x 3) = 4.

When we apply these considerations to digraphs we have 'q = n (n – 1)', the maximum number of branches, and 'r = (n – 1)', the number of branches in a 'tree'. Considering the digraph in Figure 5.14., the number of nodes is 5. Hence, 'n (n – 1) = 20' and '(n – 1) = 4'.

Using eq.5.31. we have (20 x 19 x 18 x 17)/(1 x 2 x 3 x 4) = 4845 which is the *maximum* number of '(n -1)' groups which the digraph in Figure 5.13. can have. A very large number considering that it has been obtained from a digraph with 5 nodes. However, the actual number of branches in the digraph in Figure 5.14. is 7. Thus, the number of different groups of '(n – 1)' is given by (7 x 6 x 5 x 4)/(1 x 2 x 3 x 4) = 35.

However, not all groups of '(n – 1)' are trees or suitable trees for the construction of wholes or conceptual boundaries as given by eq. 5.24. Some are loops (i.e. not trees) others have two emanating branches from the same node (i.e. not suitable trees), they contravene Rule 3. Now we want to describe how to find the number of suitable groups of '(n – 1)' or trees which then determine the number of wholes or conceptual boundaries, 'sp', or variety of wholes i.e. eq.5.24. which can be generated from a given array or digraph.

From a static, linguistic network using the expression for combination or the alternative to eq. 5.31. [Durell, 1959, Korn, 2018], we have eq 5.32.

$$_{N(N-1)}C_{(N-1)} = [(N(N-1) - 0)\ (N(N-1) - 1)(N(N-1) - 2)....]/[1\ 2\ 3...(n-1)\ !]\quad \textbf{5.32.}$$

in which 'N' is the number of nodes in a static, linguistic network, the number of terms in the nominator is 'N – 1' divided by 'N – 1' factorials. For example, when 'N = 3', we have $_6C_2$ = (6 x 5)/(1 x 2) = 15. This number shows all the possible variations of the topology or configuation of the product of which only a few are 'trees'.

We demonstrate the method of how to use the incidence matrix and eq.5.31. by a simple example which gives sufficient background for further use in this book. Generalisation is attempted in [Korn, 2009]. We assume we are given an array eq.5.33. like eq.5.22. or eq.5.23.

$$\begin{array}{ccc} 0 & n_{12} & n_{13} \\ n_{21} & 0 & n_{23} \\ n_{31} & n_{32} & 0 \end{array}$$ 5.33.

which is represented by the digraph in Figure 5.15.

Next we construct the incidence matrix from eq.5.32. and the digraph in Figure 5.14. following the convention in eq.5.30.

branches		n_{12}	n_{13}	n_{21}	n_{23}	n_{31}		
	n_1	1	1	− 1	0	− 1	0	
nodes	n_2	− 1	0	1	1	0	− 1	5.34.
	n_3	0	− 1	0	− 1	1	1	

Using eq.5.32. the total number of combinations of '(n − 1) = 2' terms from 'n (n − 1) = 6' can be calculated from C (6, 2) = 15 which we write out in a pattern. The pattern is formed by combining the branches in the columns in eq.5.34. in groups of '(n − 1) = 2' in all possible ways as shown in eq.5.35.

$$\begin{array}{lllll} n_{12}\,n_{13} & n_{13}\,n_{21} & n_{21}\,n_{23} & n_{23}\,n_{31} & n_{31}\,n_{32} \\ n_{12}\,n_{21} & n_{13}\,n_{23} & n_{21}\,n_{31} & n_{23}\,n_{32} & \\ n_{12}\,n_{23} & n_{13}\,n_{31} & n_{21}\,n_{32} & & \\ n_{12}\,n_{31} & n_{13}\,n_{32} & & & \\ n_{12}\,n_{32} & & & & \end{array}$$ 5.35.

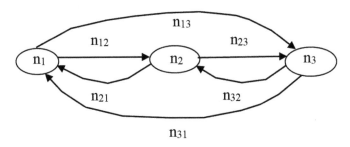

Figure 5.15. Digraph representation of eq.5.33. or eq.5.23.

The combinations in eq.5.35. contain C (6, 2) = 15 terms = All possible '(n – 1)' terms including those which violate Rule 3. and those which form loops. Inspection of eq.5.35. leads to sort out the categories as follows:

$$n_{12}\, n_{13}\, n_{21}\, n_{23}\, n_{31}\, n_{32}$$ which violate Rule 3

$$n1_2\, n_{21}\, n_{23}\, n_{32}\, n_{13}\, n_{31}$$ which form loops

$$n_{13}\, n_{21}\, \underline{n_{23}\, n_{31}}\, n_{13}\, n_{23}$$

$$n_{21}\, n_{31}\, \underline{n_{12}\, n_{23}}\, n_{21}\, n_{32}$$

$$n_{12}\, n_{31}\, n_{13}\, n_{32}\, n_{12}\, n_{32}$$

5.36.

which are genuine 'trees', those underlined correspond to Figure 5.13. and eq.5.23., they *make sense*

The network representation of a 'tree' which contravenes Rule 3 is shown in Figure 5.16. The 9 genuine 'trees' from eq.5.36. are depicted in Figure 5.17.

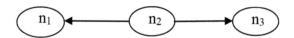

Figure 5.16. Tree which contravenes Rule 3

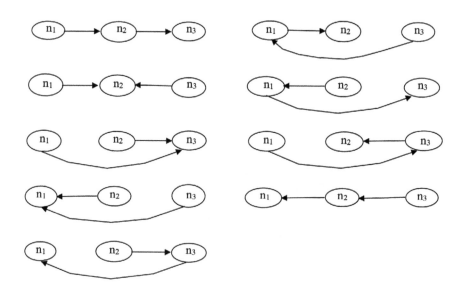

Figure 5.17. Trees for generating wholes

We apply the 'trees' in Figure 5.17. to the example in eq.5.23. to show the wholes or 'sp' as given by eq.5.24.

$(sp)_1 = n_{12}$ (top is supported by legs) $(sp)_2 = n_{12}$ (top is supported by legs)
$\quad\quad n_{23}$ (legs stand on carp) $\quad\quad\quad\quad n_{31}$ (carp is top)

$(sp)_3 = n_{12}$ (top is supported by legs) $(sp)_4 = n_{13}$ (top is supported by carp)
$\quad\quad n_{32}$ (carp is legs) $\quad\quad\quad\quad n_{21}$ (legs stand on top)

$(sp)_5 = n_{13}$ (top is supported by carp) $(sp)_6 = n_{13}$ (top is supported by carp)
$\quad\quad n_{23}$ (legs stand on carp) $\quad\quad\quad\quad n_{32}$ (carp is legs)

exp 5.37.

$(sp)_7 = n_{21}$ (legs stand on top) $(sp)_8 = n_{21}$ (legs stand on top)
$\quad\quad n_{31}$ (carp is top) $\quad\quad\quad\quad n_{32}$ (carp is legs)

$(sp)9 = n_{23}$ (legs stand on carp)
$\quad\quad n_{31}$ (carp is top)

from which we regain the original sentence in $(sp)_1$, we recognise an 'upside down table' in $(sp)_4$, $(sp)_5$ is not a whole as we discussed in section 5.2. The rest of (sp)'s make no sense. In making these judgements we rely on our understanding of the semantic content of each ordered pair.

Remark &&&

The method for *identifying genuine 'trees'* in a static, linguistic network outlined can be used for networks with any number of nodes. It may be seen somewhat cumbersome but perhaps 'software' could be developed to deal with it or an analytical method could be attempted as in [Korn, 2009].

The conversion of algebraic expressions or arrays of ordered pairs like eq.5.19., 5.20. into static, linguistic networks, and vice versa, has been achieved. The advantage of this method is that the concept of 'tree' has been identified as the unique structure which defines a construction. A method is offered for explicit investigation the number of 'trees' in static, linguistic networks. 'Products [3]' in the scheme of Figure 3.1. can be represented as static, linguistic networks where the method is applied and if a 'tree' is not found, modification to 'production/user [2]' can be suggested. Also, the variety offered by a static, linguistic network may lead to developments of *novel constructions* of product [3].

To summarise: We have arrived at the scheme of expression of natural language as 'linguistic networks' through the concept of 'ordered pairs' which is shown in Figure 5.18.

Further to the representation of product [3], in section 3.2. we suggest four particular cases of the scheme in Figure 3.1. Here we make a general statement regarding product [3] as follows

106. --- 'In case of 'Utilising systems' a product [3] receives <u>properties</u> which *stimulate* it to produce *interaction* within the framework of Part B. In case of 'Producing systems' a product [3] receives <u>properties</u> which *contribute* to its physical or mental *construction* to enable it to produce eventually when delivered and sold, an *interaction*.'----

When used in a Utilising system, a product [3]
Is complete and selected from a store in the course of implementing Part A. as demonstrated in section 4.3.,
When used in a Producing system, a product [3]
At its *creation* stage = Is fabricated, manufactured and assembled into a whole and is represented by 'Static, linguistic network',

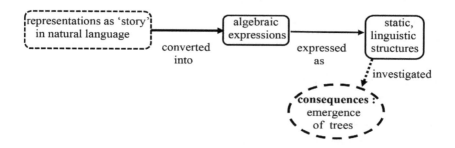

Figure 5.18. Expression of language as networks

At its *customer* stage = Is delivered and sold in the course of implementing Part B. This kind of activity of User/Producer [2] and product [3] in Figure 3.1. is represented by 'Dynamic, linguistic network'.

Accordingly, a unified application of dynamic and static, linguistic network representation has emerged. Properties can be resourced from the choice as discussed in section 4.1.

End of **Remark &&&**

5.4. Uncertainties in qualified, simple sentences

In section 5.1. we discussed the concepts of 'context – free' and 'context – dependent' sentences. Using the latter a scenario can be located in the *space of meaning* [Popper, 1972, Magee, 1985]. It is the adjectival and adverbial qualifiers which can do this leading to representations as 'dynamic, linguistic networks'. So far we have used qualifiers in a kind of 'on or off way', there was no intermediate possibility or *uncertainty*.

Perhaps the first, comprehensive analytical method of using 'uncertainty' was 'fuzzy set theory' [Zadeh, 1965]. We used this method at the beginning of its development of the current work but it produced an ever decreasing value of certainty in the 'propagation of state' in a semantic diagram or dynamic, linguistic modelling. This led to using the method offered in [Durkin, 1994] and further developed in [Korn, 2009] which is presented here with modifications.

In section 5.1. we have discussed qualifiers which are used to modify the 'meaning' of 'objects or agents' i.e. noun phrases and 'relations and interactions' i.e. stative and dynamic verbs. In other words, qualifiers can modify the *emergence of outcomes* or 'changes of equilibrium states'. Therefore, if these qualifiers vary the possibility of outcome also varies. How this **_variation_** can be accomplished is considered here.

By 'variation of qualifier' we mean the following. We have seen that the term qualifier refers to properties or, in grammatical terms, to adjectival and adverbial phrases and clauses or sentences which act as such. There are qualifiers which we may call 'exact' with precise cut off point. For example, we can say: 'The cross section of the output shaft of the car engine is (circular)' or 'The hole in the wall is (square)' or 'This car is travelling (at a speed of 50 km/h)'. Adjectival phrases like the ones shown in brackets, are exact, something is either 'square' or 'not square', there cannot be any variation.

On the other hand, there are adjectival and adverbial phrases which are **_vague_**. For example, in the sentence 'This man is (tall)' the adjective 'tall' is vague and, to a large extent, what we consider 'tall' is a matter of opinion. There is a range of measurements which can be expressed 'in metres and centimetres' which may be accepted as 'tall'. Below '1.7 m', for example, a man may not be regarded as 'tall', above '2.5 m' no man or woman is likely to exist but between, say, 1.7 m and 2.2 m a man may be regarded as 'tall'. The essential point is that there is a range of measurement rather than a clear cut off point as in case of 'square' or not 'square'.

There are many 'linguistic variables' [Zadeh, 1965, Durkin, 1994] such as height, speed, age which can be expanded into a range of numerical values which is called 'fuzzy set'. Repeating the remark above: In our work as described in this book, some time ago we used fuzzy set theory to introduce 'variation of qualifiers' but abandoned this approach as use of fuzzy sets always leads to a declining or diminishing possibility expressed as *acquired properties of states* as they progress in time. Improvement or increased possibility of occurrence of outcomes cannot be achieved [Korn, Takats, 1995].

Vague qualifiers can be expanded into a series of values. For example, we can say: 'This man's height is 1.65 m' which is a single value but we can also say that 'Looking at him, this man appears of medium height or short or he is a dwarf'. We are no longer certain, we cannot assign a single value. We rather volunteer an expression of view or opinion or offer a 'grade' to the linguistic variable 'height'.

At this point we note that:

1. Any vague linguistic term like adjectives, adverbs and so on, which is used for alleging something about something else, can be used as a *linguistic variable* or a 'concept'. For example, we can say: ' Among these, say, 200 persons we can find employees (concept) who are very loyal or loyal or disloyal (which are called grades)',

2. We can *expand* a linguistic variable into values or grades such as, for example, 'height (very short, short, medium, tall, very tall)', 'sense of duty (strong, weak, do not care)', 'employee (very loyal, loyal, disloyal),

In general, we can write

$$(\text{concept})_i = (\text{concept})_i \, (\text{grades})_{i,l} \qquad\qquad \textbf{5.38.}$$

which says that a particular concept 'i' can be expanded into 'l' grades. For example,
$(\text{concept})_3 = (\text{concept})_3 \, ((\text{grade})_{3,1}, (\text{grade})_{3,2}, ...)$ or $(\text{height})_3 = (\text{height})_3$ $((\text{very short})_{3,1}, (\text{short})_{3,2}, (\text{medium})_{3,3}, (\text{tall})_{3,4}, (\text{very tall})_{3,5})$ where we have inserted commas for clarity.

3. A particular object with a concept can have one grade or another but *not more than one* at the same time,

4. An object, in particular living objects, can change their grade *in time* or as a result of *intervention* like training, medical treatment, persuasion etc. For example, we can have from eq.5.38.: 'age = age(baby, young, middle aged, elderly, old)' and a person as he/she ages travels along the grades, or 'receptionist = receptionist (very friendly (yesterday), friendly (today), indifferent (tomorrow)),

5. A set of concepts with grades can be specified. Persons, for employment, for example, can be selected to fit *particular combination of grades* from each concept. For example, we can say:

employee (very loyal, loyal), with training (high, medium), personality (very pleasant, pleasant, can cope).

In accordance with point 5. just above, we can select any combination which appears to be suitable for some specific purpose. For example, considering employment of a person, we select as requirements: 'person (employee (loyal), with training (medium), personality (pleasant)) in which the meaning of terms may need to be further elaborated.

Vagueness of qualifiers has resulted in uncertainty which is reflected in the multi-valued nature of qualifiers. Fuzzy set theory assigns numerical measures to concepts and places a grade within a selected range of these measures. For example, the concept 'age' can be expanded in terms of the measure 'years' from 0 to 100 and the grade 'baby' can be considered to fall within the range of years from 0 to 3. We propose to use *certainty theory* (Durkin, 1994) instead which we briefly outline as far as necessary for its application in linguistic modelling.

Certainty theory uses the idea of expressing a subjective belief, an opinion or view regarding the existence of a state or the occurrence of an event. The measure of belief is called the certainty factor 'cf' which varies from + 1 to – 1 and is assigned to a statement carrying the belief. Cf's can be interpreted by linguistic terms as shown in Figure 5.19.

We discuss certainty theory under headings following approximately the approach in [Durkin, 1994]:

A. Uncertain evidence or sentences with uncertainty

A sentence which expresses uncertainty and used in inexact reasoning contains expressions like the ones given in Figure 5.19. For example, we can say: 'The hotel on the Riviera is very likely going to be full of guests this summer'. The term 'very likely' shows uncertainty regarding the occurrence of an event and it is close to 'almost certainly' in Figure 5.19. with cf = 0.8. So we can replace the original sentence

'The hotel on the Riviera is very likely to be full of guests this summer' with another
'The hotel on the Riviera is going to be full of guests this summer', cf = 0.8.

We have replaced the sentence with uncertainty with a sentence without doubt or uncertainty and added a cf as a 'measure of certainty'. Thus, certainty factors

cf	uncertain term
- 1	definitely not
- 0.8	almost certainly not
- 0.6	probably not
- 0.4	may be not
- 0.2 to 0.2	unknown
0.4	may be
0.6	probably
0.8	almost certainly
1.0	definitely

Figure 5.19. Cf values expressed in linguistic terms

'cf' are *informal measures of confidence* for a piece of evidence expressed as a sentence or statement. They represent the degree to which we believe the evidence to be true.

B. Uncertain rules

Cf values can also be attached to rules expressed as *logical conditionals*. A conditional consists of an antecedent, here called 'evidence', 'E', and a consequent or 'hypothesis', 'H' joined by 'If… then…' connectives as discussed in sections 1.3. and 4.2.

Given that 'E' is true or it can be observed to be so, the value of cf represents the level of belief in 'H'. For example, we can say: 'If the summer is hot (E) then the hotel on the Riviera will be full of guests, with cf = 0.8'. In other words, the evidence 'E' is there for all to see 'the summer is hot' then from Figure 5.19. we are 'almost certain' that 'the hotel on the Riviera will be full of guests'.

C. Propagation of certainty for rules with one uncertain term in the antecedent

In point B. we assumed that the evidence or antecedent, 'E', in the conditional was true. Here we consider the case when this evidence is uncertain as in point A. and we are interested in the certainty of consequent or hypothesis, 'H'. The procedure to work out this certainty is:

First, we assign a cfe, the level of belief, to the sentence with 'E' as in point A.,
Second, we assume that the sentence with 'E' is true or cfe = 1 and assign a
cfh, level of belief, to the sentence with 'H' as in point B.,
Third, we multiply the two cf values which then gives the final level of belief
in 'H'.

For example, we can say: 'If the summer this year looks pretty hot then the
hotel on the Riviera is likely to be full of guests'.

First, we assign to the evidence or antecedent, cfe = 0.6, or 'probably' from
Figure 5.19. as equivalent to '.looks pretty',
Second, we assume that the evidence is 'true' i.e. 'If the summer this year is
hot then the hotel on the Riviera is likely to be full of guests' with 'likely' taken
as equivalent to 'probably' with cfh = 0.6 from Figure 5.19.
Third, the final level of belief in the hypothesis 'H' is cff = 0.6 x 0.6 = 0.36
which tells us that uncertainty in the evidence reduces the assumed certainty
of the hypothesis as expected.

We can set this procedure out in a formula as follows

$$\text{If } [E \text{ (with } cf_e)] \text{ then } (cf_h) \text{ } [H \text{ (with } cf_f = cf_e \times cf_H)] \qquad \textbf{5.39.}$$

D. Propagation of certainty for rules with more uncertain terms in the antecedent

A conditional with more than one uncertain term in the antecedent has more
than one sentence acting as evidence. These sentences are connected either
by logical AND or logical OR functions. The procedure for calculating cf,
level of belief, in the hypothesis is similar to that in point C. above.

When sentences are connected by logical AND functions:

First, we assign cf values, cf_{e1}, cf_{e2}.... to all sentences acting as evidence 'E' in
the antecedent as in point A.,
Second, we assume that all sentences as evidence 'E' in the antecedent are
true i.e. cf = 1 and assign a cf_h to the sentence with hypothesis 'H' in the
consequent as in point B.,

Third, we take the **minimum** of cf_{e1}, cf_{e2}.... and multiply it by cf_h to give the final value, cf_f, or level of belief, of the hypothesis 'H'.

For example, we can say: 'If the summer this year looks pretty hot and the foreign exchange is not too favourable then the hotel on the Riviera is not very likely to be full of guests'.

First, we assign the evidence or antecedent, $cf_{e1} = 0.6$ or 'probably' from Figure 5.19. as equivalent to '.looks pretty'. and $cf_{e2} = 0.4$, the effect of 'too' we assume to be 'may be' from Figure 5.19.,
Second, we assume that the evidence is true i.e. 'If the summer this year is hot and the foreign exchange is not favourable then the hotel on the Riviera is not likely to be full of guests' with our belief that '.exchange is not favourable' having strong influence on the certainty of hypothesis. So from Figure 5.19. we take $cf = 0.9$.

The first evidence is against the hypothesis but the second strongly favours it. Given that people are sensitive to 'foreign exchange fluctuations', it is fairly certain that 'the hotel is not likely to be full of guests'.

Third, the minimum value of cf in the evidence is 0.4. Therefore, $cf_f = 0.4$ x $0.9 = 0.36$ which indicates 'may be' in Figure 5.19. or a low possibility of outcome due to the moderating effect of $cf_{e2} = 0.4$. This indicates that although '...exchange is not favourable', when assumed to be true, has a strong positive effect on the outcome but its certainty is estimated only at a low level. Because the minimum function favours low levels of certainty, it is not all that certain that 'the hotel on the Riviera is not likely to be full of guests'.

This example reveals a *weakness of certainty theory* approach when it comes to having multiple antecedents. It is the minimum value of cf in the antecedent which influences the hypothesis. The hypothesis is sensitive to this value only. We could be certain that 'the summer this year is hot' with $cf = 1$ but this would not make any difference to the certainty of the hypothesis. On the other hand, if we believe that 'the summer this year is hot' to an extent of $cf = 0.2$ that would make a large difference to the hypothesis, $cf = 0.2$ x $0.9 = 0.18$. This is reasonable since now the lowered certainty of 'the summer this year is hot' contributes strongly to the hypothesis 'the hotel on the Riviera is not likely to be full of guests'.

Another difficulty appears when, as in points B., C. and D., the method asks for the evidence to be regarded 'true'. The truth value of a sentence may be possible to assess through visualisation when the constituents of the sentence are expressed in concrete terms such as 'the summer is hot' or 'the value of a particular currency fluctuates'. However, when we come to a sentence used as evidence like 'there is a great deal of cruelty taking place in this ship' establishment of truth value needs further investigation towards obtaining its *empirical content* or seeking tangible evidence amenable to sensual input.

When sentences of evidence are connected by logical OR functions, the procedure for calculating cff is the same except the **maximum** value of cfe is taken instead of minimum.

The description can be captured by the relationship similar to eq.5.39. as

If $[E_1$ (with $cf_{e1}) \land E2$ (with $cf_{e2}) \land ...]$ then (c_{fh}) $[H$ (with $cf_f = cf_h \times \min(cf_{e1}, cf_{e2}.)]$

where 'x' means multiplication.   **5.40.**

E. Propagation of certainty when cf values arise from different sources

We propose to construct more complex reasoning schemes representing 'stories' as descriptions of scenarios or the 'primary model' using sequences of elcons. The introduction of uncertainty into the logical conditionals such as exp 5.3. discussed in section 5.1. depends on regarding 'dp' with 'ip' and 'in' with 'ep' as 'evidence' connected by the logical AND function and 'in' and 'ap' as 'hypothesis'. Thus, sentences with *vague adjectival* qualifiers are considered as evidence.

Treatment of uncertainty changes when we come to calculating properties, 'cp'. We intend to regard these properties as evidence which originates from sources not directly connected with objects which form the structure of a reasoning scheme as seen in Figures 5.5. and 5.6. considered in section 5.1. 'Cp' properties bring into the scheme the possibility of calculations, decisions based on comparisons and they can be used for expressing conditions which can introduce *improvement* in the progression of 'cf' values as the state propagates in a dynamic, linguistic network, thus, reversing a possible *downward trend.* Accordingly, the structure of the antecedent in equations like exp 5.3. can be divided into two parts depending on whether there is a 'cp' property or not. Following exp 5.3. the form of antecedent becomes as in exp 5.41.

$$[dp(1,1)\ (cf_1) \wedge ip(1,1)\ (cf_2)...] \times [cp(1,1)\ (cf_c)] = antecedent \qquad \textbf{5.41.}$$

in which each of the two parts is enclosed in square brackets and are connected by 'x' sign indicating the 'method of combination' as worked out below.

In order to find the resulting cf of the antecedent we take the minimum of cf's connected by the AND functions designated 'cf_m' in the first square brackets and combine this value with that of 'cp' designated 'cf_c' in the second square brackets according to the following relations

If both cf's are greater than 0

$$cf_x = cf_m + cf_c\ (1 - cf_m) \qquad \textbf{5.42.}$$

If one cf is less than 0

$$cf_x = (cf_m + cf_c)/(1 - min(|cf_m|\ |cf_c|)) \qquad \textbf{5.43.}$$

where the vertical dashes '|' indicate absolute value of the enclosed cf.

If both cf are less than 0

$$cf_x = cf_m + cf_c\ (1 + cf_m) \qquad \textbf{5.44.}$$

The combined value of cf or 'cf_x' is then multiplied by 'cf_h' as shown in eq.5.40. to obtain cf_p the final value of cf of the hypothesis or outcome, the *measure of our belief* in the *certainty of its occurrence.*

We look at an example which leads to a 2 – place sentence, to illustrate how the formalism of exp 5.3. and the application 'certainty theory' introduced so far. Using a kind of 'distorted' linguistic modelling in relation to that introduced in section 5.1., the 'story' is as follows:

'A housewife was short of provisions so wearing her smart hairdo and being well versed in operating machinery, drove her car which was in good, running order, to the shops where she had friends as well'. We identify from the sentence:

The context free sentence 'housewife drove car' in which we regard 'housewife' as initiating and 'car' as affected object, and

Qualifiers which are shown as predicates of sentences or statements as follows

dp – housewife was short of provisions
ip – housewife was well versed in operating machinery
ep – car was in running order
np – housewife was wearing smart hairdo which is a 'neutral property' judged to play no part in the scenario
cp – there were friends
ad – housewife drove (to the shops) which is an adverbial qualifier
(pp – Background knowledge – 'The housewife knew where the shops were' which we assume. 'Housewife' ended up 'at the shops' because 'she knew where they were and preferred to go there', 'she could have gone 'to the market' to get her provisions as far as 'dp' is concerned. So we conclude that there is a need to introduce 'pp' properties so as to be able to select 'ad' properties, a step which is usually omitted in casual conversation.)

The 'context dependent sentence', a 2 – place sentence, is represented as a 'dynamic, linguistic network' or semantic diagram in Figure 5.20.

Following the method in section 5.1., from Figure 5.20. we obtain eq.5.45.

$$dp(1,1) \wedge ip(1,1) \rightarrow in(1,2)$$
$$in(1,2) \wedge ep(2,2) \text{ and } cp(2,2) \rightarrow \mathbf{ap(3,3)}$$

exp 5.45.

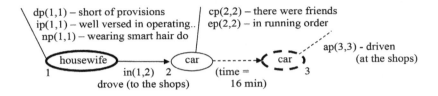

Figure 5.20. Semantic diagram of housewife-car example

where 'cp' is part of the second conditional since it affects the change of state: whether the 'car is driven to and is (at the shops)'. It adds additional motivation for change. The nature of connection of the 'cp' property is left open for the moment. We did not include 'neutral properties' since being 'neutral' we assume that it contributes nothing to the relations in the conditionals. A 'np' can become relevant at a later stage.

The pair of 'conditionals. eq.5.45. can be 'read' as follows:

'If ('dp', the housewife was short of provisions) and ('ip', she was well versed in operating machinery) then ('in', she drove her car to the shops)'

'If ('in', the housewife drove her car to the shops) and ('ep', her car was in running order) 'and' ('cp', there were friends near the shops) then ('ap', the car was driven to the shops)'.

where the 'cp' property is fitted into the conditional through the connective 'and' which is not the logical 'and' function.

We look at this example to illustrate the use of certainty factors in eq.5.45. We reproduce the verbal form of eq.5.45., without 'cp' to begin with, in which we have inserted cf values in brackets as measures of confidence dictated by our belief in the uncertainty of sentences representing evidence. Using eq.5.40. we have

'If ('dp', the housewife was short of provisions) (- 0.6) and ('ip', she was well versed in operating machinery) (0.8) then (0.9) ('in', she drove her car to the shops)' (0.9 x min (- 0.6, 0.8)) = - 0.56

in which the values of cf's from Figure 5.19. mean that:

1. 'The housewife was probably 'not' short of provisions' (- 0.6),
2. 'It is almost certain that she was well versed in operating machinery' (0.8),
3. 'From case C. above, to obtain the cf of rule we assume that the 'evidence' is true 'The housewife was short of provisions' (1.0) and 'She was well versed in operating machinery' (1.0) then it is more than almost certain that 'She drove her car to the shops' (0.9).

Application of eq.5.40. to the second part of eq.5.45. gives

'If ('in', the housewife drove her car to the shops) (- 0.56) and ('ep', her car was in running order) (0.8) then (1.0) ('ap', the car was driven (to the shops)) (1.0 x min (- 0.56, 0.8) = - 0.56

which means that 'the housewife probably did not drive her car to the shops'.

The meaning of cf's in the expressions above can be interpreted from Figure 5.19. Further to the remark regarding the weakness of certainty theory in point D., we note that again it is the minimum value of cf, in this case - 0.56, which dominates the *propagation of certainty*. We assessed the level of confidence in the driving property 'dp' as we believe that 'housewife was probably not short of provisions' which has led to 'the housewife probably did not drive her car to the shops' and has propagated through the unit of change. The assessment then results in outcome 'ap', the acquired property, which says that 'the car was probably not driven (to the shops)' which is consistent with what is asserted by the 'driving property', 'after all if there is no shortage of provisions then there is no need to drive to the shops'.

However, if we now reinstate the 'cp' property in eq.5.45., using eq.5.41. we have

'If ('dp', the housewife was short of provisions) (- 0.6) and ('ip', she was well
   versed in operating machinery) (0.8)
then (0.9) ('in', she drove her car to the shops)' (0.9 x min (- 0.6, 0.8)) = - 0.56

'If ('in', the housewife drove her car to the shops) (- 0.56) and ('ep', her car was
   in running order) (0.8) 'and' ('cp', there were friends near the shops) (0.9)
then (1.0) ('ap', the car was driven to the shops)' (1.0 x (min (-.56, 0.8) 'and'
0.9)) = 0.77

where we combine the minimum of the antecedent which is – 0.56 with cf of
'cp' which is 0.9 as explained following eq.5.41. We use eq.5.43. because one
cf is negative and substituting we have

$$cf_x = (- 0.56 + 0.9)/(1 - \min|- 0.56||0.9|) = 0.77$$

Remarks &&&

We see that as a result of including the 'cp' property the outcome 'ap' has
changed from 'the car was probably not driven to the shops' to 'the car was
more than almost certainly driven to the shops' from Figure 5.19. This change
has taken place despite 'the housewife was probably not short of provisions'
but presumably the attraction of 'there were friends' overrode 'her decision of
probably not to drive to the shops'. We see the effect of introducing additional
evidence into the reasoning scheme. At this point we add a generalisation

107. --- 'A story or narrative of a scenario in natural language, the primary
model, yields by linguistic analysis or 'meaning preserving linguistic
transformations' the 1 – and 2 – place sentences, the *homogeneous language*'
leading to expressions like exp 5.3. and 5.45.'----

By inserting this generalisation we want to stress that the source of
'homogeneous language', the analytical part of the linguistic approach, is
the *story* and is obtained by meaning preserving transformations not yet
discussed. The reasoning scheme with certainty factors as developed here
allows to engage in exploration of imaginary scenarios or the consequence of
'what would happen if we changed this particular aspect into that'.

We have mentioned two methods: fuzzy sets and certainty theory as ways of having *numerical measures of uncertainties* which arise as a result of using vague qualifiers. These methods may not be the only ones, further research may uncover others that can fit into linguistic modelling. Here we shall be using certainty theory. Later research might lead back to the use of fuzzy set theory in conjunction with calculating properties and their way of combining with other properties as shown by eq.5.41.

The assignment of certainty factors, 'cf', to sentences with *vague qualifiers* is based on subjective estimate of how certain an observer or what his/her level of belief is in a state of affairs. In other words, how confident one is that a state of affairs exists or an event will happen. Following Durkin (1994), we have outlined how cf can be used for propagating uncertainties from premises or antecedents towards conclusions or hypotheses or outcomes using logical conditionals. This approach fits into the reasoning scheme described by expressions such as eqs.5.3. and 5.45. We have introduced the notion of combining cf values through computing properties, 'cp', which allows regulation of values of certainties 'cf' as 'acquired properties' or states propagate in time in a dynamic, linguistic network obtained from the *homogenous language* which is derived from a 'story' of a scenario by 'meaning preserving linguistic transformations' [Korn, Huss, Cumbers, 1988].

End of **Remarks &&&**

5.5. Variation of uncertainties in qualifiers

We have outlined a 'certainty theory' which appears to be suitable for taking into account uncertainties associated with qualifiers in reasoning schemes such as the semantic diagram in Figure 5.5. Uncertainties arise, for example, from reliability of a technical component like a washing machine or from features associated with human components like mood changes, getting tired as time goes on and properties decline or acquired, rational or irrational wishes and ambitions. In fact, we can assign uncertainty to any statement acting as evidence with a *vague qualifier*. In case of properties with sharp cut off points such as possessed by 'square' we have certainty.

In sections 4.1. and 5.1. we introduced a *classification of qualifiers* which, as we have seen in section 5.4., are the carriers of uncertainties. We demonstrated in that section how variation of certainty factors affects the outcome or 'acquired properties' of a reasoning scheme such as exp 5.3. However, we assigned a single certainty factor to a sentence with words like likely, nearly, too much etc. which signal uncertainty, serving as evidence which propagated through a reasoning scheme or 'dynamic, linguistic network' as in Figure 5.5. We now want to work out cf values for vague qualifiers which show **variations** or **grading** as shown by eq 5.38. This requires a notation which admits this variation using certainty factors within a qualifier or variation of level of confidence in a qualifier. This notation with further variation allows qualifiers to fit into expressions like exp 5.3. or 5.45.

Uncertainties due to vagueness of qualifiers are expressed by:

A. Grading of adjectives and adverbs,
B. Assignment of certainty factors, 'cf', to grades,

which are the two components of *variation of uncertainty*.

We need to describe the 'notation' for adjectival qualifiers and for interaction. The structure of eqs.5.3. and 5.45. and that of more complex semantic diagrams like Figure 5.5. which are constituted from such expressions, are defined by **objects and their interactions**. Members of each category are modified by adjectival and adverbial qualifiers respectively. Thus, as we have seen in Figures 5.4., 5.5. and 5.6., for objects and interactions to fit into a semantic diagram, the notation for *adjectival qualifiers* needs to specify:

1. Their location in a semantic diagram in relation to the object or agent to which they belong,
2. Properties constituting an adjectival qualifier,
3. Grading and certainty factors.

The notation for *interactions* should describe:
1. Their location in a semantic diagram in relation to the objects or agents which interact,

2. Adverbials which qualify an interaction,
3. Grading and certainty factors.

Since the notation is the same for all adjectival qualifiers in the pair like exp 5.5., we use 'dp' as demonstration of how the notation is developed:

$$dp(object, property set) \qquad\qquad \textbf{exp 5.46.}$$

$$object = (object\ position\ in\ the\ semantic\ diagram) \qquad \textbf{exp 5.47.}$$

$$property\ set = ((property)_1, (property)_2...(property)_i... (property)I) \qquad \textbf{exp 5.48.}$$

where the number of properties in the set can vary from 1 to I. A property in the set is given by

$$(property)_i = ((property\ name)_i, (grade\ set)_i) \qquad\qquad \textbf{exp 5.49.}$$

$$(grade\ set)_i = (grade, cf)_{il} \qquad\qquad \textbf{exp 5.50.}$$

Exps 5.47. to 5.50. define exp 5.46., substituting the former into exp 5.46. and using abbreviated forms of the terms, we have

$$dp(objname/pos, (prop/name)_i, (grade, cf)_{il}) \qquad\qquad \textbf{exp 5.51.}$$

which:
1. Allows an adjectival qualifier to consist of a number of properties: i = 1, 2, ...I,
2. Includes eq. 5.38.,
3. Includes all three points mentioned above regarding how to specify qualifiers and as such defines an adjectival qualifier, 'dp', 'ip', 'ep' or 'cp'.

Exp 5.51. has the same form *for all adjectival qualifiers* and is used in exp 5.3. and other like it following the pattern set by eqs.5.40. and 5.41. We show how this is done using an example as we go along to give the terms a tangible meaning. We can say:

'A number of girls who were trained secretaries, willing to work, needed money and looked for (well paid, interesting jobs)'.

This is a one-place sentence if we assume that the noun 'jobs' is used for qualifying the verb, with dp – number of girls needed money, ip – number of girls were trained secretaries, willing to work.

Following the first part of exp 5.3. or 5.45., the general predicate logic form of a 1 – and 2 – place sentence, we have

If ('dp', the number of girls needed money) $\wedge$ ('ip', they were trained … and willing…)
then ('in', they looked for well paid, interesting jobs) **exp 5.52.**

Taking 'ip' as the example to show how to grade properties and to insert cf values in exp 5.51., the procedure is:

1. In exp 5.51. the 'property name' means the same as 'concept' in eq.5.38. We obtain a 'property name' as the *vague qualifier* from a sentence in the story of a scenario. Property name admits grading. Here property names are 'trained….' and 'willing…',

2. Next we divide a vague qualifier into grades. The number of grades is arbitrary. The more grades we assign the finer the division of the qualifier. Here we can have 'trained (very high, high, low)' and 'willing (strong, weak)',

3. To each grade we assign two numbers which lead to certainty factor, cf. The first number between – 100 and + 100 designated by the symbol 'ai', is intended to express the *significance, importance or relevance of the grade* as part of a property as far as the *outcome in the consequent of the conditional* is concerned. The second number between – 1 and + 1 designated by the symbol 'bi', is intended as a *measure of belief or confidence in certainty* as shown in Figure 5.19. that an object has a particular grade of a particular property. Assignment of both numbers is based on subjective judgement.

Here the outcome or consequent of the conditional is 'they looked for jobs'. Bearing this outcome in mind, we assign numbers as follows ---

trained (very high, 80/0.4, high, 70/0.9, low, 50/0.3)
willing (strong, 90/0.8, weak, 40/0.5)   **exp 5.53.**

which reflect our belief that in 'looking for jobs' 'very high training' was important (80) but not many of the 'number of girls' had it (0.4). Most of the 'number of girls' had 'high training, with measure of belief, 0.9'. Also, 'strong willingness' appeared significant (90) and it is believed that most of the 'number of girls' had it (0.8).

At this point we can apply exp 5.51. to this adjectival qualifier as follows

ip(ngirls1,1,(traid(vhigh,80/0.4, high,70/0.9, low,50/0.3),
wilg(st,90/0.8, wk,40/0.5)))

exp 5.54.

4. If there is more than one property name in an adjectival qualifier as there is in exp 5.54., then their grades need to be combined as shown by exp 5.50. to construct a **'property profile'**. A property profile shows the combined characteristics or grades of the object or agent to which they refer together with their significance and extent of possession of grades. This might serve as a criterion of employment for the 'number of girls...'.

Using exp 5.50. we have in this example:

Grade sets, $i = 1, 2$ (trained and willing), for $i = 1, l = 1, 2, 3$ and for $i = 2, l = 1, 2$. In general terms we expand exp 5.50. as follows

for 'trained': $(\text{grade set})_1 = (\text{grade, cf})_{11} (\text{grade, cf})_{12} (\text{grade, cf})_{13}$ and
for 'willing': $(\text{grade set})_2 = (\text{grade, cf})_{21} (\text{grade, cf})_{22}$ **exp 5.55.**

We substitute exp 5.53. into exp 5.55.

$(\text{very high, } 80/0.4)_{11} (\text{high, } 70/0.9)_{12} (\text{low, } 50/0.3)_{13}$
$(\text{strong, } 90/0.8)_{21} (\text{weak, } 40/0.5)_{22}$ **exp 5.56.**

using the numerals only we combine exp 5.55.

11, 21	11, 22	(and in words	very high, strong	very high, weak
12, 21	12, 22	from exp 5.56.)	high, strong	high, weak
13, 21	13, 22		low, strong	low, weak

exp 5.57.

which tells us that the first term in the first row of exp 5.55. is combined with all terms in the second followed by the second term and so on.

The example above shows how to combine grades of different adjectival qualifiers. The example that follows intends to work out the **personality profile** of the 'number of girls'.

To show a slightly more complicated example of how to combine grades and cf's, we have three properties i.e. $i = 1, 2, 3$:

For the 1st property --- $i = 1$ we have $l = 1$
For the 2nd property --- $i = 2$ we have $l = 1, 2, 3$
For the 3rd property --- $i = 3$ we have $l = 1, 2$

Following exp 5.55., exp 5.50. becomes
$$(\text{grade set})_1 = (\text{grade, cf})_{11}$$
$$(\text{grade set})_2 = (\text{grade, cf})_{21}, (\text{grade, cf})_{22}, (\text{grade, cf})_{23}$$
$$(\text{grade set})_3 = (\text{grade, cf})_{31}, (\text{grade, cf})_{32}$$

which using just the subscripts, we combine into

11, 21, 31	11, 21, 32
11, 22, 31	11, 22, 32
11, 23, 31	11, 23, 32

exp 5.58.

which is equivalent to exp 5.57. and gives 6 combinations: 1 x 3 x 2 or the product of 'il' terms.

5. Each combination or property profile has a resulting certainty factor, cfr, which is obtained from

$$p = il$$
$$cf_r = \Sigma \ (a_1 \times b_1 + a_2 \times b_2 + \ .... + a_p \times b_p)/(|a_1| + |a_2| + \ ... + |a_p|)$$
$$p = 1 \hspace{6cm} \textbf{exp 5.59.}$$

where ap = − 100 to + 100 and bp = -1 to + 1 as defined in point 3. above for *each combination of (grades, cf)* or 'i'. The vertical strokes in the denominator indicate absolute values of numbers enclosed in case the confidence number is negative.

Having demonstrated how to work out the 'grade set' in case of a 'slightly more complicated example, we now return to the 'first example'. Application of exp 5.59. to exp 5.56. and 5.57. gives for 'each combination of (grades, cf)'

11, 21 (very high, strong) = (80 x 0.4 + 90 x 0.8)/(80 + 90) = 0.61
11, 22 (very high, weak) = (80 x 0.4 + 40 x 0.5)/(80 + 40) = 0.43
12, 21 (high, strong) =   (70 x 0.9 + 90 x 0.8)/(70 + 90) = 0.84
12, 22 (high, weak) =   "   = 0.75
13, 21 (low, strong) =   "   = 0.62
13, 22 (low, weak) =   "   = 0.39

$$\hspace{10cm} \textbf{exp 5.60.}$$

which shows the variation of certainty factor, cfr, of the adjectival qualifier 'ip' or the **property profile** as a function of variation of the combinations of instances of 'grade sets' i.e. 'grades, cf' with the assumed significance and confidence numbers.

Remark &&&

We note from exp 5.60. that the highest cfr is 0.84. This tells us that in exp 5.52. if the 'number of girls' have 'high training' and 'strong willingness' then from Figure 5.19. they are 'more than almost certainly' facilitate the interaction: 'number of girls looked (for well paid, interesting jobs)'. In other words, 'the number of girls' do not need 'very high' training which, in any case, few of them have (confidence number is 0.4). 'Low training' and 'weak willingness' as one would expect facilitates the interaction least.

End of **Remark &&&**

If in exp 5.51. i = 1 and l = 1, 2, 3,... or there is only one property which has a number of grades, then the certainty factors, 'cfr', are given by the second or confidence numbers as discussed in point 3. above. For example, for the first term in exp 5.53. or if we have only 'trained (very high, 80/0.4, high, 70/0.9, low, 50/0.3)' then from exp 5.59. we have

$$p = 1, l = 1, 2, 3, \ldots\ldots L$$
$$cf_r = \Sigma((a_1 \times b_1)/(|a_1|)) = \Sigma(\pm b_1) \qquad\qquad \textbf{exp 5.61.} .$$
$$p = 1$$

In exp 5.61. the *summation sign* means: Calculate each quantity in the brackets for all grades 'l' under the same property 'i = 1' From the first term in exp 5.53. which is 'training', application of exp 5.61. gives cfr is $(80 \times 0.4)/80 = 0.4$, $(70 \times 0.9)/70 = 0.9$ and $(50 \times 0.3)/50 = 0.3$.

6. Having obtained a value for certainty factor, cf_r, for an adjectival qualifier, it is ready to be included into exp 5.3. or eq. 5.41. as appropriate.

We now return to the example:

'A number of girls who were trained secretaries, willing to work, needed money and looked for (well paid, interesting jobs)'.

The sentence is a 1 – place sentence, its context – free form is: 'Girls looked

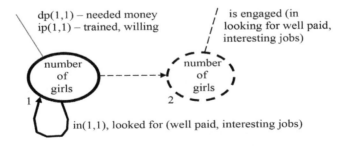

Figure 5.21. Semantic diagram of 'number of girls'

for' and diagrammed in Figure 5.21.

With reference to Figure 5.21. we obtain

$$dp(1,1) \wedge ip(1,1) \rightarrow in(1,1) \text{ and } in(1,1) \rightarrow \mathbf{ap(2,2)} \qquad\qquad \mathbf{exp\ 5.62.}$$

Using exp 5.51., 5.54. and the results of calculations by exp 5.59., the first part of exp 5.62. is expanded into

dp(ngirls,1,1,(needmon(badly,100/1.0))) (1.0) $\wedge$
ip(ngirls,1,1,(traid(vhigh,80/0.4, high,70/0.9, low,50/0.3), wilg(st,90/0.8,
wk,40/0.5))) (0.61, 0.43, 0.84, 0.75, 0.62, 0.39) $\rightarrow$ $\qquad\qquad$ **exp 5.63.**
(cf of rule = 1, .8, .6, .4
in(lokedfor,1,1,(wellpaid(verywell,well),interesting(very,just)))

in which
1. We assume the single uncertainty in 'dp',
2. The result of calculations from exp 5.61. or the 'cf' is written after 'dp' which is a general convention in further calculations,
3. There are 4 values of cf of rule each asserted here arbitrarily for illustration as there are 4 combinations of 2 grades of each adverbial qualifier: (verywell, very), (verywell, just), (well,very), (well,just).

To do the calculations using exp 5.40. we have: (1, 0.8, 0.6, 0.4) x
min ((1.0, 0.61), (1.0, 0.43), (1.0, 0.84), (1.0, 0.75), (1.0, 0.62), (1.0, 0.39))

for each cf of rule.

Thus, for each 'minimum value' in the brackets and for each combination, the results of calculations of cf for the adverbial qualifier of 'in' or the consequent are:
for (verywell, very) --- 1 x (.61, .43, .84, .75, .62, .39) = .61, .43, .84, .75, .62, .39
for (verywell, just) --- .8 x (.61, .43, .84, .75, .62, .39) = .49, .34, .67, .6, .5, .31
for (well, very) --- .6 x (.61, .43, .84, .75, .62, .39) = .37, .26, .5, .45, .37, .23
for (well, just) --- .4 x (.61, .43, .84, .75, .62, .39) = .24, .17, .34, .3, .25, .16

We note that exp 5.63. conforms to the pattern of exp 5.40. since there are two terms in the antecedent.

For the second part of the 'unit of change' exp 5.62., we have:

in(lokedfor,ngirls,1,ngirls,1,(wellpaid(verywell,well),interesting(very,just))) with 24 terms of cf values, 6 for: ((verywell, very), (verywell, just), (well, very), (well, just)) →

exp 5.64.

(1) ap(ngirls,2,2,(engagedinlookingfor (wellpaid, interestingjobs)))(with 24 terms of cf values, 6 for each combination: ((verywell, very), (verywell, just), (well, very), (well, just))

which conforms to the pattern of exp 5.39. since there is one term in the antecedent.

We now describe the details of *how to develop exp 5.63. and 5.64.* with variation of qualifiers, as follows:

1. Exp 5.51. is the equation of which the adjectival qualifiers in 'units of change' in their operational form are constructed. A particular case of this equation is the first part of exp 5.63.
2. In the first line of exp 5.63. for 'dp', a particular case of exp 5.51., we assume that the 'number of girls 'definitely' (from Figures 5.19. and 5.20., 100/1.0) needed money' with 'badly' indicating the grade. Here an adverb is used to qualify 'needed', a stative verb.
3. Details of the second line of exp 5.63. for 'ip', a particular case of exp 5.51., are shown in exps 5.53. and 5.60.
4. After the conditional sign signifying 'then', the horizontal arrow, the cf of rule are asserted. For example, when cf of rule = .8, 'almost certain' from Figure 5.19., means that the 'certainty that the number of girls looked for (very well paid, just interesting) jobs ranges from .49 to .31. as shown above by the second line (verywell, just) of the calculations for cf of adverbial qualifier.
5. In the first part of exp 5.64. for 'in' to obtain cf values for the interaction, we use the 'calculations for the minimum values' above, 24 values.

6. 'In the calculation for the minimum values' we use the **adverbial profiles** which are worked out in point 3. following exp 5.63.

7. In exp 5.64. values of cf for 'ap' follow that of in(1,1) because the cf of rule is assumed to be 1.0 and the interaction is the only term in the antecedent, no 'ep' property as in the 'unit of change' exp 5.45., for example.

Remarks &&&

We note the increase of the number of cf values of the conditional as a result of variation of adjectival and adverbial qualifiers, 24 in this case. When certainty is propagated further this number increases further unless regulated by 'cp' properties as discussed in section 5.4. A feature of propagation of certainty is the *rapid increase in the variety of possibilities of outcomes* expressed by certainty factors.

Exp 5.63. and 5.64. are a particular case of exp 5.3. or **unit of change** which repeatedly recurs throughout 'linguistic modelling', with details of variation of adjectival and adverbial qualifiers. When a 'story' of a scenario is transformed into *homogeneous language* of 1 – and 2 – place sentences the result is sequences of 'units of change' represented as a semantic diagram or dynamic, linguistic network.

Additional remarks:

1. In the second part of a unit of change such as exp 5.3 or 5.45. in general and in exp 5.64. in particular, according to generalisation **102.**, a change of state, 'ap', will occur since change is necessarily followed by interaction. However, the certainty of change depends on the levels of certainty of the constituents in a 'unit of change'. For example, in exp 5.64. cf of rule in front of 'ap' is taken as 1.0 since we believe that change is a certainty given that the antecedent, in(1,1) can be true.

2. In exp 5.64. there are six conditionals for each of the four variations of the adverbial qualifier of the interaction or there are 24 possibilities or there are 24 acquired properties, 'ap', to occur. This is the case as we can see in exp 5.3. or 5.45. but in general

acquired property 'ap' = past participle of the
dynamic verb designating interaction
qualified by adverbials **exp 5.65.**

However, in general

108. --- 'An object or an agent can have one grade at a time under a property name'. ----

We can trace each conditional following the appropriate cf values.

For example, using abbreviations in exps 5.63. and 5.64., we can have

dp(1,1) (1.0) ∧ ip(1,1) (0.61) → (0.8) in(1,1) (0.8 x min(1.0, 0.61) = 0.49) for:
(verywell, just)

exp 5.66.

in(1,1) (0.49) for: (verywell,just) → (1.0) ap(2,2) (1.0 x 0.49) = 0.49 for:
(verywell, just)

similarly for all the others. We can repeat this expansion for each of all cf values in exp 5.63. and 5.64. and regard it as a time sequence of variation of properties as time passes or just select one or more 'expressions' for transmission. We bear in mind the time taken for 'change of state' to acquire a new property 'ap' as indicated by the dotted directed line in Figure 5.20. for each cf expansion.

Exps 5.63. and 5.64. with acquired property, ap(2,2), can be expanded in words:

'**If** there is a number of girls with very high training and strong willingness who badly needed money **then** they looked for [very well paid and very interesting job] or [very well paid and just interesting job] or [well paid and very interesting job] or [well paid and just interesting job]', and

'**If** they looked for [very well paid and very interesting job] or [very well paid and just interesting job] or [well paid and very interesting job] or [well paid and [just interesting job] **then** they are engaged in looking for [very well paid and very interesting job] or [very well paid and just interesting job] or [well paid and very interesting job] or [well paid and just interesting job]'.

3. Here we see a range of adverbial profiles carried by the interaction belonging to a particular cf value. However, an 'ap' property can have only one adverbial profile at a time, according to generalisation **108.** here there are 24. The selection of a specific adverbial profile is aided by performance related properties, 'pp' [Korn, 2009]. For example, if we assume that the 'number of girls are very ambitious and highly intelligent' then they are more likely 'to look for very well paid and very interesting jobs'. This will then select the first of the four choices of the adverbial profiles in exp 5.64.

4. The acquired property, outcome, 'ap(2,2)' or the consequent in exp 5.64. can occur with each of 6 certainty factors for the 4 adverbial profiles. Therefore, in total, 'ap(2,2)' can occur on 24 different occasions. There is no preference, each occurrence can happen with equal probability. In other words, 'ap(2,2)'or the 'number of girls engaged in looking for (well paid, interesting jobs etc)' can be in any one of 24 **equally probable states**. At the moment they are seen to happen in sequence or as described in point 3.

End of **Remarks &&&**

5.6. Product and systems design parameters, products as 'static, linguistic networks'

According to the 2nd hypothesis put forward in section 3.1., we say that '[systems or structures] are created for [changing equilibrium states from an initial to a final state]'. This statement is reflected in Part B. and Part A. respectively in the scheme diagrammed in Figure 3.1. The means to effect the change itself is the 'interaction' in any of the variety of its manifestations as discussed in section 4.2. With reference to Figure 3.1., the instrument which actually exerts the 'interaction' is 'product [3]'.

In section 3.1. we mention four particular cases of 'systems' of the general scheme diagrammed in Figure 3.1. Here we are concerned with 'Utilising and Producing systems'.

In BOTH CASES: For the product [3] to exert 'interaction' it needs to be **ready**. The term 'ready' means the following ----

A. *In case of Utilising systems*
As considered in section 4.3. product [3] is 'available from store' i.e.
1. 'When a person wants to travel from a suburb to the city centre, the prompt, h/she goes to the bus station and catches the appropriate 'bus', the product [3], which is capable of accomplishment of the desired change of state i.e. 'h/her body's position changes.' or
2. 'To achieve the same outcome, h/she can call a 'taxi' which functions as product [3] when prompted by the 'driver.'' or
3. 'If h/she wants to insert a nail in a piece of wood, the prompt, h/she uses a 'hammer', the product [3], which when used properly by 'skilled power' discussed in section 4.2., will change the position of the nail'.
4. 'In this case, if the nail is regarded as the product [3] which when inserted will hold the piece of wood tightly to another. Accordingly, there is a progression of the concept of product [3].' or
5. 'If h/she has the inspiration and wants to occupy h/her mind, the prompt, borrows a 'book', the product [3], from the library which can affect the mental state of the reader.'

As indicated in Figure 3.1., we note that in all cases the product [3] itself is 'prompted or driven' by the 'User/Producer system [2]' *before* exerting interaction.

So 'ready' means the product [3] is 'available' and *capable of or is in a state of* receiving an input to prompt or to enable it to exert the required interaction'. Both, 'input' and 'interaction' are expressed in terms of **'properties'**, 'stimulating properties' as suggested by generalisation **106.** in section 5.3.

B. *In case of Producing systems*
In this case, the product [3] does not yet exist, it has to be fabricated or manufactured or employed [in case of living things as in case of a 'person being trained for the position of waiter'] by using 'constructing properties' followed by assembling, if required, and delivering to MARKET [4] to sell as indicated in Figure 3.1. Reaching this stage of existence means 'ready' for a product [3].

The diagrammatic representation of 'Product and System design parameters' is shown in Figure 5.22. The interpretation of this figure needs knowledge of:

A. Figure 3.1. in section 3.2.

B. The variety of interactions considered in section 4.2.

C. Stages of 'Implementation of Part A.' of Figure 3.1. in section 4.3.

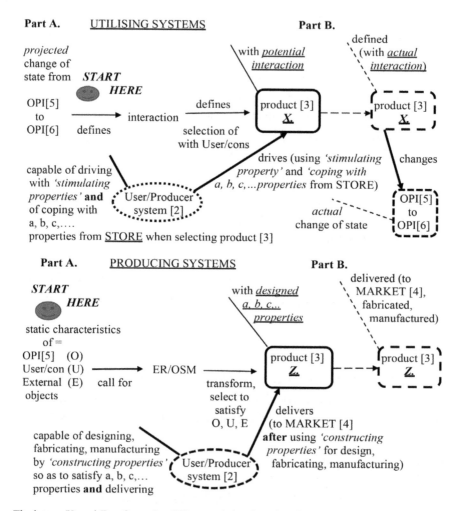

The letters X. and Z. refer to the different origin of product [3].

Figure 5.22. Diagram of Product and System design parameters

The term 'design parameters' means those 'properties' which a product [3] and a user/producer [2] must have in order to fit into or to match **requirements** generated by implementation of Part A. of the scheme in Figure 3.1. Further to 'Implementation of Part A.' and with reference to Figure 5.21., the *design parameters* are formulated as follows

For *Utilising systems*

Product [3] is to
1. Be selected so as to exert the correct kind and magnitude of *interaction*, and
2. Have the specified a, b, c,... *properties*,

User/Producer [2] is to be capable of
1. Driving product [3] using 'stimulating properties' which are selected from point B. above,
2. Coping with issues arising from prevailing a, b, c,.... properties.

For *Producing systems*

Product [3] is to have the
1. Designed a, b, c,.... *properties*, and
2. Required kind and magnitude of *interaction*,

User/Producer [2] is to be capable of
1. Designing, fabricating, manufacturing product [3] using 'constructing properties' so as to satisfy a, b, c, ... properties, and
2. Delivering product [3] to MARKET [4] with the view to sell.

The application of 'Design parameters' in particular cases is aided by the 2nd criterion, the scheme in Figure 1.1. in section 1.3. and Figure 4.2. in section 4.2.

Products as 'static linguistic networks

The product [3] in Utilising systems appears as a 'whole', it is recognised and designated as such when selected from STORE by the 'systems designer' or 'observer' or 'customer'. However, in Producing systems a product [3] as required in the scheme in Figure 3.1. does not exist, it has to be constructed by a User/producer systems [2] using *constructing properties* carried by 'contingent sentences'. Contingent sentences are modelled by 1 – and 2 – place sentences such as exp 5.3. and diagrammed as Figure 5.4. in section 5.1.

A 'static, linguistic networks' are introduced in section 5.3. Here they are used for representing 'products [3]'. The intention is to express products [3] as networks so that

1. The *'tree'* as a necessary condition for unique definition of a network i.e. product [3], can be found, and
2. The multiplicity of *'trees'* can be made explicit to show the variety of possibilities of existence of products [3] leading to emergence of *unexpected* as well as useless forms.

A product [3] is constructed from 'acquired properties, ap,' as given by exp 5.65. [Past participle or passive voice of a dynamic verb + its adverbial qualifier] when they **no longer change** in a dynamic, linguistic network. The concept of dynamic verb is familiar but that of 'adverbial qualifier' is not which is now introduced.

The structure of the *'acquired property'* consists of:

1. The 'ap' symbol carried by the dotted line attached to the *changed object* of the 'affected object' at the end of the directed, dotted line in the second of the 'unit of change' such as exp 5.3. or semantic diagram,
2. The relation which is formed from the passive voice of the dynamic verb derived from the active voice which designates the interaction which changes the affected object,
3. The adverbial which qualifies the dynamic verb can be:

x. Adverbials which are in a **1**st bracket = [manner, degree, time, cause, purpose, reason, assertion, 'information', 'energy', properties in section 4.1.], and

y. Adverbials which are in a **2**nd bracket = [place, object, thing, parts of sentences treated as adverbs (The boy jumped {off the table})].

Adverbials in the 1st bracket result in 'reduced ordered pairs' since they lack a concrete or abstract second object. Adverbials in the 2nd bracket result in 'ordered pairs' because they are objects.

Information or energy are treated as adverbials and are either given as part of a story, inserted to complete a story or needed in 'design specifications' [Korn, 2009, 2013].

They are carried by *specific dynamic verbs*. For instance, 'to push' carries mechanical energy flow or physical power or 'to notice' carries information as a subordinate clause as in 'the boy noticed that 'the ball is stuck on the roof'' [Burton, 1984, Korn, 2009].

For example adverbs in contingent sentences:

1st bracket === Manner: He works carefully, Degree: He is totally exhausted, Time: They arrived late, Cause....: She is consequently dismissed, Assertion: She will surely be dismissed by boss (true or false),

2nd bracket === Place: They went {to Spain} for the winter, Part of sentence: Man covered the door {with paint} in which 'to Spain', case of location, and 'with paint', case of instrument, is regarded as adverb [Fillmore, 1968].

The subsequent action results the 'door' becoming

door (is covered (well) with) paint

or 'door' and 'paint' were separate entities at time = 0 but later the two objects are brought together and we conclude that the 'door is painted'. Otherwise the sentence is regarded as a 'three – place sentence' requiring *linguistic analysis* to convert it into 1 – and 2 – place sentences [Korn, 2009].

This completes the description of the notion of '*adverbials*'.

The 'changing or affected object' in a dynamic, linguistic network or semantic diagram such as exp 5.3. depicted in Figure 5.4. in section 5.1., exhibits an **affected object**, 'ep' property which is carried over to the changed object with 'ap' property since an object when changes keeps this property. This property is understood to facilitate or to hinder the change of state of a changing object or has features of the changing object describing its **state**.

An 'ep' property acts as an adjectival qualifier of the affected object which is positioned in a semantic diagram at the arrowed end of the continuous line designating 'interaction' and is carried over to the 'ap' property. It is shown in a linguistic network of an *ordered pair* as a continuous line attached to the first object of the ordered pair.

Using examples from the 1st and 2nd brackets, we convert an 'acquired property' into elementary, static, linguistic network of 'reduced and ordinary ordered pairs' as shown in Figure 5.23. The notation is also shown with the lower case letter 'n' to replace 'ap'.

Considering another example with 'story': 'The long, passenger train braking hard arrived punctually at platform 4'.

The semantic content and assignment of 'ep' properties and 'reduced order pairs' are the subject matter of 'conventional science', they contribute nothing to the *structure* of a linguistic network formed by 'ordinary ordered pairs' which is a matter for 'systems science' as shown by Figure 5.24., for example.

Generalised expressions for ordered pairs

Only adverbs of 'place, object, thing' in the 2nd bracket can contribute to the structure of a 'product' and as such forms 'ordinary ordered pairs'. All other adverbial phrases form 'reduced ordered pairs'. In a linguistic network they are represented by directed lines connecting two nodes and by self -loops respectively. A 'reduced ordered pair' occurs when we have adverbials from the 1st bracket or when a noun phrase in a 'case' in Case Grammar terms other than 'agentive' is represented as an adverbial [Fillmore, 1968].

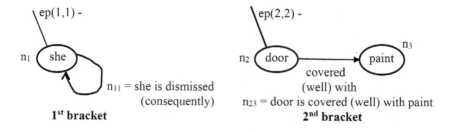

Figure 5.23. Ordered pair representation of 'acquired properties'

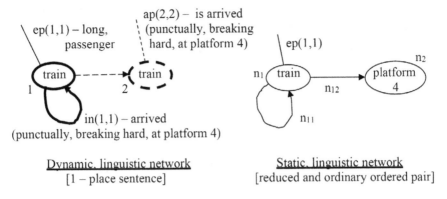

Dynamic, linguistic network
[1 – place sentence]

Static, linguistic network
[reduced and ordinary ordered pair]

Figure 5.24. Semantic diagram and linguistic network of 'train' scenario

A verb can be qualified by more than one adverbial phrase from the 1st bracket leading to a 'reduced ordinary pair'. Only *one adverbial* of 'place, object, thing' or 'assertion' can be attached to a verb to form an 'ordinary ordered pair' otherwise Rule 3. in [Korn, 2009] will be contradicted. For example, we can say 'the long, passenger train arrived punctually [time], breaking hard [manner] at platform 4 [place]' which is represented as a semantic diagram of 1 – place sentence with outcome as linguistic network in Figure 5.24.

In Figure 5.24. we have

n_{12} = [long, passenger] train (is arrived at) platform 4 (place)

exp 5.67.

n_{11} = [long, passenger] train (is arrived at [punctually (time), braking hard (manner)])

and at ap(2,2) in Figure 5.24., the ordered pair is written as n_{12} (n_{11})

or the 'acquired property' is related to a 'reduced' and an 'ordinary' ordered pair.

Accordingly, in *general* we have

$n_{cx}(n_{cc})$ = [ep(b,b)]object c (passive/active voice of verb [adv(from 1st bracket)]) object x (from 2nd bracket) [adj]

exp 5.68.

where the passive/active voice of a dynamic/stative verb is an *obligatory* component, 'b' and 'c' designate the affected and changed object, 'x' designates an object from the 2nd bracket.

Alternatively

$$n_{cx} (n_{cc}) = [ep(b,b)] \text{ object } c \text{ } [ap(c,c)] \qquad \textbf{exp 5.69.}$$

Exp 5.68. and 5.69. signal the achievement of *'acquired properties'* and have been expressed as *'ordered pair'*.

Using the 1st and 2nd brackets, from exp 5.68. we can have the following particular cases

1. No adverbial qualifiers
    $n_c = [ep(b,b)]$ object c (passive/active voice of verb)

2. Using the 1st bracket
    $n_{cc} = [ep(b,b)]$ object c (passive/active voice of verb [adv from 1st bracket])

3. Using the 2nd bracket **exp 5.70.**
    $n_{cx} = [ep(b,b)]$ object c (passive/active voice of verb) object x (2nd bracket))[adj]

4. Using the 1st and 2nd brackets when written separately
    $n_{cx} (n_{cc}) = ncc + n_{cx}$

Note: All qualifiers are written in *square brackets*.

We look at an example reproduced from [Korn, 2013] but modified which is intended to demonstrate the *emergence* of a product [3] as a structure of 'ordered pairs' arising from 'acquired properties' of objects and to explore the consequences. In general

109. --- 'A product [3] consists of 'acquired properties' as described by exp 5.65., carried by objects or agents which are part of the dynamic, linguistic network and no longer change, in addition to objects or agents as adverbials from the 2nd bracket as shown in exp 5.68.' ---

The narrative or 'story' of the scenario: 'There is a farm with land for grazing but in the winter for the cows to be able to give milk, they must eat hay which is delivered to them by the farmer who uses a tractor, from the store to the cow shed twice a day. The cows are milked every morning by means of machines. Having accomplished these jobs, the farmer is content'.

The STAGES of 'linguistic modelling' are

A. Homogeneous language of context – free, 1 – and 2 – place sentences derived from the story by *meaning – preserving, linguistic transformations* [in this case there is no need since all sentences are already in this form]

The farmer [1] delivered hay [2]
The farmer placed to cows [5]
The farmer connected machines [8]
Machines milked cows

All are 2 – place sentences and constitute the *topology of scenario*, thus, enables the 'semantic diagram' to be constructed.

B. Semantic diagram
Shown in Figure 5.25.

C. Adjectival qualifiers with grading or other modifiers [such as certainty factors [Durkin, 1994, Korn, 2009]]. No grading etc. is used in this example.

$dp(1,1)$ – for the cows
$ip(1,1)$ – uses tractor
$ep(2,2)$ – nutritious
$ep(5,5)$ – hungry
$ep(8,8)$ – working

D. Interactions with adverbial qualifiers

in(1,2) – The farmer delivered hay [from store to shed, twice a day]
in(,5) – The farmer placed [hay] to cows
in(,) – The farmer connected machines [to cows]
in(,) – Machines milked cows [until no milk]

E. Logic sequences or topology of the scenario with graded adjectives and adverbials

No grades are introduced in this example, how to obtain 'causal chains' is explained in the example in Figure 5.5. in section 5.1.

Causal chains: 1. 3,2,1   2. 10,6,5,4   3. 9,8,7   4. 12,11

For causal chain 1.
$dp(1,1) \land ip(1,1) \rightarrow in(1,2)$
$in(1,2) \land ep(2,2) \rightarrow \mathbf{ap(3,3)}$ no more change of state, we form an ordered pair to be part of product [3]

At ap(3,3) from exp 5.70. the ordered pair is written as

$ap(3,3) = n_{1,4} =$ [nutritious] hay (is delivered [twice a day, from store to]) shed

For causal chain 2.
$ap(3,3) \rightarrow in(3,1)$ feedback link 'prompts' change of state ap(4,4),
$in(3,1) \rightarrow ap(4,4)$ **decision junction**
$ap(4,4) \rightarrow in(4,5)$
$in(4,5) \land ep(5,5) \rightarrow ap(6,6)$
$in(9,6) \land ap(6,6) \rightarrow \mathbf{ap(10,10)}$ link in(9,6) is assumed to exist, no more change of state, we form an ordered pair to be part of product [3]

$ap(10,10) = n_{2,5} =$ [hungry] cows (are milked [until no]) milk

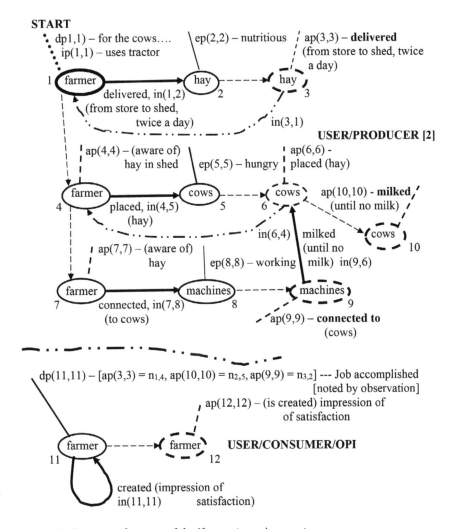

Figure 5.25. Semantic diagram of the 'farmer/ cows' scenario

For causal chain 3.

ap(6,6) → in(6,4) feedback link 'prompts' change of state ap(7,7),

in(6,4) → ap(7,7) **decision junction**

ap(7,7) → in(7,8)

in(7,8) ∧ ep(8,8) → **ap(9,9)** no more change of state, we form an ordered pair to be part

ap(9,9) = $n_{3,2}$ = [working] machines (are connected to) cows

$ap(9,9) \rightarrow in(9,6)$
$in(9,6) \wedge ap(6,6) \rightarrow ap(10,10)$

For causal chain 4.
$dp(11,11) \rightarrow in(11,11)$
$in(11,11) \rightarrow ap(12,12)$

Development of product

There are 5 objects or agents in the scenario which can be identified in Figure 5.25. as follows with numerals assigned arbitrarily:
Hay 1, cows 2, machines 3 which are active part of the dynamic, linguistic network
Shed 4, milk 5 which act as adverbs to dynamic verbs designating 'interaction'.

Using these objects or agents in exps 5.20., 5.21. in section 5.2., we set up the array in exp 5.71.

n_{11}	n_{12}	n_{13}	$\mathbf{n_{14}}$	n_{15}	
n_{21}	n_{22}	n_{23}	n_{24}	$\mathbf{n_{25}}$	
n_{31}	$\mathbf{n_{32}}$	n_{33}	n_{34}	n_{35}	**exp 5.71.**
n_{41}	n_{42}	n_{43}	n_{44}	n_{45}	
n_{51}	n_{52}	n_{53}	n_{54}	n_{55}	

in which the symbols in bold designate the 'ordered pairs' derived from the semantic diagram in Figure 5.25. and are reproduced below
$ap(3,3) = n_{1,4} =$ [nutritious] hay (is delivered [twice a day, from store to]) shed
$ap(10,10) = n_{2,5} =$ [hungry] cows (are milked [until no]) milk
$ap(9,9) = n_{3,2} =$ [working] machines (are connected to) cows

In exp 5.71. the 'ordered pairs' in bold result in a *disconnected* linguistic network as depicted in Figure 5.26. without the bold, dotted branch.

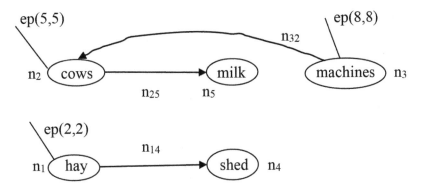

Figure 5.26. Static, linguistic network of 'farmer/cows' scenario

Remarks &&&

1. This example uses terminology from the scheme in Figure 3.1. in section 3.2. and represents an instance of Part B. The story omits any reference to a 'problematic situation', Part A. does not enter the example, it relates a number of events that results in what is interpreted as a 'product [3]' expressed in terms of 'ordered pairs'. The product [3] is perceived by the 'farmer' who could be User/consumer or OPI, who after h/she completed h/her work to express satisfaction or otherwise.

2. The product [3] as it appears in Figure 5.26. is disjointed which could not deliver a single interaction. The static, linguistic network needs to be completed to form a 'tree' as discussed in section 5.3. by inserting in this case a single link.

To satisfy Rule 3 and 4 in section 5.3., this link can be selected from either of the last two rows of exp 5.71. since $n = 5$ and $(n - 1) = 4$ in exp 5.71. We can have the following choice:

n_{42} = shed, cows $\quad n_{43}$ = shed, machines $\quad n_{45}$ = shed, milk
n_{51} = milk, hay $\quad\quad n_{54}$ = milk, shed

The rest of the links form loops in the static, linguistic network in Figure 5.26. The ordered pair 'milk, shed' is selected because it can be expressed like 'milk (is carried to) shed' or 'milk (is stored in) the shed' which makes sense and is inserted in Figure 5.27. forming a 'tree'.

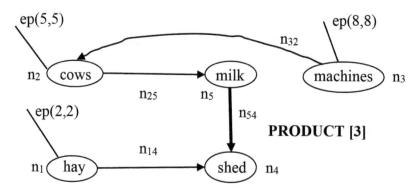

Figure 5.27. Representation of product [3] as a tree

The introduction of an additional ordered pair in Figure 5.27. calls for an additional 'system' in the User/Producer [2] in Figure 3.1.

3. Here we introduce the notion of *measure of complexity* of a scenario which is given by exp 5.72.

measure of complexity = number of ordered pairs that constitutes a product

exp 5.72.

which in this case is 4. We note that the 'measure of complexity' reflects on the 'complexity' of User/Producer [2]. In this example to construct the product [3] an additional 'producer system' is needed.

4. We can calculate the number of groups of ordered pairs 'n − 1' in a digraph from eq.5.32. in section 5.3. For 'n = 5' and the 'total or maximum number of branches is 'n (n − 1', this equation gives (20 x 19 x 18 x 17)/(1 x 2 x 3 x 4) = 4845. This is the number of variations of 'trees' one of which is given in Figure 5.26. and produced by the User/Producer [2] as depicted in Figure 5.25.

The growth of the number of possibilities of connections of objects or nodes as the number of nodes increases offers an immense number of choices to *chance*.

5. After constructing the *structure* of a scenario or without it, a branch of 'conventional science' can enter for working out problems associated with aspects of the scenario. Here we are concerned with 'business science' (finance, accounting, law, marketing and so on) with its own story encapsulating it interest which can be the continuation of the narrative of the scenario:

'The herd of cattle consists of 56 cows each eating 15 kg of hay a day during winter time assuming there is no grass and gives 18 litres of milk a day. The price of hay is £250 a tonne. The question for the farmer is --- 'If the winter lasts 90 days what is the minimum selling price of milk to break even ???"

The mathematical model: Total cost of hay is 56 x 0.015 x 250 x 90 = £18900 from which the minimum selling price of milk 18900 = 56 x 18 x 90 x price which is about £0.2 per litre.

6. This example is a manifestation of the application of generalisation **500.** considered in section 4.2. concerning *interactions* and their structural symbolism represented as 1 – and 2 – place sentences seen as a semantic diagram or dynamic, linguistic model, the 'elementary product [3] in section 5.1. in Figure 5.3.

The application of 'elementary products' to contribute to the construction of a 'total product [3]' in Figure 5.26. and 5.27. delivered by User/Producer [2] in Figure 5.25. and sensed by the User/consumer in the same figure.

End of **Remarks &&&**

5.7. Consideration of 'meaning preserving, linguistic transformations'

In section 1.3. we discussed that a *symbolic structure* has to have a basic element just like any physical structure of which it is seen to consist. In constructing a *systems theory* such element needs as far as possible to satisfy the 'generality of the systemic or structural view of the world' which is introduced as the 1st hypothesis of systems thinking in section 3.1.

This means that when constructing a 'symbolic structure' of a part of the world along the lines as indicated in Figure 1.1. in section 1.3., there has to be a *transformation* performed by the brain/mind apparatus from the results of observation to 'elementary constituents' of some kind. For example, from observing the change of position of a 'railway carriage' from standing on level ground, we can produce the sentence of the symbolic structure of 'natural language': 'The 'engine' attached to the 'railway carriage' pushed it resulting in its motion'. Physical scientists then went into a great deal of effort to conceptualise this kind of experience into the abstract notion of 'force' with the symbol 'f' and unit 'newton'. Over the centuries the discipline of physics followed by engineering have evolved a coherent 'system' of 'abstract, measurable notions' of physical properties and variables to be used for constructing mathematical models of varying generality [Pledge, 1966, MacFarlane, 1970, Boylestad, 1987, Korn, 2007].

We note that the immediate result of observation is the production of symbolic structure leading to structural model [embodiment of the former in a medium] of 'natural language'. Natural language is available to all, it is the first stage of development of all kinds of models although it may not be explicitly formulated as the practice is in the 'performing and fine arts', it is called the *primary model*.

No disciplines other than the physical sciences such as physics and chemistry, have succeeded in achieving the development of 'elementary constituents (elcon)' of comparable fundamentality. To develop a 'systems theory' it is a requirement to suggest an elcon which can serve as an acceptable 'basic building block' of systems or structures. Quantifiable properties which are the elcon of the various disciplines of physical sciences, are not suitable because they are too restrictive, they exclude properties like *emotive and intellectual* such as 'anger' and 'clever'. So, the effect on behaviour of possession of this kind of properties cannot be estimated and included in the dynamics of scenarios.

The only symbolic structure of generality that approaches the generality of the 'systemic view' is **natural language**. However, natural language formulated into a 'story' or 'narrative', is too complex, with too much expressive power, too vague and with highly abstract terms, to serve as elcon as used by people in its raw form. *Specific, linguistic expressions* need to be *transformed* into 1 – and 2 – place sentences, the elcon proposed in section 1.3. so as to preserve the *meaning* of the original expression as far as possible. This kind of transformation is called *meaning preserving, linguistic transformation* (MPLT).

The **intention** is to demonstrate the *application of MPLT* to *'specific expressions'*.

This means breaking down *linguistic complexities* into their components 1 – and 2 – place sentences which show the following general features:
1. They are the *minimal* linguistic structures which make 'complete sense' [Burton, 1984],
2. They clearly exhibit the structure of 'subject – predicate' with one noun as the 'subject' and another in the 'predicate' with any one playing the roles of
    a. Initiator,
    b. Affected participant
    c. Neutral participant i.e. neither a. not b.

A. Passivisation

Passivisation is a grammatical transformation process which relates sentences of the *active form*:
NP1 + V + NP2 (noun phrase1 + verb + noun phrase2)
to sentences of the form = NP2 + be + V'ed + NP1.

The effect of this is to bring into prominence NP2 of the active sentence. As far as diagramming is concerned, the effect of passivisation is to turn the direction of directed lines joining a pair of contours in a semantic diagram towards the contour carrying the 'affected object' or noun phrase. Passivisation has been used in the feedback loops of Figure 5.25. designated by the chain dotted lines.

For example, using the sentence 'Alfred [NP1] burnt [V] the cake [NP2]', after passivisation it becomes 'The cake [NP2] was [be] burnt [V'ed] by Alfred [NP1]'

B. Conversion of 3 – and 4 – place sentences

There are verbs which combine with three or four noun phrases and there are *two, general ways* of doing the 'conversion' which is demonstrated by an example for each = =

First, 'Combination of 2 – place sentences'.

For example, the 3 – place sentence: 'John sent the letter to Bill' can be replaced by
'John sent the letter' [deleting the NP3] AND
'The letter was sent to Bill' [passivizing the original sentence with deleted NP1]

in which 'John is the 'initiator' and the inanimate object 'letter' is the 'affected' object: 'It has acquired the new property of 'being on the way to Bill''.

For example, the 4 – place sentence: 'The men carried the food from the kitchen to the canteen' which can be replaced by
'The men carried the food' [deleting the NP2 and NP3] AND
'The food from the kitchen was carried to the canteen' [passivising the original sentence with deleted NP1]

Second, Treating the noun phrases in the predicate as 'qualifiers'

Using the sentences above as demonstration, we have

3 – place sentence: 'John sent [the letter] to Bill' where the noun in bracket is an adverb,
4 – place sentence: 'The men carried [the food from the kitchen) to the canteen' where the phrase in square brackets is an 'adverb'.

In both cases, the result of transformation is a 2 – place sentence with a dynamic verb which can be diagrammed as shown in Figures 5.28. and 5.29.

C. Treatment of clause relations

By clause relation is meant the way in which the 'information' of one clause

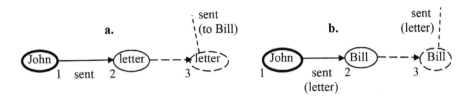

Figure 5.28. Result of transformation of a 3 – place sentence

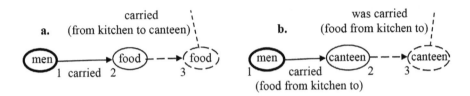

Figure 5.29. Result of transformation of a 4 – place sentence

is understood in the light of 'information' contained in another. Each of the statements is meaningful, has full sense, on its own and their relation is indicated by *connectives* the function of which is:

1. To signal the semantic content of the clause to which they are attached,
2. To join the two adjacent clauses.

There are many ways of expressing 'connectives', here we give only one example of each relation. The following clauses are used for demonstrating the *method*:

'Wilson appealed to technologists to support his party'. 'He won many middle-class votes.'

If we assume that 'Wilson's appeal' was successful and 'technologists' had middle-class votes then these two clauses express a sequence in which one event follows the other. Within this broad meaning, we have available a number of possibilities of relations between the two clauses which can be made explicit by the use of 'connectives' as follows:

a. Cause

BECAUSE Wilson appealed to technologies, he won many middle-class votes.

b. Means

BY appealing to technologies, Wilson won many middle-class votes.

c. THOUGH Wilson appealed to technologists, he DID NOT win many middle-class votes.

The *method* to fit 'clause relations' into 'linguistic modelling' i.e. to express their meaning by 1 – and 2 – place sentences, is to replace the 'connectives' by statements which contain respectively verbs:

a. 'causes', **b.** 'enables', **c.** 'contrasts' and shown in Figure 5.30.

Remarks &&&

We note that a 2 – place sentence with a dynamic verb can be discerned in both, the 3 – and 4 – place sentences. The rest of the sentences are treated as adverbs which differ in complexity. However, depending on which noun is selected as an 'affected object or agent', the semantic diagram is different. Otherwise it is the same for both kinds of sentences.

Further to Figures 5.28. and 5.29., in both cases in the 'first' method in part a. the 'accusative case' in case grammar term is the 'affected object'. In

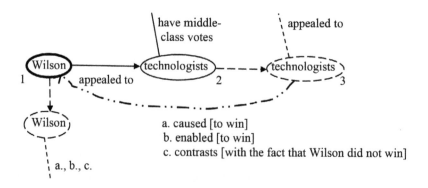

Figure 5.30. Examples of treatment of clause relations

the 'second' method in part b. we have the 'dative' case or the 'case of the *beneficiary*' which, although the topology of the semantic diagrams is the same, is naturally more 'acceptable' to an 'observer' because the notion of 'acquire property' is closer to that of 'beneficiary' than to that of 'direct object'. [Fillmore, 1968]

End of **Remarks &&&**

CHAPTER 6

APPLICATIONS OF ASPECTS OF *SYSTEMS THEO-RY/PROBLEM SOLVING*

---- The aim of CHAPTER 6.: The basic ingredients of a 'systems theory' are put forward in the introduction to CHAPTER 5. by exp 5.2.: The general principles to be tested and the linguistic model which can do it [when needed]. The general principles or hypotheses are presented in section 3.1. In CHAPTER 4. we developed the basis of 'systems theory' and in CHAPTER 5. we described the techniques including an introduction to 'linguistic modelling', which are needed to work out the details of 'systems theory'. The intention in this chapter is to apply the preceding material to scenarios which yield particular cases of various complexity as measured by exp 5.72. in section 5.6.----

6.1. Linguistic modelling of scenarios with energetic and informatic interactions

In section 4.2. we discussed the different kinds of 'interactions'. This simple 1st example is intended to demonstrate how interaction as 'physical power' is modelled in linguistic modelling.

The **1st EXAMPLE** is from the technical field of energy conversion which shows explicitly the 'flow of energy' or physical power. The terms 'energy' and 'power' are well defined in physics and described as a form of interaction [Korn, 2009].

The 'story' goes as follows: 'Water is stored in an artificial lake restricted by a dam. When released, the water drives a very efficient turbine. The output power of the turbine is 8 MW when its shaft is rotating at 120 rad/s which it delivers to an ac generator with overall efficiency of 0.6. The generator supplies power 24 h a day into the local electricity distribution grid'.

Following the pattern in section 5.6., the linguistic model representation of the description of the scenario or its story is:

A. Homogeneous language of context – free, 1 – and 2 – place sentences derived from the story by *meaning – preserving, linguistic transformations* [in this case there is no need since all sentences are already in this form]

Water [1] drives turbine [2]
Turbine [3] delivers generator [4]
Generator [5] supplies grid [6]

C. Adjectival qualifiers with grading or other modifiers [such as certainty factors [Durkin, 1994, Korn, 2009]]. No grading etc. is used in this example.

dp(1,1) – released
ip(1,1) – restricted by dam
ep(2,2) – very efficient
ep(4,4) – efficiency 0.6
ep(6,6) – local [assumed adjectives]

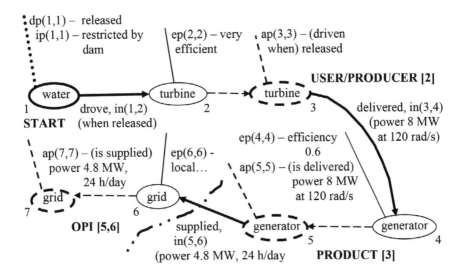

Figure 6.1. Semantic diagram of energy flows in 'water' scenario

D. Interactions with adverbial qualifiers

Water drives [when released] turbine
Turbine delivers [power 8 MW at 120 rad/s] generator
Generator supplies [power 4.8 MW, 24 h/day] grid

B. Semantic diagram

Shown in Figure 6.1.

E. Logic sequences or topology of the scenario with graded adjectives and adverbials

From the semantic diagram in Figure 6.1. we write the single causal chain by following the direction of arrows in reverse starting at an object without further change of state which is the 'grid'. [No grading in this example]

Causal chain: 7,6,5,4,3,2,1

which is followed by the predicate logic sequence [Korn, 2009]
1/1 $dp(1,1) \land ip(1,1) \to in(1,2)$
1/2 $in(1,2) \land ep(2,2) \to ap(3,3)$
1/3 $ap(3,3) \to in(3,4)$
1/4 $in(3,4) \land ep(4,4) \to ap(5,5)$
1/5 $ap(5,5) \to in(5,6)$
1/6 $in(5,6) \land ep(6,6) \to \mathbf{ap(7,7)}$

in which acquired properties act as a driving properties. This means that an object will have acquired a property which it then uses to drive another.

The acquired property of the 'generator', $ap(5,5)$, functioning as the product [3] is represented as 'ordered pair' and shown as 'static, linguistic network' in Figure 6.2. [Korn, 2009].

We calculate the output power of the generator as 4.8 MW as its efficiency is 0.6 [Korn, 2012].

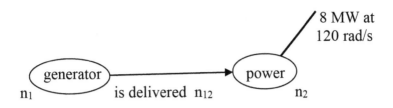

Figure 6.2. Linguistic network representation of 'generator'

Remarks &&&

This example demonstrates the representation of a straightforward, technical scenario by means of linguistic modelling to show that interaction as physical power is carried as 'adverbial qualifier'. The example gives a clear view of structure of an 'energy conversion scenario' i.e. objects interacting in terms of physical power and the effect of the qualifiers on its **outcome** i.e. interaction [5,6] assuming the 'generator is regarded as 'product [3]. Having made the structure explicit or demonstrated the 'systemic view' in concrete terms, particular problems can be considered in depth using the appropriate 'product and system design parameters', not considered here, from aspects of mechanical and electrical engineering.

The example considers only Part B. of the 'problem solving' scheme in Figure 3.1. There is no User/consumer with 'acceptability conditions' so the 'grid' regarded as OPI accepts whatever value of power the 'generator' supplies.

The structure in Figure 6.1. shows a Utilising system as shown in Figure 5.22. in section 5.6. with 'generator', product [3], selected so as to deliver 'electrical power' stimulated by 'mechanical power', it is an 'energy converter' [Korn, 2012]. The User/Producer [2] is subject to 'Point I/1. to supply physical power as interaction as discussed in section 4.3. Its other design parameters, 'a, b, c, ... properties' are not given. The medium part of the interactions are 'water, shaft and copper wire' shown as energy conversion proceeds.

End of **Remarks &&&**

The 2nd **EXAMPLE** is intended to demonstrate an understanding of the concept of 'information' and its application as a mode of interaction as discussed in section 4.2. A brief background of this concept is also described.

A historical background of the concept of information

An early reference to the use of information, although oblique, was made by Maxwell in his paper on 'engine governors' [Maxwell, 1868] and through the notion of 'demon' [Jeans, 1921]. In both, information is considered in the context of operation of a purposive system. The job of the demon was to recognise molecules with different speeds enclosed in a closed container separated by a wall with a hole. The demon then opened and closed the hole to let the faster molecules into one part and the slower ones into the other. By this means the demon raised the temperature in one section of the container and lowered it in the other, apparently, without expenditure of work. This contradicts the 2nd law of thermodynamics, a paradox which was not resolved until recently. Nowadays we recognise that Maxwell pointed to the operation of control systems consisting of energy and information bearing regions interfaced by an amplifier with appropriate power supply which, theoretically, requires zero physical power at its input port to operate [Korn, 1995].

Szilard recognised that the demon was acting on information. He invented the term 'negentropy' in this connection [Szilard, 1929]. Brillouin made important contribution to the link between thermodynamics and information [Brillouin, 1956]. The question of information was raised later in the context of transmission of electrical signals [Nyquist, 1924, Hartley, 1928] leading to Shannon's work [Shannon, Weaver, 1964]. Information as a concept with meaning was investigated [Bar-Hillel, 1964]. A theory of information was proposed by Devlin [Devlin, 1991]. Information theory appears to be a subject still developing and is a topic of intense interest [Winder, 1997, Flynn, 1998].

Although systems for the transmission of information had been in existence since living things felt the need to communicate, the notion of information system has evolved as a result of development and extensive use of personal computers and their effect on methods of management and business [Stair et al, 2008]. The nature and principles of operation of information systems is not established and a suggestion is made to this effect here.

Considering the literature, the concept of information appears to have been treated in isolation without a theory of information systems. Such systems are immensely pervasive in their use by living things in the context of 'purposive configuration', they are **innate** as pointed out in section I.1. in humans, animals and plants at micro and macroscopic levels and used by the vast variety of organisations formed by these things. Information is used by physical objects predominantly as part of purposive systems, inclusive of hardware type of control systems, to bring about a mental change of state directly or indirectly, in much the same way as energy is utilised. Accordingly, we intend to discuss:

1. The concept of information from the point of view of its = Playing a part in the operation of information systems, and Modelled by 'linguistic modelling',
2. The application of linguistic modelling of scenarios to the design of such systems using the method described in section 4.3.

Concept of information

We discuss the notion of information from the point of view of its acting as a *kind of interaction* as discussed in section 4.2. for the change of *mental states* of chosen, changing objects, OPI [5-6] in Figure 3.1. in living things. There are many kinds of mental states described by abstract terms like 'sadness', 'cleverness' summarised under 'Properties' in section 4.1. which can be caused or alleviated by 'informatic products'. In general, in the context of information, we are concerned with two forms of change of mental states:

A. From *uncertainty* (when we are aware of a choice or selection of objects or possibilities) towards more *certainty*. For example, in 'The passenger (product [3] generating information) 'notices' (information bearing dynamic verb) that 'the train has 5 carriages with 20 rows of seats each with 4 seats (subordinate clause carrying *information with uncertainty*)'" [Burton, 1984]. The passenger (also playing the part of OPI [5] receiving information) may be prompted by this information to find a particular seat which leads to h/her having acquired *certainty* (OPI [6] Final state).

B. From *ignorance* (when we are not or partially aware or not certain about an aspect of a part of the world) towards *awareness* or *certainty*. For example, in 'The guard (product [3] generating information) 'warned' (information bearing verb) the waiting passengers (OPI [5] with ignorance or Initial state) that 'the train overdue by 20 min or 30 min, is now approaching (subordinate clause carrying *information with awareness*)". We assume that the purpose of the 'guard' (product [3]) in creating and transmitting this information is to input awareness to passengers (OPI [6] Final state of mind) to get them ready for boarding the train (action, see Figure 1.1. in section 1.3.) when it arrives at the station.

Accordingly, we have two types of information which are used to alleviate:
1. The means of relieving uncertainty is called *selective information* (selection of a particular item from a group of items or ensemble like choosing a letter from a number of letters or a seat on a train or an arrangement of on/off switches).
2. The means of relieving ignorance or introducing certainty where there is uncertainty, is called *semantic information* (generation of messages like issuing notices, instructions or commands, giving advice, transmitting feelings like pain, love etc).

The notion of information flow in section 4.2. as a 'kind of interaction' which has been given in the context of linguistic modelling applies to *both types of information* since they are both transmitted in the same way:
'Carried by a medium and the concept is signalled by 'information bearing, dynamic verbs' with information itself is contained in subordinate clauses as demonstrated by the examples just given and as such can be covered by the same definition'.

Classical communication theory is concerned with 'selective information' only. In this theory
1. The length of strings of two symbols made up of 1 and 0 required to assign distinguishing labels to each of the number of items in an ensemble [such as the number of tools in a toolbox] called *Information* is given by the *'logarithm to the base 2'* of the total number of item in the ensemble, or
2. There is a number of possibilities [numerals on the sides of a dice] of occurrence of events and any one of them can occur with equal probability then the *amount of Information* is given by the *'logarithm to base 2'* of the inverse of probability of all possibilities of occurrence of events.

For example, the ensemble or set 'Table, chair, bed, wardrobe' consists of 4 items and '$\log_2 (4) = 2$' is the length of strings to assign distinguishing labels to the 4 items in the set i.e. 11, 10, 01, 00. Or there are 8 sides of an object with equal possibilities of occurrence when the object is thrown like a dice or there are 8 items in an ensemble. Then the probability of occurrence of any one is 0.125 and the Information given by '$\log_2 (1/0.125) = 3$ which means that there are 8 strings 1 and 0 of length of 3 to distinguish every single possibility i.e. 111, 110, 101, 100, 011, 010, 001, 000. Accordingly, both kinds of information are given by the same mathematical expression [Hartley, 1928, Shannon, Weaver, 1964].

The above brief consideration is intended to demonstrate that both kinds of information are identical from the point of view *labelling*. Our intention is to relate both kinds of information to the *choice arising from variation of qualifiers of sentence elements* in 1 – and 2 – place sentences in processed natural language. These sentence are carried by 'special, dynamic verbs' designating interactions as subordinate clauses acting as adverbials. Unprocessed natural language is called the *primary symbolism* that can be manipulated by the mind and in terms of which other symbolisms can be expressed such as 'road signs [triangle means 'danger']' or a 'mathematical model [two apples plus one apple equal three apples' [Johnson-Laird, 1988].

1st: *Consideration of selective information*

Further to the 'Acceptability conditions' discussed in section 4.3., the problem here is similar in that we face a number of items available from which we have to select one or more subject to 'acceptability conditions' in the context of an informatic situation.

Let us look at the example above which is an 'information bearing' sentence.
'The passenger   (product [3] generates information)
'notices'   (information bearing dynamic verb)
that 'the train has   5 carriages with 20 rows of seats each with 4 seats.
                        (subordinate clause carrying *information with uncertainty*)'''.

There is uncertainty as far as the 'passenger' is concerned because h/she needs only 'one seat' and confronted with 5 x 20 x 4 = 400, a very large 'choice' or 'selection' to choose from.

The 'passenger' now plays the User/consumer [7] to formulate the *Acceptability conditions*' so as to create a guidance in selecting the required seat:

H/she is aiming at = Sitting in the first carriage nearest to the front of the train
which reduces the choice to 1 x 20 x 4 = 80
Sitting in a forward facing seat, there are 10 rows
which reduces the choice to 1 x 10 x 4 = 40
Sitting next to a window
which reduces the choice to 1 x 10 x 2 = 20 (1 seat on each side)
Sitting at the end of the row of seats
which reduces the choice to 1 x 1 x 2 = 2, *the final choice.*

The method described generates an 'Acceptability condition' with 'properties of seats' which are outside the 'properties' or adjectival and adverbial phrases of the 'noun phrases' given in the information. For example, 'Given in the information: A carriage has 20 rows of seats', and 'Given in the Accessibility condition: A carriage has forward facing seats.' The fulfilment of this kind of Acceptability condition requires 'human perception and judgement'.

The Acceptability condition is narrower if we restrict its formulation to contain the 'kinds of properties' which are used to qualify the nouns and the verb which comprise the information i.e. the subordinate clause. However, the method becomes amenable to mathematical manipulations by Cartesian products like the exp 5.5. in section 5.2. We consider a simpler example but along the same lines as the previous one: 'The train has 2 coaches each with 2 compartments and in each compartment there are 4 seats'. We want to find the total number of possibilities of different arrangements of seats or the size of *choice.*

We introduce the notation: coaches, $A = \{A1\ A2\}$, compartments, $B = \{B1\ B2\}$, and seats, $C = \{C1\ C2\ C3\ C4\}$ which are regarded as sets. The Cartesian product or the ensemble of the three sets is given by exp 6.1.

A1 B1 C1	A2 B1 C1
A1 B1 C2	A2 B1 C2
A1 B1 C3	A2 B1 C3
A1 B1 C4	A2 B1 C4
A1 B2 C1	A2 B2 C1
A1 B2 C2	A2 B2 C2
A1 B2 C3	A2 B2 C3
A1 B2 C4	A2 B2 C4

exp 6.1.

Since each item is different, from exp 6.1. we have, for example, for: A1 B2 C3 = 'The seat is in the first coach, compartment two and it is number three'. The person seeking a particular seat can formulate h/her Acceptability condition from the *choice* offered by exp 6.1.

2nd: *Consideration of semantic information*

Semantic information is about introducing *variation* of qualifiers of sentence elements in a simple sentence occupying the position of subordinate clause of an information bearing verb. The diagrammatic representation of semantic information is shown in Figure 6.3.

The variation of qualifiers introduces *ignorance* and *uncertainty* into a statement because we no longer know which of the possibilities offered is valid or true. and a 'choice' needs to be made to relieve it which can be

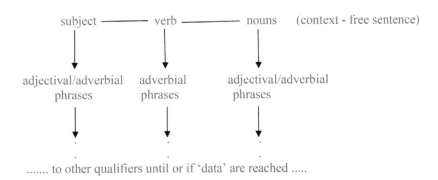

Figure 6.3. Diagram of semantic information

done by formulating 'acceptability conditions' in the context of operating an *information system*. This is going to be demonstrated now.

Figure 6.4. shows an example of the sentence: 'John was bored with his job so he wrote a letter to his boss saying that he, a high wages man, unwillingly resigns from the company, with good working conditions, in 1 week' in which the qualifiers are expanded as given in Figure 6.4.

The notation to designate the three sets in Level 1 is introduced:

$X = \{A(hw), B(lw)\}, Y = \{C(uw), D(wi)\}, Z = \{E(gwc), F(pwc)\}$ from which we generate the ensemble by expanding the sets using *Cartesian product* as exp 5.5. in section 5.2. with 2 x 2 x 2 = 8 items to obtain

$$
\begin{array}{ll}
A\,C\,E & B\,C\,E \\
A\,C\,F & B\,C\,F \\
A\,D\,E & B\,D\,E \\
A\,D\,F & B\,D\,F
\end{array}
$$
exp 6.2.

which is the *variation* of qualifiers at Level 1. Each variation makes a sentence in the subordinate clause i.e. the information, for example, ACF = 'A high wages man unwillingly resigns from a company with poor working conditions'. So a choice of 8 variation of information has been created.

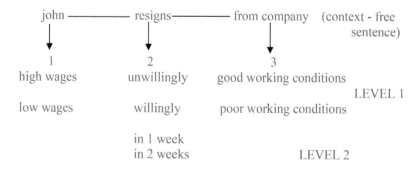

Figure 6.4. Semantic information in 'john/company' example

In addition, in Figure 6.4. any or all of the qualifiers in LEVEL 1 can be expanded, for example, we have

(1 w), (2 w) for Y = {C(uw), D(wi)} which when inserted into exp 6.2. gives a *vertical* expansion in exp 6.3.

A C1 E	B C1 E
A C1 F	B C1 F
A C2 E	B C2 E
A C2 F	B C2 F
A D1 E	B D1 E
A D1 F	B D1 F
A D2 E	B D2 E
A D2 F	B D2 F

exp 6.3.

Any of the items in exp 6.2. or 6.3. can appeal to the 'boss' since they are equally likely to occur before formulation of *'Acceptability conditions'*. For example, the statement in the 1st line of the 1st column in exp 6.3. is read as follows:

'A C1 E': 'The boss becomes aware of the letter written by john who is on 'high wages' resigns 'unwillingly' in '1 week' from the company with 'good working conditions'' which is one of the 16 alternatives.

In general, the schemes depicted in Figures 6.3. and 6.4. can be expanded indefinitely: In LEVEL 1 any number of 'vague' adjectival phrases can be added *horizontally* to qualify the subject and the other nouns and to qualify the verb with adverbial phrases. LEVELS 2, 3 and so on, or the *vertical* expansion, can be created under each adjectival and adverbial phrase in LEVEL 1 leading to 'nested' qualifiers at this level. This idea can be expressed symbolically as follows:

$$\text{For any: (LEVEL1 QUAL)}\left[\prod_{i=1}^{i=I} (L2Q)_i\right] \text{ for any } \prod_{j=1}^{j=J} (L3Q)_j \text{ and so on} \qquad \textbf{exp 6.4.}$$

We look at an example to demonstrate the use of exp 6.4.

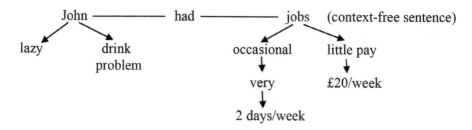

Figure 6.5. Representation of semantic information

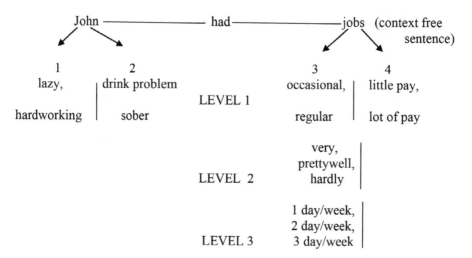

Figure 6.6. Variation of qualifiers in semantic information

'John was a lazy kind of man with a drink problem who had very occasional jobs 2 days a week on the average with little pay of about £20 per week'. This sentence is regarded as a subordinate clause i.e. information and is shown diagrammatically in Figure 6.5. Each qualifier in the semantic information in the diagram in Figure 6.5. can be varied as shown in Figure 6.5. The selection of terms in a variation, or choice or possibility, or the manner of variation is guided by selecting 'opposites' or 'grading' so as to vary the character trait of a person carrying the information. In case of 'lazy' the alternative is 'hardworking'. We have also graded 'very' and '2 days/week'.

For the context free sentence 'john had jobs' we can construct a possible qualified sentence 'john, lazy and sober, had jobs which are pretty well occasional, 2 days/week, with little pay'.

To work out the possible variations of sentences in Fig.5.5., we introduce abbreviations for the qualifiers from which sets are constructed as follows:

X = {A(lazy), B(hardworking)}, Y = {C(drink, D(sober)}, Z = {E(occa), F(reg)}, W = {G(little), H(lot)}

from which we can construct the *horizontal variations* of qualifiers at LEVEL 1 using Cartesian product

A C E G	A D E G	B C E G	B D E G	
A C E H	A D E H	B C E H	B D E H	
A C F G	A D F G	B C F G	B D F G	**exp 6.5.**
A C F H	A D F H	B C F H	B D F H	

giving 2 x 2 x 2 x 2 = 16 variations or 16 items in the ensemble. We can pick any of the variations to reproduce a sentence. For example, 'B C F H' means 'John, hardworking with drink problem, had regular jobs with a lot of pay'.

However, there are *vertical variations* as the qualifiers at LEVEL 1 are further qualified towards data. Referring to Figure 6.6. we introduce the abbreviations:

For E(occa) – x(very), y(prew), z(hard), and for y(prew) – 1(1d/w), 2(2 d/w), 3(3 d/w),

which is expressed by the symbols as follows: E x, E y 1, E y 2, E y 3, E z. This expression means:

  E x = occasional (very),

  E y 1, 2, 3 = occasional (prettywell, (1 day/week or 2 day/week or 3 day/week)),

  E z = occasional (hardly).

As exp 6.4. indicates, other terms like 'regular', 'little pay' etc. in Figure 6.6. can also be graded in a similar way.

The vertical variations are substituted into the horizontal variations

A C E x G	A D E x G	B C E x G	B D E x G	
A C E x H	A D E x H	B C E x H	B D E x H	
A C E y 1 G	A D E y 1 G	B C E y 1 G	B D E y 1 G	
A C E y 1 H	A D E y 1 H	B C E y 1 H	B D E y 1 H	
A C E y 2 G	A D E y 2 G	B C E y 2 G	B D E y 2 G	
A C E y 2 H	A D E y 2 H	B C E y 2 H	B D E y 2 H	**exp 6.6.**
A C E y 3 G	A D E y 3 G	B C E y 3 G	B D E y 3 G	
A C E y 3 H	A D E y 3 H	B C E y 3 H	B D E y 3 H	
A C E z G	A D E z G	B C E z G	B D E z G	
A C E z H	A D E z H	B C E z H	B D E z H	
A C F G	A D F G	B C F G	B D F G	
A C F H	A D F H	B C F H	B D F H	

For expansion of LEVEL 1 qualifiers 'E', exp 6.4. becomes

$$\begin{array}{ll} i = 3 & i = 3 \\ E(x, y, z) \text{for 'y'} E(1, 2, 3) = 5 \\ i=1 & j=1 \end{array}$$

which occurs 8 times resulting in 40 terms, plus 8 unexpanded terms in exp 6.5. gives 48 terms altogether in exp 6.6. Thus, if a diagram like Figure 6.6. and exp 6.5. are known
exp 6.4. can be used for calculating the number of terms in the expanded form of exp 6.5. which is exp 6.6.

Remark &&&

We have suggested the notions of 'selective' and 'semantic' information and introduced a single method for modelling the notion of information which fits into linguistic modelling. In both cases it is a *choice* of a particular occurrence out of a variety which is the common factor to attempt to alleviate uncertainty or remove ignorance.

Particular cases of the concept of information are:

1. According to interpretation here, the context – free sentences like the one in the top line of in Figure 6.5., for example, contains 'zero' information because it cannot be used for effecting a 'choice'. However, such sentences carry 'meaningful' statements and people happy to use them because they are an efficient way of exchanging messages and people are aware of and can supply additional *background* meaning as required. For example, we can say 'John gave money to Mary' and, although this is a context – free sentence, we can be sure that 'Mary knows what John is doing'. Her state of mind has been changed by 'zero' information. In other words, human beings can have their minds changed by 'zero interaction', unlike material objects which need external stimulus as suggested by generalisation **102.** in section 5.1.

2. A context – dependent sentence such as the one shown in Figure 6.5. locates to a limited extent sentence elements in the 'space of their meaning' giving no 'choice' but certainty or awareness of a state of affairs. This is 'one' information.

3. When we make a statement expressing a thought about an aspect of a scenario of which we are not sure, we use the term *impression*. For example, we can say 'My impression is that you are not happy about the outcome of our conversation'. The term 'impression' calls for a subordinate clause which carries the substance of the 'message' and which can change 'mental states' so we accept this as 'one vague' information.

4. A change of mental state can take place when we experience the sensation of *temptation* as long as the sensation is expressed in terms of a sentence. For example, we can say 'That bed looks comfortable I am tempted (to lie down and may go to sleep)'. Here the phrase in brackets is 'one' information.

5. As considered here, information is carried by a *medium* which is a necessary condition for making it sensitive to perception by 'living things' so as to change their mental states in response to 'signals' from external sources including own body. The difference between humans and non – humans is that the brain/mind of the former can turn signals into thoughts which they can express as symbolic models of high expressive power. There are animals which can do the same resulting to symbolic models of limited expressive power.'

End of **Remark &&&**

Formulating the 'Acceptability conditions'

To make a 'choice' in a scenario like 'buying a dress in a store of dresses' can be done by *guessing* or by constructing an *informed judgement* for effecting a 'selection' or for accepting a 'suggestion' of a number of items. Formulating Acceptability conditions is a way of constructing an informed judgement based on *reasoning*. The 2nd Stage of implementation of Part A. of the scheme in Figure 3.1. in section 4.3. is concerned with Acceptability conditions for selecting products [3] for producing 'selective' as well as 'semantic' information.

In section 6.1. we have discussed what is meant by 'information' in the context of 'linguistic modelling'. As considered in section 4.2. physical power as well as information flow is a form of 'interaction' produced by product [3] as shown in the scheme in Figure 3.1.

Here we intend to elucidate how an 'object or agent [inanimate or animate, artificial or natural]' responds to an interaction based on h/hers or its physical, mental and/or intellectual perceived or imagined, make up or construction. The notion of *interaction* is seen as discussed in section 4.2. and carried by the product [3] in section 4.3. i.e.

interaction = Material object carrying *energy*

        ditto   ditto   *qualities/quantities* including *use*

        ditto   ditto   *influence* including *information* and *inference*

This is proposed to be done in the following *STEPS*:

1. Assignment of a *designation* to an individual or group which recognises it and carves it out of the background environment as a whole or concentrates attention on a part of the world,
2. Selection of *parameters* which puts the individual or group in the *context of interest* from the point of view of the 'investigator' or observer of the 'problematic situation' or any scenario. This step is a start of implementation of the general statement VWX. in section 2.2. regarding the restriction of knowledge when making symbolic statements or modelling parts of the world,

3. Assignment of particular instances of 'parameters' called *identifying properties*, IP, which narrow down the designation to a particular case as appears in a scenario under consideration,

4. Using the 'identifying properties' we ask 'If such an object or agent has such properties which *instance of the choice* of *interaction* h/she finds acceptable, or in case of inanimate objects, which instance of the choice is acceptable or match as seen by an *observer*.

Alternatively,

5. For a given set of 'identifying properties' of a designation, which *designed* or *selected instance* of *interaction* can be *'offered'* to the object or agent.

STEP **4.** is carried out by using the *Entailment Relations* shown in Figure 4.5. in section 4.3.

We consider an example which involves 'information flow' attached to a 'dynamic verb' for changing mental state [Korn, 2009, 2013]. The 'story' is as follows: 'Local inhabitants in a village are retired people with symptoms of withdrawal into isolation which may result in mental and physical illness. Health workers use young persons for delivering letters with information to 'locals''.

The dynamic, linguistic network or semantic diagram without details of linguistic modelling, is shown in Figure 6.7.

The 'Acceptability conditions' are developed by 'health workers' and they are as follows:

1. Designation – Locals

2. Parameters –   **3.** Identifying properties -

          Age   IP1 – Elderly, 70 and over

          Occupation   IP2 – Formerly professional

          Social status   IP3 – Retired, reluctant to change

          Personality traits   IP4 – Perhaps prone to worry

          State of health   IP5 – Reduced hearing, eyesight

                                      IP6 – Tendency to physical, mental isolation

IP act as *initial state*, IS, of *object or agent.*

4. Following the scheme in Figure 4.5., application of the Entailment Relation to this example

A. There are IP 3, 6, the *initial mental state*, AND
B. To change or to improve mental state implied by the properties in A.,
C. *REQUIRES* delivery of *information* to attempt to change to *final mental state* 'to become more amenable to accept changes' and 'to reduce the feeling of being isolated'.

In view of IP3 and 6, the *information* to be delivered is likely to be: Health workers feel that 'information is about activities for locals' [context – free sentence]

available   attracting
A walks   D opportunity to talk
B exercise   E opportunity to play games in doors
C putting on plays

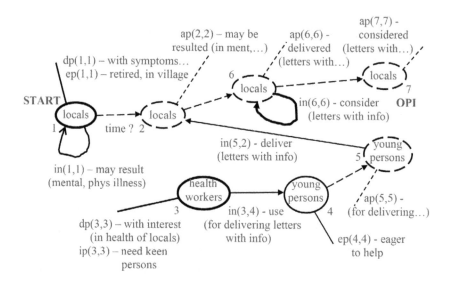

Figure 6.7. Semantic diagram of 'locals' scenario

Following Figure 6.6., we have X = {A(W), B(E), C(P)}   Y = {D(T), E(G)} which are grouped as before

| A D | B D | C D | <u>Walk Talk</u> | <u>Exind Talk</u> | <u>Play Talk</u> |
| A E | B E | C E which mean: Walk Games | Exind Games | Play Games |

from which the health workers conclude that 'if locals engage in the underlined activities they will achieve their 'final mental state'.

Comparing the semantic diagram in Figure 6.7. with the scheme in Figure 3.1., we can say that: Locals – OPI, Product [3] – young persons, User/producer [2] – health workers who created the product [3] by recruiting the 'young persons' and produced the 'interaction'.

We now return to the *'John/company' example* for which the diagram of 'information' is depicted Figure 6.4. The 'story' is reproduced here: 'John was bored with his job so he wrote a letter to his boss saying that he, a high wages man, unwillingly resigns from the company, with good working conditions, in 1 week'.

The STAGES of 'linguistic modelling' are
A. Homogeneous language of context – free, 1 – and 2 – place sentences derived from the story by *meaning – preserving, linguistic transformations,* MPLT, when necessary
John wrote a letter
Letter was noted by boss (MPLT: Necessary for perception and passivised)
Boss was told (MPLT: Passivised to make 'boss' the affected object)
Boss considered

Note: The last 3 sentences have been added to enable a meaningful, semantic diagram to be constructed. These sentences constitute the *topology of a scenario*, thus, leads to construction of a semantic diagram or dynamic, linguistic network.

C. Adjectival qualifiers with grading or other modifiers [such as certainty factors]

dp(1,1) – fedup (very, just)

ep(2,2) – written in capital letters (Added to qualify 'letter')

ep(4,6) – understanding, gentle (qualifier of 'boss' at object 4 but becomes effective at object 6)

D. Interactions with adverbial qualifiers

in(1,2) – wrote (strongterms, mildterms)

in(3,4) – was noted by

in(5,5) – was told (info: resigns…)

in(6,6) – considered (acceptance of letter…)

in which we have added grades and adverbial qualifiers or have modified the original story of the scenario as considered appropriate. This is an instance of the freedom of choice or the liberty to manipulate thoughts offered by linguistic modelling. We now introduce uncertainties [Durkin, 1994, Korn, 2009].

E. Logic sequences/topology of the scenario

Causal chain: 7, 6, 5, 4, 3, 2, 1

1/1 dp(1,1) → in(1,2)

1/2 in(1,2) ∧ ep(2,2) * ap(3,3)

1/3 ap(3,3) → in(3,4)

1/4 in(3,4) → ap(5,5)

1/5 ap(5,5) → in(5,5)

1/6 in(5,5) → ap(6,6)

1/7 ap(6,6) → in(6,6)
1/8 in(6,6) ∧ ep(4,6) → **ap(7,7)**

F. Logic sequences with graded qualifiers/data for cf

1/1 dp(john,1,1,(fedup(very,90/0.8, just,50/0.4)))(0.8,0.4) →
      (0.7)in(wrote,john,1,letter,2,(written(strongterms)))(0.7 x 0.8 = 0.56),
      alternatively
      (0.7)in(wrote,john,1,letter,2,(written(mildterms)))(0.7 x 0.4 = 0.28)

in which, according to exp 5.61., there is one term in the antecedent, therefore,
(90 x 0.8)/90 = 0.8 and (50 x 0.4)/50 = 0.4 and
in this and subsequent statements, according to exp 5.39.:
'cf of consequent = (cf of antecedent x cf of rule)' [Korn, 2009]

1/2 in(wrote,john,1,letter,2,(written(strongterms,0.56))) →
      (1)ap(letter,3,3,(written(strongterms,0.56))), alternatively

in(wrote,john,1,letter,2,(written(mildterms,0.28))) →
      (1)ap(letter,3,3,(written(mildterms,0.28)))

1/3 ap(letter,3,3,(written(strongterms,0.56))) →
      (1)in(noted,letter,3,boss,4,(written(strongterms,0.56))), alternatively
      ap(letter,3,3,(written(mildterms,028))) →
      (1)in(noted,letter,3,boss,4,(written(mildterms,0.28)))

1/4 in(noted,letter,3,boss,4,(written(strongterms,0.56))) →
      (1)ap(boss,5,5,(awareofletter(0.56), alternatively
      in(noted,letter,3,boss,4,(written(mildterms,0.28))) →
      (1)ap(boss,5,5,(awareofletter(0.28)))

1/5 ap(boss,5,5,(awareofletter(0.56))) →
      (1)in(told,boss,5,5,(byletterabout(resig,0.56))),
      alternatively
      ap(boss,5,5,(awareofletter(0.28))) →
      (1)in(told,boss,5,5,(byletterabout(resig,0.28)))

1/6 in(told,boss,5,5,(byletterabout(resig,0.56))) →
    (1)ap(boss,6,6,(awareofletterabout(resig,0.56))), alternatively

    in(told,boss,5,5,(byletterabout(resig,0.28))) →
    (1)ap(boss,6,6,(awareofletterabout(resign,0.28)))

1/7 ap(boss,6,6,(awareofletterabout(resig,0.56))) →
    (1)in(consid,boss,6,6,(acceptletter(strongterms,aboutresign,0.56))),
    alternatively

    ap(boss,6,6,(awareofletterabout(resig,0.28))) →
    (1)in(consid,boss,6,6,(acceptletter(mildterms,aboutresig,0.28)))

1/8 in(consid,boss,6,6,(acceptletter(strongterms,aboutresig,0.56))) ∧
    ep(boss,4,6,(nature(gen/und,100 x 1/100 = 1))) →
    (1)**ap(boss,7,7,**(withconsid(acceptletterinstrongterms,aboutresig,
    0.56))), alternatively

    in(consid,boss,6,6,(acceptletter(mildterms,aboutresig,0.28))) ∧
    ep(boss,4,6,(nature(gen/und,100 x 1/100 = 1))) →
    (1)ap(boss,7,7,(withconsid(acceptletterinmildterms,aboutresig,
    0.28)))

in which there are two terms in the antecedent, therefore, according to exp 5.40., 'cf of consequent = min of cf of antecedent x cf of rule' [Durkin, 1994, Korn, 2009]. Here we have TWO 'certainty factors' and the states, ap, can propagate *alternatively* along either depending on whether: 'John was *very* fed up, with cf = .56, probable, or *just* fed up, with cf = .28, may be, from Figure 5.19. in section 5.4.'

B. Semantic diagram

Shown in Figure 6.8.

Further to Figure 6.8. the 'boss becomes aware of John's letter' at contour 5 and h/she sees that the 'letter' is about 'his resignation' at contour 6 the 'acceptance' of which is considered at contour 7.

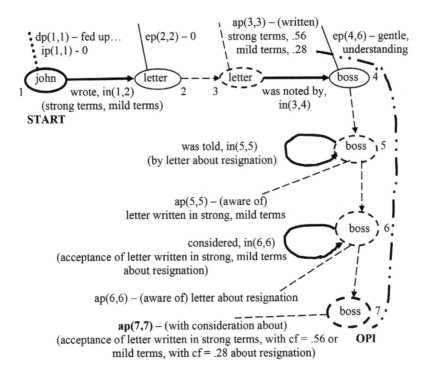

Figure 6.8. Semantic diagram of 'john/boss' problem

The 'information content of the letter' is evaluated and is presented by exp 6.3. and any one of the 16 alternatives can be seen by the 'boss'.

The likely alternatives for 'acceptance' are considered by the 'Acceptance conditions' which is set out below.

1. Designation – Boss

2. Parameters –
    In control
    Manage
    Knows people
    Tends to be emotional
    Tends to be rational

3. Identifying properties -
IP1 – Mild
IP2 – Good at managing
IP3 – Knows people well
IP4 – See ep(4,6)
IP5 – Not h/her strong point

4. Application of the Entailment Relation gives

A. There are IP 3, 4, 5, the *initial mental state*, AND
B. To rely on this mental state to bring about 'acceptance of resignation',
C. REQUIRES delivery of information with any one of the *choice* of 16 possibilities in exp 6.3. to the 'boss' as shown in the semantic diagram in Figure 6.8.

It is not known which of the possibilities comes to the 'boss' attention because 'John' can write any one. However, judging from IP 3, 4, 5, the most likely 'instance of information' which may lead to 'acceptance of resignation', is 'B C1 or 2 E' because 'Although, 'John is on low wage' but despite 'good working conditions' he is still 'unwilling to resign in 1 or 2 weeks''. This view is supported by the 'higher certainty of John feeling 'fed up''.

Remarks &&&

Commenting on the 'John/boss' problem in Figures 6.4. and 6.8., we note the three stages of *information processing*:
1. Modelling the scenario with means of carrying information [letter] as shown in Figure 6.8.,
2. Preparing information as depicted in Figure 6.4., and
3. Constructing the 'Acceptance conditions',
in this case, have been carried out independently, there is no *'design thinking'* involved. In other words, 'John' or anybody else is not engaged in identifying a 'problematic issue' followed by the procedure suggested by the scheme in Figure 3.1. The 3 points are demonstrated by this example.

However, we can relate the parts in the example to those in Figure 3.1. as suggested by exp 1.1. in section 1.3. The 'boss' is OPI [5,6] who receives 'interaction' as 'information' from 'John' who prepares it, thus, he is product [3]. Presumably, he also prepares the medium to carry information i.e. the 'letter' and arranges for its delivery to 'boss', 'John' plays the part of User/producer [2] as well, also, 'John' plays the part of User/consumer [7] and that of brain/mind [1] who monitors his own satisfaction with 'resignation'.

We note that information, *emotive* such as 'strong terms, mild terms' and *factual* such as 'about resignation' is carried as adverbial qualifier of the dynamic verb designating 'informatic interaction' which is another general feature of the method of linguistic modelling [Korn, 2009].

We note that the 'boss' can be exposed to a large number of variations or 'choice' of information as shown by exp 6.3. of which one is selected as guided by the 'Acceptability conditions'. Construction of 'Acceptability conditions' requires expert knowledge of people and it sets in motion a methodical selection of interaction from a choice for the accomplishment of change of state of OPI [5,6].

Apart from selecting a particular case of 'information' from the *choice* offered, information may affect the mental state of a person by
A. Timing the release of information, for example, 'The government announces increase of tax when there is a perceived outside threat to the country', or
B. Order of release of information when there is more than 'one' simple sentence, for example, 'A parent tells his son [first] that there is a present of a sailing boat waiting for him', followed by [second] 'The news that he failed his entrance examination'.

All these suggestions are debatable and carried out depending on the intellectual and mental state of the parties involved.

In this section we have discussed examples related to 'energetic and informatic' interactions as considered in section 4.2. We have also introduced the notions of 'selective' and 'semantic' information and a method which models both in the same way that fits into the use of 'linguistic modelling'.

End of **Remarks &&&**

6.2. Linguistic modelling of scenarios with material interaction

Scenarios involving material interaction which is discussed in section 4.2., occur commonly in everyday practice. The symbolism of any kind of 'interrelation' is physically implemented in terms of 'matter' exhibiting *properties* tangible to senses or to instruments called 'model' and produce a *signal* or a *sign* which can be 'interpreted' or deciphered by the brain/mind. The 'brain/mind' can then decide which particular kind of 'interrelation' is carried by the model.

This idea is captured by the diagrams in Figures 1.1. in section 1.3. and in 4.2. However, the whole process can be carried out 'instinctively' without resorting to the works of imagination. In this case, energetic interaction carrying 'force', for example, can be felt directly and creates a change of state of material body of a person or any other body like a mountain when it is affected by an 'earthquake', for example.

Here we consider particular cases involving 'material interaction' and as the 1st **example** we use the application of SSM in section 2.2. [Checkland 1982] for demonstration of how to put the 'systems theory' as proposed here, into practice. The intention is to apply the complete scheme diagrammed in Figure 3.1.

Implementation of Part A.

The *story* of the 'problematic situation' is as follows: 'A householder having inspected his garden fence made of timber, concluded that it needed redecorating or changing. He decided to do the job himself so as to ensure that it will enhance the visual appearance of the property to fit in with h/her neighbour's property'.

1st STEP

The *investigator* of the problematic situation thinks that according to the 'story' the 'timber, garden fence' is identified by the 'householder' as the object needing redecoration or the source of the problem. In other words, it carries the 'problematic issue'. This interpretation implies that

OPI [5] = = Garden fence

or Initial state [IS] of OPI [5] is identified as the
'Timber, garden fence is in 'unsatisfactory state of decoration'.

2nd STEP

The 'householder' plays the part of User/consumer. H/her 'expectation' is

or Initial, mental state [IS] of User/consumer [7] is recognised as the 'Garden fence is to be in a satisfactory state of decoration and to accomplish this is to cost the least of the alternative means. Also, to achieve the completed state is to be done as noiselessly as possible since the neighbour dislikes noise.'

3rd STEP

Considering the initial state of the 'garden fence' as described in the 1st STEP, the corresponding final state is expressed as 'satisfactory state of decoration achieved as cheaply and as noiselessly as possible'

or Final state [FS] of OPI [6] is seen as
'The garden fence is to be in a 'satisfactory state of decoration achieved as cheaply and as noiselessly as possible.'

4th STEP

The *investigator/householder* when comparing the results of the 2nd and 3rd STEPS, feels that the EXPECTATION of User/consumer [7] appears sufficiently close to the FINAL STATE of OPI [6] to allow the

Final state [FS] of User/consumer [8] to happen and monitored by the brain/mind [1].

5th STEP

The *investigator/householder* thinks that the following products [3] can produce the 'Material interaction' discussed in section 4.2. to affect the change of state of OPI [5 – 6] or the 'garden fence' to create the *right impression* in the User/consumer [7]:

Current timber, garden fence is to be = = =

1. Replaced by [grey, plastic fence] or,
2. Replaced by [wire mesh fence] or,
3. Covered with [grey paint applied with a brush i.e. becomes a painted fence] or,
4. Covered with [grey paint applied with a spray i.e. becomes a painted fence],

All suggestions of product [3] are capable of producing the same *interaction*: 'To turn [the unsatisfactory state of decoration of the timber, garden fence] into [satisfactory state of decoration as cheaply and noiselessly as possible]'. The 'interaction' is consistent as far as its adjectival component is concerned [unsatisfactory to satisfactory (however vague it is)]. The additional part is the adverbial component.

6th STEP

Static property of OPI (O) or the size of the garden fence: '1. 15 m long and 2. 1.5 m high'

Static property of User/consumer (U) i.e. 'householder': '3. He is elderly', 4. 'Cost conscious'

Static property of External 'object or agent' (E) i.e. 'neighbour': '5. He is sensitive to noise'.

7th STEP

The properties which a product [3] need to have to fit O, U and E, can be worked out using the 'Entailment Relation [ER]' discussed in section 4.3. Accordingly, we have

A. The fence which is: 1. 15 m long, 2. 1.5 m high, Householder who is: 3. Elderly, 4. Cost,

5. Neighbour who is sensitive to noise,

B. There is to be a 'product [3]' with properties which can fit those in A.,

C. REQUIRES properties of 'product [3]' to *match* those in A. which are: a. long enough, b. high enough, c. not tiring to use, d. low cost, e. makes little noise,

Followed by the Object Selector Matrix [OSM] to choose the product [3]

possible products [3]	2nd set of qualifiers				
	a.	b.	c.	d.	e.
grey, plastic fence	1	1	0	0	0
wire mesh fence	1	1	0	0	0
grey paint applied with a brush	1	1	0	1	1
grey paint applied with a spray	1	1	0	0	1

The product [3] 'fence covered with *grey pain applied with a brush*' scores the most '1' and is *selected* by the 'householder' which, although 'tiring to use', meets the 'low cost' and the 'noise' requirement.

Accordingly, the *'product design parameters'* of 'product [3]' from section 4.3. and from the 3rd STEP, are:
Interaction == 'To turn [the unsatisfactory state of decoration of the timber, garden fence] into [satisfactory state of decoration as cheaply and noiselessly as possible]' and
Static properties == a. long enough, b. high enough, c. somewhat tiring to use ?, d. low cost (applied with a brush), e. makes little noise.

We have here a Utilising system as considered in section 3.2. and a User/ Producer [2] in Figure 3.1. which is capable of

'Supplying the required interaction and adding the 'additional static properties' to the already existing product [3] so as to satisfy the *product design parameters* as Points I./1. and I./3. in exp 4.3. in section 4.3., and consequently to fit into the scheme of Figure 3.1.'

These are the *systems design parameters*. We now come to

Implementation of Part B.

From the 'static properties' of product [3] and the Object Selector Matrix, the 'householder' can find that

X. 'Fence is long and high' implies: The right quantity of grey paint is available
Y. 'Grey paint applied with a brush' implies: A well prepared brush is required

which are the 'accommodating properties' as considered in **section 4.3.** Point I./2.

In order to produce the symbolic model as a 'linguistic model' of Part B., we need to add to the original 'story' of the scenario the model of which, when put into practice, fits to Part A. of the scheme. The 'story' is based on the information gained from the preceding considerations.

The 'story' is: 'The householder needs to obtain grey paint in the right quantity from the local store and prepare a suitable brush ready for painting. Having 'manufactured' the product [3], the householder proceeds to paint by hand the fence which has rough surface'.

The STAGES of 'linguistic modelling' are = = =

A. Homogeneous language of context – free, 1 – and 2 – place sentences derived from the 'story' by *meaning – preserving, linguistic transformations* [in this case, there is no need since all sentences are already in this form]

1. Householder obtained paint
2. Householder prepared brush
3. Householder painted fence

These sentences define the structure or topology or the algorithm of the scenario and lead to the 'semantic diagram' or 'linguistic network' of the scenario in Figure 6.9.

C. Adjectival qualifiers with grading
Grading can be assigned to qualifiers to vary their effect on the **performance** of the object which they qualify. The technique is explained in detail in [Korn, 2009].

$dp(1,1)$ – householder having inspected property, wants to do the job [strongly, just]
(in keeping with the overall decoration scheme of the property so as to enhance the visual appearance of the property)
$ip(1,1)$ – householder's hands are in good order
$ep(2,2)$ – paint is grey
$ep(5,5)$ – quality of brush [hard, soft]
$ep(8,8)$ – rough surface

D. Interactions with adverbial qualifiers

in(1,2) – householder obtained paint [from local store]

in(4,5) – householder prepared brush [for painting]

in(7,8) – householder painted the fence [by hand] bearing in mind 'dp(1,1)' selected 'ep(2,2)'

B. Semantic diagram

The semantic diagram in Figure 6.3. demonstrates the 'structure' of the scenario and acts as an aid in pointing out the qualifiers or 'properties' which are demanded by the symbolism of the diagram [dp, ep etc as considered in

START activities at object 1. initiated by 'dp' property :

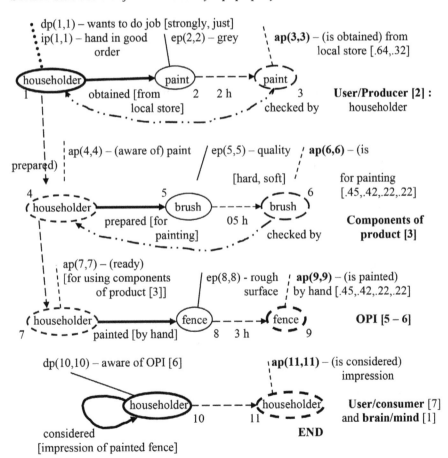

Figure 6.9. Semantic diagram of 'householder/painting' scenario

section 5.1.]. The required qualifiers are obtained from the 'story' or invented to satisfy the rules of linguistic modelling.

START activities at object 1. initiated by 'dp' property:

E. Logic sequences/topology of scenario with graded adjectives and certainty factors [cf]
Causal chains from Figure 5.5.: 1. 9, 8, 7, 4, 6, 5, 4, 1, 3, 2, 1 2. 11,10

For causal chain 1.

$dp(1,1) \land ip(1,1) \rightarrow in(1,2,[adv,1,2])$	delivering precondition for
$in(1,2,[adv,1,2]) \land ep(2,2) \rightarrow \textbf{ap(3,3)}$	application of 'product'

$ap(3,3) \rightarrow in(3,1)$
$in(3,1) \rightarrow ap(4,4)$

$ap(4,4) \rightarrow in(4,5,[adv,4,5])$	delivering precondition for
$in(4,5,[adv,4,5]) \land ep(5,5) \rightarrow \textbf{ap(6,6)}$	application of 'product'

$ap(6,6) \rightarrow in(6,4)$
$in(6,4) \rightarrow ap(7,7)$

$ap(7,7) \rightarrow in(7,8,[adv,7,8])$
$in(7,8,[adv,7,8]) \land ep(8,8) \rightarrow \textbf{ap(9,9)}$

For causal chain 2:

$dp(10,10) \rightarrow in(10,10)$
$in(10,10) \rightarrow \textbf{ap(11,11)}$ **User/utiliser**

F. Logic sequences with graded qualifiers/data for certainty factors [cf]
For causal chain 1.

$dp(hhol,1,1,(job(strong,90/0.8,just,40/0.4))) \land$
$ip(hhol,1,1,(hand(good,90/0.9))) \rightarrow$
(cf of rule, 0.8) $in(obt,hhol,1,paint,2,(from(store)))(0.64,0.32)$

in which to each grade we assign two numbers which lead to certainty factor, cf. The first number between − 100 and + 100 designated by the symbol 'ai', is intended to express the 'significance, importance or relevance of the grade' as part of a property as far as the 'outcome in the consequent of the conditional' is concerned. The second number between − 1 and + 1 designated by the symbol 'b$_i$', is intended as a 'measure of belief or confidence in certainty' as shown in Figure 4.3. in [Korn, 2009] that an object has a particular grade of a particular property [Durkin, 1994].

The resultant 'cf' of the consequent is obtained from

(cf of rule) x min(cfdp,cfip) = 0.8 x ((min(0.8, 0.9), min(0.4, 0.9)) = .64, .32) [Durkin, 1994].

The assignment of certainty factors is based on subjective judgement and follows the explanation in [Korn, 2009].

in(obt,hhol1,paint,2,(from(store)))(0.64,0.32) ∧ ep(paint,2,2,(paint(grey,100/1)))
→ (1)**ap(paint,3,3,(paint(obtained))) (0.64,0.32)**
cf = 1 x (min(64, 1), min(.32, 1))

ap(paint,3,3,(paint(obtained)))(0.64,0.32) →
(1)in(check,paint,3,hhol,1,(fed(back)))(0.64,0.32)
in(check,paint,3,hhol,1,(fed(back)))(0.64,0.32) →
(1)ap(hhol,4,4,(awar(paint)))(0.64,0.32)

ap(hhol,4,4,(awar(paint)))(0.64,0.32) →
(1)in(prep,hhol,4,brush,5,(for(paint)))(0.64,0.32)
in(prep,hhol,4,brush,5,(for(paint)))(0.64,0.32) ∧ ep(brush,5,5,(qual(hard,
80/0.8,soft,50/0.6)))→(0.7)**ap(brush,6,6,(prep(paint)))(0.45,0.42,0.22,0.22)**
cf = .7 x (min(.64, .8), min(.64, .6) , min(.32,.8), min(.32,.6)) = .45,.42,.22,.22

where the certainty factors of 'ap' are calculated by taking all combinations of certainty factors of 'in' and 'ep' and using the minimum of each term to be multiplied by 0.7, the certainty factor of the rule [Korn, 2009, Durkin, 1994]. The same way as is done for the 'dp' statement and can be written as

$$7 \text{ x} \begin{bmatrix} \text{min (prepared .64 hard brush .8)} \\ \text{min (prepared .64 soft brush .6)} \\ \text{min (prepared .32 hard brush .8)} \\ \text{min (prepared .32 soft brush .6)} \end{bmatrix} \begin{matrix} .45 \\ .42 \\ = .22 \\ .22 \end{matrix}$$

ap(brush,6,6,(prep(paint))) (0.45,0.42,0.22,0.22) →
        (1)in(check,brush,6,hhol,4,(fed(back)))(0.45,0.42,0.22,0.22)
in(check,brush,6,hhol,4,(fed(back)))(0.45,0.42,0.22,0.22) →
        (1)ap(hhol,7,7,(ready(paint)))(0.45,0.42,0.22,0.22)

ap(hhol,7,7,(ready(paint)))(0.45,0.42,0.22,0.22) →
        (1)in(paint,hhol7,fence,8,(paint(byhand)))(0.45,0.42,0.22,0.22)
in(paint,hhol7,fence,8,(paint(byhand)))(0.45,0.42,0.22,0.22) ∧
ep(fence,8,8,(qual(rousurf,100/1))) →
        (1)ap(fence,9,9,(painted(byhand))) (0.45,0.42,0.22,0.22)

For causal chain 2.

dp(hhol,10,10,(awar(product,100/1))) →
        (1)in(con,hhol,1,hhol,1,(imp(paintedfence)))(1)
in(con,hhol,1,hhol,1,(imp(paintedfence)))(1) →
(1)ap(hhol,11,11,(cons(impression)))

The dotted, directed lines carry the **time** it takes for a change of state to take place.

Ordered pairs corresponding to components of the *product* are written as

At: ap(3,3) $n_{3,20}$ = [ep(2,2)] paint (obtained from) (l/store) (.64,.32)
At: ap(6,6) $n_{6,6}$ = [ep(5,5)] brush (prepared for [painting]) (.45,.42,.22,.22)

The ordered pairs in words and the static, linguistic network in Figure 6.10., are

From $n_{3,20}$ = grey paint [related to] is obtained from the local store
From $n_{6,6}$ = hard or soft brush [related to] is prepared for painting

Remarks &&&

1. This example shows an application of 'systems theory' to a 'problematic situation'. Part A. is the 'speculative part' but conducted in a methodical way in natural language to arrive at the 'product and systems design parameters' discussed in section 4.3. which enable Part B. to proceed. Problem solving and systemic or structural thinking is discussed under a single umbrella.

The dynamic verbs in the semantic diagram of Part B. are 'abstract' and the 'householder' who is the instigator of the 'problematic issue' carried by OPI [5] or the timber, garden fence, and the judge of its resolution or no resolution i.e. the User/consumer [7], is likely to think in these terms. This is the case because

a. This type of verbs are the most efficient way of carrying thought, and
b. The ability of problem solving in the living sphere is *'innate'* as discussed in section I.1. and the 'householder' is able to carry out the *operational steps* without going into further details. This is a general point expressed in

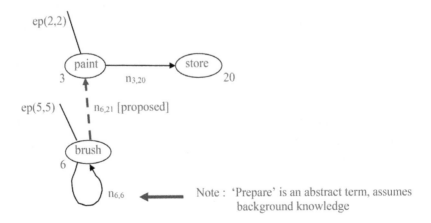

Figure 6.10. Static, linguistic network of product of 'householder' scenario

110. --- 'In 'systems theory' which uses the symbolism of processed natural language, the 'abstract' verbs can, if desired' be broken down in their *operational components'* to arrive at a 'detailed algorithm' or recipe for a robot or a person to carry out a task'. ---

For example, from Figure 6.9. in the sentence the dynamic verb with its adverb which sets the direction of *operationalisation*, we have:

'The householder 'prepared' [for painting] the brush' which can be expanded into *operational components* such as
'Brush is prepared [for painting] means = = (cleaned [with water] which means = (dipped [into a bucket] which means (lifted [up] (lowered [into bucket]))))

in which each of the terms can be further expanded until *visualisable* details are achieved that an individual can actually carry out, a 'subjective mental step'.

Both, Parts A. and B., although expressed in terms of 'processed, natural language', show the instances at which *quantitative methods* enter the reasoning scheme. For example, the 'geometric properties' of the garden fence at the 6th STEP are needed to estimate the amount of paint required for painting.

2. The linguistic network in Figure 6.10. is disjointed, therefore, it cannot be put forward as a 'product' as discussed in section 5.3. However,
n6,21 = 'Brush is dipped in paint', a new connection, objects 6 – 3, makes the network connected. It becomes a 'product [3]': *Connection of paint to brush was missing* [Korn, 2018].

We note: The accomplishment of the 'acquired property, (ap)' for generating this ordered pair requires an additional 'system' in the diagram of Figure 6.9. which can be generated by the pair of context – free sentences:

'The householder dips the brush [in paint]'

which is a 3 – place sentence but if the noun 'paint' is treated as an 'adverb of location' then the sentence becomes a 2 – place sentence and the corresponding 'acquired property' can be written

'The brush is dipped (in paint)'

and the 'ordered pair', $n_{6,21}$ = [ ] brush (dipped in [ ]) paint [ ].

3. Using the verbal equivalents of certainty factors as listed in Figure 5.19. in [Korn, 2009, Durkin, 1994], we can say for objects 3 and 6

$n_{3,20}$ = Grey paint is obtained [.64: probably] or [.32: less than may be] from the local store
$n_{6,6}$ = Brush is prepared for painting [from calculations attached to 'ap(brush,6,6,....', hard brush [.45: may be prepared] or soft brush [.42: may be prepared] or hard brush [.22: unknown] or soft brush [.22: unknown]

The variation of certainty of the 'problematic issue' to be resolved at object 9 in Figure 6.9. is as follows

$n_{9,22}$ = Fence painted by hand in good order [.45... .22: varies from 'may be' to 'unknown']

which tells us that 'enhancement of visual appearance of the property' is subject to uncertainty which varies from 'probably and may be' to 'less than may be and unknown'.
This is what object 10 in Figure 6.9. the 'householder' perceives through 'dp(10,10)' property.

The *uncertainty* arises from the activities depicted in Figure 6.9. being prone to adverse characteristics expressed by adjectival and adverbial phrases attached to objects or agents. Figure 6.9. should also show ways and means of how to improve the performance of the scenario.

We can say that the semantic diagram in Figure 6.9. carries the *structure* of the scenario through objects or agents and interactions, the topology of the scenario, on which properties or *characteristics* or features of agents are superimposed. Structural aspects are the matter of **systems science,** the question of characteristics and their relations is a matter for aspects of **conventional science** together called the **scientific enterprise.**

4. The dynamics of semantic diagram in Figure 6.9. shows the *'algorithm'* as it is or sequence of production:

'Paint has been obtained from the store' then 'Brush is prepared for painting' then 'Fence is painted by hand'. The first two acquired properties are the components of the product.

Although times for the accomplishment of each task is indicated along the dotted lines, the dynamics of the scenario is not worked out. Development of *software* is needed.

5. Variation of product: From a static, linguistic network using the expression for combination eq. 5.32. discussed in section in section 5.3. [Durell, 1959, Korn, 2018]

$$_{N(N-1)}C_{(N-1)} = [(N(N-1) - 0)(N(N-1) - 1)(N(N-1) - 2)....]/[1\ 2\ 3...(N - 1)\ !]$$

in which the number of terms in the nominator is 'N – 1' divided by 'N – 1' factorials. In the modified Figure 6.10. 'N = 3', we have $_6C_2$ = (6 x 5)/(1 x 2) = 15. This number shows all the possible variations of the topology or configuation of the product: more than one such configuration could be 'feasible' and would provide an unexpected *novelty*.

6. This example is an application of the scheme in Figure 3.1. The procedure of Part A. is demonstrated together with Part B. showing the semantic diagram in Figure 6.9. Particular cases of the User/Producer [2], User/consumer [7] and product [3] are also shown in Figure 6.9. without further details of 'expectation'.

7. In this example it is possible to shift the parts which objects or agents play in the scheme in Figure 3.1. For example, the text can be interpreted so that the 'householder' is the OPI [5] or the 'object carrying the problematic issue'.

H/her mental state may be seen initially 'unsatisfactory' by an individual and the 'garden fence' plays the part of product [3]. The dynamic verbs 'obtain' and 'prepare' then constitute part of User/Producer [2] together with the 'householder'. In this case, the semantic diagram has to accommodate the 'householder' in h/her new role.

8. The application of the scheme in Figure 3.1. to the 'problematic situation' discussed in this example, can be compared with the application of SSM to the same 'problematic situation' discussed in section 2.2. The comparison is shown by putting forward advantageous features which the SSM does not appear to have as follows:

A. The identification and resolution of problematic issues are expressed in terms of a 'systems theory' which conforms to the general pattern [principles + symbolism] followed by in depth, wide ranging theories of science shown in the preamble to CHAPTER 5. [Korn, 2018],
B. The 'systems theory' is rooted in branches of accepted knowledge,
C. The 'systems theory' has the symbolism of 'linguistic modelling' which is the alternative, general symbolism to mathematics capable of taking into account emotive, mental and intellectual as well as quantitative aspects of objects or agents and interrelations. Processed natural language is capable of coping with the generality of the systemic or structural view of parts of the world,
D. The resulting dynamic, linguistic network or semantic diagram such as Figure 6.9. can be expanded to operational level and as such can serve as the algorithm for carrying out concrete tasks.

End of **Remarks &&&**

For the **2**nd **example** we use the 'story' or narrative of the scenario: 'A shopkeeper wants to increase h/her takings from customers who appear rather unhappy at present possibly because their level of satisfaction is low. This is the shopkeeper's impression and h/she is seeking ways and means to effect improvement which is in the interest of customers as well since h/her shop is the only one around that sells the product which is needed in the area. H/her main line of merchandise is cheese, ham and tuna sandwiches which are delivered to the shop all mixed up'.

Implementation of Part A.

1st STEP

Consideration of the text shows that according to the *shopkeeper's* impression the 'customers do not generate sufficient takings and they appear to be unhappy'. Therefore, they are the source or carrier of 'problematic issue'. This interpretation implies that

OPI [5] = = Customers

or the Initial state [IS] of OPI [5] is identified as the
'Customers' initial, mental state is unhappiness due to 'low level of satisfaction"

2nd STEP

The *shopkeeper* is the person who can judge the 'state of happiness and level of satisfaction of customers'. H/her 'expectation' is

or the Initial state [IS] of User/consumer [7] is recognised as the *'expectation'* of the
'Customers are to be happy due to 'high level of satisfaction"

3rd STEP

Considering the initial, mental state of customers, the corresponding final, mental state is expressed as 'Customers are happy due to their 'high level of satisfaction"

or Final state [FS] of OPI [6] is seen as
'Customers are in a happy, mental state due to their 'high level of satisfaction"

4th STEP

The *shopkeeper* when comparing the results of the 2nd and 3rd STEPS, feels that the EXPECTATION of User/consumer [7] appears sufficiently close to the FINAL STATE of OPI [6] to allow

Final state [FS] of User/consumer [8] to happen and monitored by the brain/ mind [1] which is 'being satisfied with expectation having been achieved'.

5th STEP

The *shopkeeper* thinks that the following products [3] can produce the 'Material objects' carrying the appropriate 'influence' which can exert through *impression* discussed in section 4.2., the change of state of mind of 'customers' so as to satisfy the 'expectation' of the User/consumer [7].

Current state of mind of 'customers' is suggested to be changed by offering =
= =
1. Sandwiches cheese, ham, tuna arranged and labelled on shelves or,
2. Free coffee available when buying 2 sandwiches of any kind or,
3. Seats with tables are to be available inside the shop,

All of the suggested products [3] appear to be suitable for generating the same 'impression': 'To turn the state of mind of 'customers' from [unhappy due to 'low satisfaction'] into [happy due to 'high satisfaction']'.

6th STEP

Static properties of O, U, E or OPI, User/consumer, External objects

W. Static properties of *OPI [5]* or 'customers' can be suggested from the 'Acceptability conditions' introduced in section 6.1. as follows

1. Designation – Customers

2. Parameters –	**3.** Identifying properties -
Age group	IP1- youngish
Personality	IP2 – go ahead type
Occupation	IP3 – banks, finance

4. Following the scheme in Figure 4.5., application of the Entailment Relation to this example

A. There are IP 1, 2, 3 AND
B. To have identifying properties as listed in A.
C. *IMPLIES* to have *particular properties* which are assessed as
IP1 – 1. impatient

IP2 – 2. have little time

IP3 – 3. appreciative of order

X. Static properties of *User/consumer* *[7]* or 'shopkeeper' using the 'Acceptability conditions'

1. Designation – Shopkeeper

2. Parameters –   **3.** Identifying properties –

         Age   IP4 – Around 60

         Personality   IP5 – Cautious

4. Using the Entailment Relation

A. There are IP4, 5

B. To have the identifying properties as listed in A.

C. IMPLIES to have *particular properties* which are assessed as

IP4 – 4. considering sale of business

IP5 – 5. not spending too much

Y. Static properties of External objects or 'Shop' using the 'Acceptability conditions'

1. Designation – Shop

2. Parameters –   **3.** Identifying properties

      Small, selling groceries   IP6 – relies on local custom

4. As before, using the Entailment Relation

A. There are IP4, 5, 6 AND

B. To have identifying properties as listed in A.

C. IMPLIES to have *particular properties* which is assessed as

IP6 – 6. appreciates local people

Z. Having elucidated the 'static properties' of those objects or agents which are involved in operating the product [3], we can use the Entailment Relation to at least reason out the properties with which the product [3] *needs to cope* based on the properties of O, U, and E.

A. There are *particular properties* 1.,2.,3.,4.,5.,6 AND
B. To have particular properties as listed in A.
C. IMPLIES to have the corresponding *coping properties* =

1. Impatient	a. Readily available
2. Have little time	b. Little time to prepare
3. Appreciate order	c. Well presented, arranged
4. Considering sale of business	d. Short term investment only
5. Not spending too much money	e. Not much cash available
6. Appreciates local people	f. Helps in local events

7th STEP

The Entailment Relation under point Z. yields the 'properties' with which the product [3] needs *to cope* and ALSO *to create the impression* or influence to bring about the change of mental state in 'customers' and is selected by the Object Selector Matrix as shown

	2nd set of qualifiers					
possible products [3]	a.	b.	c.	d.	e.	f
sandwiches c,h,t/arrlab	1	1	1	0	0	0
free coffee 2/sand	1	0	0	0	0	1
seats/tables	0	0	1	0	0	1

The product [3] 'sandwiches c,h,t/arrlab' scores most '1' and is *selected* by the 'shopkeeper'.

Accordingly, the *'product design parameters'* of the product [3] from section 4.3. and from the 3rd STEP, are

Interaction/impression == 'To turn [the unhappy state of mind due to 'low satisfaction] into [happy state of mind due to 'high satisfaction"] and

Static properties == Sandwiches are to be so arranged so as to be readily available, well arranged and easily identifiable or suitable for *coping* with 'customers' who are: a. impatient, b. have little time, c. appreciate order.

Production of the 'static properties' of the User/Producer [2] in a Producer system to lead to product [3] capable of creating an effective 'impression' comprise the *systems design parameters*. We now come to

Implementation of Part B.

The additional 'story' is: 'Having found the designation and the static properties of the product [3], the 'shopkeeper' has decided to clean the shelves in the shop, to place the sandwiches on the shelves, to arrange the sandwiches according to their contents and to label them so that they can be easily identified'.

The STAGES of 'linguistic modelling' are = = =

A. Homogeneous language of context – free, 1 – and 2 – place sentences

Shopkeeper [shkeep] cleaned the shelves
Shkeep placed sandwiches [sw]
Shkeep arranged sw
Shkeep labelled sw

C. Adjectival qualifiers with grading
The qualifiers are given as part of statements.

$dp(15,15)$ – shkeep wants to increase his takings, decided (after knowing....)
$ip(15,15)$ – shkeep is skilled enough
$ep(1,1)$ – shelves are dusty
$ep(3,3)$ – sw are mixed up

D. Interactions with adverbial qualifiers

Shopkeeper [shkeep] cleaned the shelves [quickly]
Shkeep placed sw1 [quickly, on shelves]
Shkeep arranged sw2 [quickly, according to contents ch, h, t on shelves]
Shkeep attached [labels to] sw3

E. Logic sequences or topology of the scenario with graded adjectives and certainty factors

Causal chains from Figure 6.11.: **1.** 2, 1, 15   **2.** 19, 18, 17, 16, 15
3. 6, 5, 4, 3

For causal chain 1.

$dp(15,15) \land ip(15,15) \rightarrow in(15,1)$
$in(15,1) \land ep(1,1) \rightarrow \mathbf{ap(2,2)}$

For causal chains 2. and 3.

$ap(2,2) \rightarrow in(2,15)$
$in(2,15) \land ep(15,15) \rightarrow ap(16,16)$ assumes that $ep(15,15)$ exists

$ap(16,16) \rightarrow in(16,3)$
$in(16,3) \land ep(3,3) \rightarrow ap(4,4)$

$ap(4,4) \rightarrow in(4,16)$
$in(4,16) \land ap(16,16) \rightarrow ap(17,17)$ 'acquired property' is used as 'ep'
property

$ap(17,17) \rightarrow in(17,4)$
$in(17,4) \land ap(4,4) \rightarrow ap(5,5)$

$ap(5,5) \rightarrow in(5,17)$
$in(5,17) \land ap(17,17) \rightarrow ap(18,18)$

$ap(18,18) \rightarrow in(18,5)$
$in(18,5) \land ap(5,5) \rightarrow \mathbf{ap(6,6)}$ which is the 'final state' of the 'sw'

$ap(6,6) \rightarrow in(6,18)$
$in(6,18) \land ap(18,18) \rightarrow \mathbf{ap(19,19)}$ which is the 'final state' of the 'shkeep'

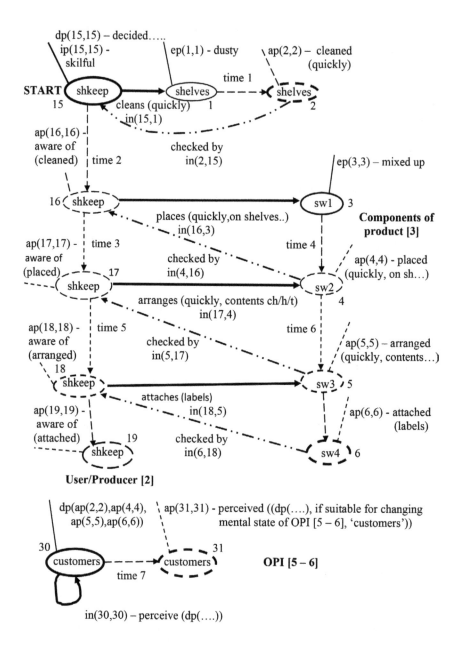

Figure 6.11. Semantic diagram of shopkeeper scenario

The ordered pairs describing the *product [3]* including 'shelves' for completeness, are written as

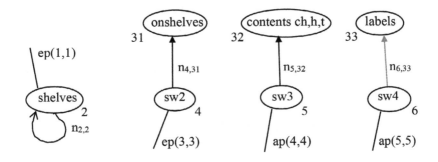

Figure 6.12. Disjointed static, linguistic network of 'sw scenario'

At ap(2,2) $n_{2,2}$ = [ep(1,1)] shelves (cleaned [quickly])
At ap(4,4) $n_{4,31}$ = [ep(3,3)] sw2 (placed [quickly]) onshelves
At ap(5,5) $n_{5,32}$ = [ap(4,4)] sw3 (arranged [quickly]) contents ch,h,t
At ap(6,6) $n_{6,33}$ = [ap(5,5)] sw4 (attached [with]) labels

which results in a disjointed static, linguistic network shown in Figure 6.12.

Remarks &&&

This example which is another particular case of the complete scheme in Figure 3.1., is presented to demonstrate an 'assembly – like' scenario in which a single object picks up 'properties' as its state proceeds in time. In particular, we see:

1. This example represents a strongly human activity scenario in which guidance is needed to assess properties of components of the scheme. The application of Entailment Relation is useful in assessment of these properties which product [3] needs to have to be able to cope with the static properties of OPI [5], User/consumer [7] and External objects or agents,

2. The use of 'ap' properties to act as 'ep' properties has been taken into account in the propagation of state under STAGE E. or 'Logic sequences' of 'Linguistic modelling',

3.The semantic diagram or the dynamic, linguistic network simulates the 'assembly – like' behaviour but has resulted in a disjointed, static, linguistic network which is not a 'tree' and as such cannot serve as product [3] as discussed in section 5.3. To turn the network in Figure 6.12. into a 'tree', we need to insert directed lines as depicted in Figure 6.13.

Following the method suggested in point 2 of the Remarks in the 'householder' example, we can write the statements with reference to Figure 6.12.

'The shkeep notionally moves the placed sw1 to sw2'
'The placed sw1 is notionally moved to sw2'

'The shkeep notionally moves the arranged sw2 to sw3'
'The arranged sw2 is notionally moved to sw3'

the second sentence of each is written as an ordered pair

$n_{4,5}$ = [placed] sw1 (moved [notionallyto]) sw2 [ ]
$n_{5,6}$ = [arranged] sw2 (moved [notionallyto]) sw3 [ ]

The term 'notionally' must be introduced because there is no actual, physical movement of 'sandwiches' takes place, only their properties change not their positions.

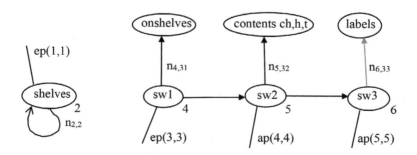

Figure 6.13. Joined static, linguistic network of product of 'sw scenario'

4. The dynamic verbs in the semantic diagram in Figure 6.11. are abstract which can be expanded into *operational form* by following the method suggested in point 1 of Remarks in the 'householder' example.

5. The statement 'The sh/keeper cleans (quickly) the shelves' represented by contours 15, 1, 2, carries an 'additional property or I./3.' as given by exp 4.3. because it arises due to the 'sandwiches' need to be 'placed on clean shelves'.

6. The next step would be the **evaluation** if the product [3] does achieve the 'change of mental state' of 'customers' which could be observed by the 'shopkeeper' through increased takings. This would mean that there is a 'causal connection' between the 'happy state of mind of customers' and their spending more on buying 'sandwiches'.

End of **Remarks &&&**

For the **3**rd **example** we look at a scenario which is a representative of a Utilising system considered in section 3.2. Such a system is recognised by its use of 'existing products [3]' which are obtained from 'stores', 'warehouses' etc. On the other hand, the operation of Producing systems is recognised by their 'creating products [3]' with reference to the scheme in Figure 3.1.

We have the following 'story' or 'narrative' of a problem situation: 'A rather obese hotel guest wants to get to the airport in 30 min in comfort which is about 25 km from h/her hotel situated out of town'. Using the scheme in Figure 3.1., we proceed as follows:

Implementation of Part A.

1st STEP

Considering the 'story', we note that the problem situation is driven by a desire, visualising a not – yet – existing state of affairs and the need to realise that desire which may have an obstacle which makes it difficult or impossible to carry out. This difficulty is seen as the 'problematic issue' which is identified by the 'investigator' or 'analyser' or, in this case, by the 'hotel guest' as the 'distance between the hotel and the airport'. This interpretation implies that

OPI [5] = = Distance between the position of the hotel guest and airport is 25 km which is the Initial state [IS] of OPI [5].

2nd STEP

The 'hotel guest' plays the part of User/consumer [7] with 'expectation'

or Initial, mental state [IS] of User/consumer [7] is recognised as the 'expectation' of the 'Hotel guest is to be at the airport in 30 min in comfort'.

3rd STEP

Considering the initial state of the 'distance', the corresponding, consistent, final state is seen as

Final state [FS] of OPI [6] 'Distance between the position of the hotel guest and the airport is 0 km'

There does not seem to be any alternative.

4th STEP

The 'investigator' or 'analyser' or 'committee' or 'hotel guest' when comparing the results of the 2nd and 3rd STEPS, feels that the EXPECTATION of the User/consumer [7] appears sufficiently close to the FINAL STATE of OPI [6] to allow the

Final state [FS] of User/consumer [8] to happen and to be monitored by the brain/mind [1].

5th STEP

The 'investigator' thinks that the following products [3] can generate the 'Material interaction' discussed in section 4.2. to affect the change of state of OPI [5 – 6] or 'To turn the distance between the position of the hotel guest and the airport from 25 km to 0 km' are

Railway
Taxi
Walking
Getting a lift in a car

All are capable of producing the same interaction i.e. delivering the material object with existing properties to accomplish the 'change of state OPI [5 – 6]' or 'Change the distance between the positions of the hotel guest and airport from 25 km to 0 km'.

6th STEP

Static properties of OPI or the 'distance' = 1. Distance is covered by motorway, and 2. by railway which needs transport to reach,
Static properties of User/consumer or the 'hotel guest' = 3. Obese, 4. Wants comfort,
5. Cover distance in 30 min,
Static properties of External objects or agents or 'hotel' = 6. Remote

7th STEP

The properties which a product [3] need to have to fit O, U and E, can be worked out from the Entailment Relation discussed in section 4.3. Accordingly, we have

A. Distance is: 1. With motorway, 2. With railway, difficult to reach, Hotel guest is:
3. Obese, 4. Wanting comfort, 5. To travel 30 min, Hotel is: 6. Remote,
B. There is to be a product [3] having properties which can fit those in A.,
C. REQUIRES a product [3] with properties which *match* those in A. which are respectively:
a. Can travel on motorway, b. Has extra transport, c. Can take the weight, d. Can provide comfort, e. Can cover distance in 30 min, f. Can cover remote distance.

Followed by the Object Selector Matrix to select product [3]

possible product [3]	2nd set of qualifiers from C.					
	a.	b.	c.	d.	e.	f
railway	0	0	1	1	1	0
taxi	1	1	1	1	1	1
walking	1	0	0	0	0	0
getting lift	1	0	1	1	1	0

The product [3] 'taxi' scores the largest number of '1' and is *selected* by the 'investigator' or 'hotel guest'.

Accordingly, the *Product design parameters* of product [3] from section 4.3. and from the 5th STEP, are:

Interaction == 'To turn the distance between the position of the hotel guest and the airport from 25 km to 0 km' using 'skilled power' as discussed in section 4.2.

Static properties of product [3] == a. Can travel on motorway, b. Has extra transport [not required], c. Can take the weight of the hotel guest, d. Can provide the comfort, e. Can cover the distance in 30 min, f. Can cover remote distance [not required].

System design parameters: Hotel receptionist [User/Producer [2]] receives a request from the hotel guest to call a taxi [product [3]] with properties a., c., d., e.

Implementation of Part B.

The 'story' of the scenario representing the problematic situation is:

'A rather obese hotel guest wants to get to the airport which is about 25 km from h/her hotel in 30 min which is situated out of town. H/she contacted the hotel receptionist to call a taxi which has properties a., c., d. and e. He could have done this h/herself using h/her mobile telephone but elected to act otherwise'.

STAGES of 'linguistic modelling' are = = =

A. Homogeneous language of context – free, 1 – and 2 – place sentences

Hguest approached hrec
Hrec called a taxi
Taxi collected
Taxi overcome distance

B. Semantic diagram or dynamic, linguistic network
This is shown in Figure 6.14.

C. Adjectival qualifiers with grading
No grading is used in this example.

dp(1,1) – hguest wants to get from hotel to airport 25 km away in 30 min
ip(1,1) – hguest is obese, likes comfort
ep(2,2) – hrec is able to communicate

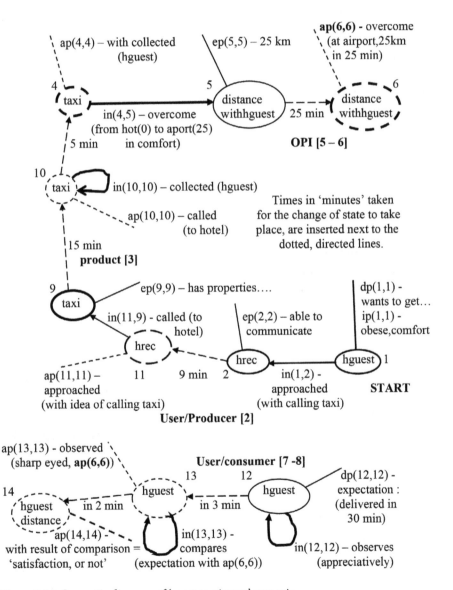

Figure 6.14. Semantic diagram of 'guest to airport' scenario

ep(9,9) – taxi has properties a., c., d., e.
ep(5,5) – distance is 25 km

D. Interactions with adverbial qualifiers
in(1,2) – Hguest approached [with calling taxi] hrec
in(11,9) – Hrec called [to hotel] a taxi
in(10,10) – Taxi collected [hguest]
in(4,5) – Taxi overcome [from hot(0) to …] distance

E. Logic sequences/topology of scenario with graded adjectives and certainty factors [cf]
From Figure 6.14., the Causal chains are:
First = 6, 5, 4, 10, 9, 11, 2, 1 Second = 14, 13, 12

For the First:

dp(1,1) $\wedge$ ip(1,1) $\rightarrow$ in(1,2)
in(1,2) $\wedge$ ep(2,2) $\rightarrow$ ap(11,11) [9 min]

ap(11,11) $\rightarrow$ in(11,9)
in(11,9) $\wedge$ ep(9,9) $\rightarrow$ ap(10,10) [15 min]

ap(10,10) $\rightarrow$ in(10,10)   Total time taken for the scenario to be
in(10,10) $\rightarrow$ ap(4,4) [5 min]   completed = 9 + 15 + 5 + 25 = 54 min

ap(4,4) $\rightarrow$ in(4,5)   which is the *outcome* or product [3] of the
in(4,5) $\wedge$ ep(5,5) $\rightarrow$ **ap(6,6)** [25 min]   scenario which generates the
'interaction' as

                    impression in the User/consumer, **ap(14,14)**

For the Second:

dp(12,12) $\rightarrow$ in(12,12)
in(12,12) $\rightarrow$ ap(13,13)

ap(13,13) $\rightarrow$ in(13,13)
in(13,13) $\rightarrow$ **ap(13,13)**

Remark &&&

Exercising the scheme in Figure 3.1. which is a methodical thinking for solving problems, for problematic situation which appears to be straightforward in this example, shows up the possibilities of choices, uncertainties in selection of 'objects or agents'. The method allows the creativity and inventiveness enter freely which, however, does not appear much in order to keep the physical size of implementations of Parts A. and B. within narrow limits.

End of **Remark &&&**

We look at a scenario with animals as 'objects or agents'as the **4th example** with the 'story' as follows: 'Feeling hungry, the hawk with his sharp eyes watched the surroundings for possible food. He noted the activities of iguanas not far away. Having noticed the hawk, one of the iguanas started to run which was his fatal mistake because his action immediately attracted the attention of the hawk. The hawk caught the iguana with his sharp claws so that he could not escape'.

We proceed along the problem solving lines suggested by the scheme diagrammed in Figure 3.1. to show how a scenario with animal agents conforms to the scheme.

Implementation of Part A.

1st STEP
The phrase 'feeling hungry' suggests that the 'hawk' carries the 'problematic issue' or he is the OPI [5].

OPI [5] = = Hawk

or Initial, mental state [IS] of OPI [5] is identified as
'Hawk feels hungry'.

2nd STEP
The 'hawk' is the agent who can expect 'the satisfaction of his mental condition'

or Initial, mental state [IS] of User/consumer [7] is recognised as the *expectation* of the 'hawk' who plays the part of User/consumer [7] which is:

'The hawk no longer feels hungry'.

3rd STEP
Considering the initial, mental state of the 'hawk', the corresponding, consistent, final state is expressed as 'The hawk no longer feels hungry'

or Final, mental state [FS] of OPI [6] is
'The hawk no longer feels hungry'.

4th STEP
Comparing the results of the 2nd and 3rd STEPS, the EXPECTATION of the User/consumer [7] is identical with the FINAL STATE of OPI [6] to allow

Final, mental state [FS] of User/consumer [8] to happen and monitored by brain/mind [1] which is 'feeling of satisfaction of expectation having been achieved'.

5th STEP
The 'hawk' needs to find 'food' or product [3] which produces the 'material interaction' discussed in section 4.2. to affect the change of state OPI [5 – 6] or the 'hawk'. This change satisfies the expectation of the User/consumer [7] as well.

According to the 'story' product [3] is named as the 'iguana'.

6th STEP
Static properties of OPI or the 'hawk': 1. Well capable of flying,
Static properties of User/consumer or the 'hawk': 2. Not too hungry,
Static properties of External objects or agents or 'atmospheric conditions': 3. Can be cloudy.

7th STEP

The properties which need *to fit* the product [3] to match O, U, E is obtained from the Entailment Relation discussed in section 4.3. Accordingly, we have

A. The 'Hawk' which is: 1. Well capable of flying, 'Hawk' who is 2. Not too hungry, Atmospheric conditions which 3. Can be cloudy,

B. There is a product [3] with properties to match those in A.,

C. REQUIRES the following properties: a. Good diver, b. One iguana is sufficient, c. Has excellent eyesight.

Followed by the Object Selector Matrix [OSM] to select product [3]

	2nd set of qualifiers		
product [3]	a	b	c
iguana	1	0	1

There is only one product [3], iguana, which is given in the 'story'. There is no 'product and system design parameters' because all necessary details are given in the 'story'.

Implementation of Part B.

We are using the 'story' given at the start of the example leading to the STAGES of 'linguistic modelling' as follows = = =

A. Homogeneous language of context free, 1 – and 2 – place sentences

These sentences define the structure or the topology or the algorithms of the scenario.

Hawk watched [the surrounding] [1 – place sentence]
Hawk noted [the activities] [1 – place sentence]
Iguana started [to run….] [1 – place sentence]
Iguana attracted hawk [2 – place sentence]
Hawk caught iguana [2 – place sentence]

B. Semantic diagram

This is shown in Figure 6.15. as the structure defined by the objects playing a part in the scenario and their interactions signified by the dynamic verbs in A. above.

C. Adjectival qualifiers with grading and certainty factors (cf)
'Grading' and 'personality profiles' can be assigned to qualifiers as discussed in section 5.5. which vary their effect on the *performance* of the objects which they qualify. Subjectively assessed certainty factors (cf) can be added to each grade to introduce numerical measures into the emergence of states as they evolve in a 'semantic diagram'.

dp(1,1) – hawk due to feeling hungry [just, .5, very, .8]
ep(1,1) – hawk sharp eyed [very, 1]
dp(5,5) – iguana having noticed
dp(9,9) – hawk is prompted by the scenario as the 'hawk', no longer hungry ?

D. Interactions with adverbial qualifiers in brackets
in(1,1) – hawk watched (surroundings for possible food)
in(2,1) – hawk is alerted by hawk (to possible food in watched surroundings)

in(3,3) – hawk noted (activities of iguanas not far away)
in(7,6) – hawk caught the iguana (with his sharp...)

in(5,5) – iguana started (to run which...)
in(6,4) – iguana attracted of hawk (attention immediately)

in(9,9) – hawk perceived (the scenario, ap(8,8))
in(10,10) – observer II decided (to act further or not)

E. Logic sequences/topology of scenario with graded qualifiers and certainty factors
The causal chains from Figure 6.15.:

First = 7, 4, 3, 1 Second = 2, 1 Third = 8, 6, 5 Fourth = 11, 10, 9

For the First and Second causal chains

1/1 dp(1,1)[just,.5, very,.8] → .7in(1,1)[.35, .56] where .7 is the cf of rule
cf = .7 x .5, .7 x .8 = .35, .56
1/2 in(1,1)[.35, .56] ∧ ep(1,1)[very, 1] → .9**ap(2,2)**[.31, .5] these cf values are
cf = .9(min(.35 x 1), min(.56 x 1)) = .31, .5   transmitted with
no further change
and worked out
using the material
2/1 ap(2,2) → in(2,1)   in section 5.4.
1/3 in(2,1) → **ap(3,3)**

1/4 ap(3,3) → in(3,3)
1/5 in(3,3) → **ap(4,4)**   to progress in the First causal chain, we
need to generate in(6,4) from the Third
causal chain

For the Third causal chain

3/1 dp(5,5) → in(5,5)
3/2 in(5,5) → **ap(6,6)**   back to First causal chain

1/6 ap(6,6) → in(6,4)
1/7 in(6,4) ∧ ap(4,4) → **ap(7,7)**   back to Third causal chain

3/3 ap(7,7) → in(7,6)
3/4 in(7,6) ∧ ap(6,6) → **ap(8,8)**[.31 .5] which says that the belief in the hawk
catching the iguana is less than 'may
be' and 'probably' using the verbal
equivalents of cf in Figure 5.19. This
acquired property is the final state of
the product to be noted by the 'hawk'.

For the Fourth causal chain

4/1 dp(9,9) → in(9,9)
4/2 in(9,9) → **ap(10,10)**

4/3 ap(10,10) → in10,10)   the final state of the 'hawk' is that his hunger
4/4 in(10,10) → **ap(11,11)**   has been alleviated or not.

Quantitative aspect of the scenario

A problem leading to a mathematical model can be formulated to show how this kind of model fits into the framework of the 'problem solving scheme in Figure 3.1', in particular that of activity by living agents.

With reference to Figure 6.15., we assume that the running speed of the iguana is 8 km/h and he is 0.4 km away from his cave when he noticed the hawk i.e. danger and started to run towards his cave. It would take him approximately 0.05 h or 3 min from this position to reach the cave using the formula: 'speed = distance over time'.

The attack speed of the hawk is 50 km/h and he is located from the iguana 1 km away on the outside of the 0.4 km away from the cave. As long as the iguana is outside his cave i.e. the maximum distance, 1.4 km, which the hawk has to cover within the 3 min time limit, it can catch the iguana. Using the same formula the hawk can reach the iguana in 1.68 min well within the time limit and catch him which confirms the 'outcome' of the scenario, ap(8,8) in Figure 6.15.

Remarks &&&

Figure 6.15. shows a 'problem solving structure' which is a particular case of the general 'problem solving scheme' in Figure 3.1. depicting the progression of mental as well as physical states in time carrying information flow and skilled power as discussed in section 4.2. Figure 6.15. depicts the activities of living agents which as such operate according to their *innate* 'purpose' directed at solving their own problems with the 'hawk' carrying out a number of functions indicated in Figure 6.15. We note that

1. The purposive activities are carried out at object level as indicated by the dynamic verbs at stage D of 'linguistic modelling',
2. Decision making is also carried out at object level, for example, at object 5 the iguana has to decide to run or to stay still, without the mechanism of decision making,

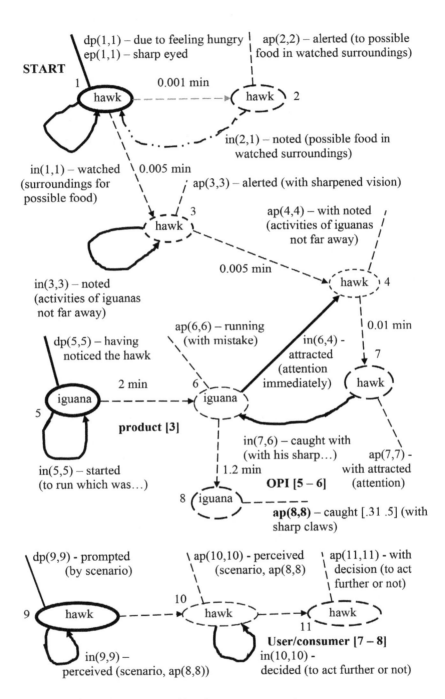

Figure 6.15. Semantic diagram of hawk – iguana scenario

3. Expressing abstract verbs and qualifiers in their concrete elements leads to *operational form* of linguistic models.

We note that an observer creates the 'linguistic model' of a cybernetic structure (Wiener, 1948) which is a human operator since only people are capable of creating symbolic models of this kind of sophistication. In case of animal agents, this kind of model can be used for studying animal behaviour.

Mathematical modelling and aspects of 'conventional science of physics' enter the structural or relational models at 'object' level by using the symbolisms expressed in terms of physical, qualitative and/or quantitative properties (Korn, 2018). Thus, mathematical models are restrictive. In the present example, 'measures of belief' attached to adjectival qualifiers enter the picture in quantitative terms. We note that there is uncertainty in the 'hawk catches the iguana' at the 'acquire property', ap(8,8), arising from the 'level of belief' at the point of adjectival property 'feeling hungry', a 'biological property' of the 'hawk'.

End of **Remarks &&&**

For the **5**[th] **example** we use a predominantly hardware based problematic situation so that the use of 'linguistic and mathematical modelling' can be shown effectively. The example demonstrates a Utilising system like the previous examples.

'Story' of the problematic situation is: 'There are people on board of a ship who need to be lowered to the sea in an emergency. For safety reason, they must hit the water at a speed not greater than 0.5 m/s.'

Following the scheme diagrammed in Figure 3.1., we have:

Implementation of Part A.

1st STEP
Considering the 'story' or 'narrative' it is 'people' who appear to be the 'object or agent' giving rise to a problem '…they need to be lowered…'. From this interpretation

OPI [5] = = People [on board of a ship]

or Initial state [IS] of OPI [5] is identified as the
'People are on board of ship, dry'

2nd STEP
There is no explicit reference in the 'story' to other human agents who could
be seen as User/consumer [7] so we assume using background knowledge
that there is a 'Sailor who operates the machinery for lowering a suitable
appliance like a lifeboat with people'. So

Initial, mental state [IS] of User/consumer [7] with 'expectation':
'Sailor sees the appliance like a lifeboat with people lowered safely from ship
to sea with minimal shock on impact with sea, dry'.

As a matter of interest, 'people' can also be seen as User/consumer [7]: 'they
can expect to be on the surface of the sea safely'. However, 'sailor' can help if
something goes wrong with 'people' OPI [6] in the course of descending.

3rd STEP
From the initial state of people in the 1st STEP, we can have

Final state(s) [FS] of OPI [6] = 1. People are on the surface of sea safely, dry,
2. People are on the surface of sea safely, wet.

4th STEP
Comparing the results of the 2nd and 3rd STEPS, we note that the 'expectation'
of User/consumer [7] and Final state [FS] of OPI [6] are not sufficiently close,
therefore, final, mental state of the former is not allowed to happen

Final, mental state [FS] of User/consumer [8] cannot happen: Depends on the
outcome of 'linguistic modelling'.

5th STEP
The following product [3] can produce the Material interaction discussed in
section 4.2. to affect the change of state OPI [5 – 6] and, consequently, to
generate the impression for the 'sailor' or

User/consumer [7 – 8]

1. People instructed to be lowered in (lifeboats),
2. People instructed to be lowered in (rafts),
3. People instructed to be dressed in (rubber suits to slide down)

where the brackets designate 'product [3]' intended to accomplish 'change of state' i.e. capable of exerting the same *interaction* which is: 'To turn [people who are on board of ship, dry] into [people who are on the surface of sea, safely dry or wet]'.

6th STEP
The 'static properties' of the following 'objects or agents' are assumed to be

Properties of OPI or 'people' (O): 1. Vulnerable, 2. Each weighs about 60 kgf, 3. Able to receive information,
Properties of User/consumer or 'sailor' (U): 4. Caring person,
Properties of External 'objects or agents' or 'sea' (E): 5. Can be rough.

7th STEP
Properties which the product [3] need to have to cope with properties of O, U, E can be worked out using the Entailment Relation (ER) as follows

A. There are people who are: 1. vulnerable, 2. each weighs about 60 kgf, 3. able to receive information, There is a sailor who is a 4. caring person, There is the sea which 5. can be rough,
B. There is to be a 'product [3]' with properties so that it can cope with those in A.
C. REQUIRES properties of 'product [3]' which are: a. protective, b. capable of taking 20 people, c. leaves ears free to hear, d. clearly visible to follow, e. can shelter people.

Followed by the Object Selector Matrix (OSM) to select product [3] resulting in selection of 'lowered in *lifeboats*' as 'product [3]'.

list of 'product [3]'	2nd set of qualifiers of 'product [3]'				
	a.	b.	c.	d.	e.
lowered in lifeboats	1	1	1	1	1
lowered in rafts	0	1	1	0	0
slid dressed in rubber suits in shutes	0	1	1	1	0

Accordingly, the *product design parameters* of 'product [3]' from section 4.3. and from the 3rd STEP, are

Interaction == 'To turn [people who are on board of ship, dry] into [people who are on the surface of sea, safely dry or wet]',

Static properties == The process of 'lowered in lifeboat is: a. protective, b. capable of taking 20 people, c. leaves ears free to hear, d. clearly visible to follow, e. can shelter people.

Implementation of Part B.

'Story' of the problematic situation on which implementation od Part A. was based is: 'There are people on board of a ship who need to be lowered to the sea in an emergency. For safety reason, they must hit the water at a speed not greater than 0.5 m/s.'

In addition, to implement the 'interaction' and to ensure that product [3] has the 'static properties', we have to exercise creativity, ingenuity and invention to devise a proposed arrangement of *hardware, software and human ware* or User/Producer [2] expressed as a 'story', which is thought to be capable of producing the **'input interaction'** to *product [3]*. This question is introduced in general terms by point I./1. in section 4.3. Usually such an arrangement is selected from a number produced by *imagination*.

The 'story' of the proposed arrangement is:
An elastic rope is wound round a winch for lowering a *lifeboat* with people in an emergency from the side of a ship into the sea as shown in Figure 6.16. Lowering is the duty of a sailor. To limit the steady state speed of the lifeboat on impact with the sea, an oil filled dashpot which is a friction device, is used with its rotating part attached to the shaft of the winch and with its casing fixed to the stationary frame. Each lifeboat can accommodate 20 people

weighing 3100 kgf total. To avoid overheating the dashpot is adjusted for the steady state speed of the lifeboat to be limited so as not to produce higher than 30 °C above atmospheric temperature.

Identification of model language with story language with reference to Figure 3.1. and suggested by **exp 1.1.** in section 1.3. is as follows:
OPI [5 – 6] = People
Product [3] = Lifeboat
Components of User/Producer [2] = Sailor, winch, dashpot, rope and so on
Brain/mind [1] = Sailor who is in contact with User/consumer [8]
User/consumer [7 – 8] = Sailor
Market [contour 4] = Notional

The STAGES of 'linguistic modelling' are:

A. Homogeneous language of context-free 1- and 2 – place sentences which are the results of 'linguistic analysis' considered in section 5.7., if needed. Additional sentences are generated from the analysis of the 'problem situation'.

Sailor allows the rope,
Rope turns the winch
Winch lowers the lifeboat,

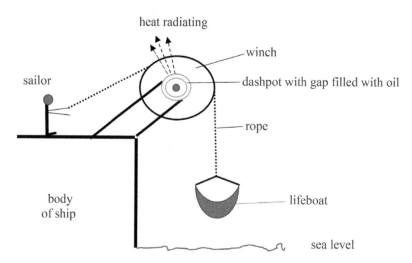

Figure 6.16. Diagram of the people lowering arrangement

Lifeboat rotates the dashpot,
Dashpot limits the lifeboat,
Lifeboat takes people.
Sailor observes
Sailor compares

B. Semantic diagram
This is initially constructed using the sentences in A. and is shown in Figure
6.17.

C. Adjectival qualifiers or 'functional properties' with grading and certainty
factors (cf)
These are called 'functional properties' and considered in section 5.1. but
reproduced here
ep = affected object properties [facilitating/hindering change of state],
dp = driving properties [motivating/stimulating],
ip = initiating object properties [facilitating/hindering interaction],

dp(1,1) – sailor with duty [strong, .9, just, .6]
ip(1,1) – none suggested
ep(2,2) – rope with elasticity [high, 1.0]
ep(4,4) – winch with elastic rope....
ip(4,4) – none suggested
ep(6,6) – lifeboat weighs 3100 kgf, with steady speed limited to 0.5 m/s to
prevent overheating, accommodate 20 people
ip(6,6) – none suggested
ep(8,8) – dashpot is oil filled, with its casing....
ip(8,8) – none suggested
ep(11,11) – people are vulnerable, weighing 60 kgf, receive information
dp(13,13) – sailor is prompted (ap(12,12))
ip(13,13) – none suggested

D. Interactions with adverbial qualifiers or 'functional properties' in brackets

in(1,2) – sailor allows the rope [to move]
in(3,4) – rope turns winch [with slip]
in(5,6) – winch lowers the lifeboat [from the side...]

in(7,8) – lifeboat rotates the dashpot
in(9,7) – dashpot limits the lifeboat [steady speed]
in(10,11) – lifeboat takes people [down to sea]
in(13,13) – sailor observes
in(14,14) – sailor compares [expectation [0.5 m/s] with actual at ap(12,12)]

E. Logic sequences/topology of scenario with graded adjectives and certainty factors

The *causal chains* from Figure 6.17.: First = 12, 11, 10, 7, 6, 5, 4, 3, 2, 1
Second = 9, 8, 7 Third = 15, 14, 13

For the First causal chain

1/1 dp(1,1)[st,.9, jt, .6] → .8in(1,2)[.72, .48]　　　　where .8 is the cf of rule
cf = .8 x .9, .8 x .6 = .72, .48
1/2 in(1,2)[.72, .48] ∧ ep(2,2)[1.0] → .95ap(3,3)[.68, .46] these cf values from
now on transmitted with no further change
cf = .95(min(1.0 x .72), min(1.0 x .48)) = .68, .46

1/3 ap(3,3) → in(3,4)
1/4 in(3,4) ∧ ep(4,4) → ap(5,5)

1/5 ap(5,5) → in(5,6)
1/6 in(5,6) ∧ ep(6,6) → ap(7,7)

1/7 ap(9,9) → in(9,7)
1/8 in(9,7) ∧ ap(7,7) → **ap(10,10)**(.68,.46)

Predicate logic sequences 1/7 and 1/8 in words [Copi, 1978]:
If the dashpot is rotated **then** the dashpot limits the lifeboat weighing 3100 kgf, with steady speed limited to 0.5 m/s which prevents overheating of dashpot,
If the dashpot limits the lifeboat weighing 3100 kgf, with steady speed limited to 0.5 m/s which prevents overheating of the dashpot **and** the lifeboat is being lowered from the side of the ship into the sea **then** the belief that the steady

speed of the lifeboat is limited to 0.5 m/s which prevents overheating of the dashpot, varies from 'slightly more than probable' to 'slightly more than may be' [Korn, 2009].

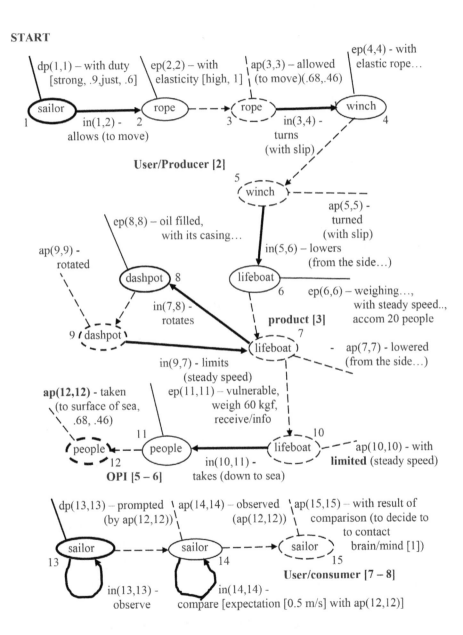

Figure 6.17. Semantic diagram of people lowering arrangement

1/9 ap(10,10) → in(10,11)

1/10 in(10,11) ∧ ep(11,11) → **ap(12,12)**(.68,.46)   which is the certainty of this event of safe 'landing of people on the sea'.

For the Second causal chain

2/1 ap(7,7) → in(7,8)

2/2 in(7,8) → ap(9,9)

For the Third causal chain

3/1 dp(13,13) → in(13,13)

3/2 in(13,13) → ap(14,14)

3/3 ap(14,14) → in(14,14)

3/4 in(14,14) → **ap(15,15)**   which says that 'sailor with expectation' faces making a decision whether to express satisfaction or ask 'brain/mind [1]' for revision to improve 'User/Producer [2] – product [delivery]"s performance.

Quantitative aspect of the 'people saving' arrangement

The application of 'network modelling of engineering systems' is demonstrated which requires a story to emphasise the 'quantitative aspects' of the scenario [Korn, 2012].

The 'story' is: 'An elastic rope which may be modelled as a linear spring of stiffness K, in the first instance, is used in conjunction with a winch of moment of inertia J and radius r, for lowering a lifeboat from a ship onto the sea as shown in Figure 6.17. The rotating part of an oil – filled dashpot which generates heat due to friction or entropy production with coefficient S, is attached to the shaft of the winch to limit the steady state speed of the lifeboat, with its casing fixed to the stationary frame. The body of the dashpot has heat capacity T, area A and heat transfer coefficient λ, radiates heat into the surrounding. The lifeboat, including people, weighs 3100 kgf.

For safety, the speed of the lifeboat on impact with the sea must be limited to 0.5 m/s and, at this speed, the temperature rise of the dashpot must not be greater than 30 °C. It is required to find whether this condition is met'.

To derive the mathematical model of a set of non-linear differential equations given by eq 6.1., the mechanical and non-isothermal networks and their topology are constructed and shown in Figure 6.18.

$$\text{torque (Nm)} \quad J\, d\omega/dt = r\, f_K - S\, \omega/\vartheta 1$$

$$\text{force (N)} \quad M\, dv_M/dt = -f_K + Mg \qquad\qquad \textbf{eq 6.1.}$$

$$\text{speed (m/s)} \quad 1/K\, df_K/dt = v_M - r\, \omega$$

$$\begin{array}{l}\text{entropy} \qquad T/\vartheta_1\, d\vartheta_1/dt = S\, \omega^2/(\vartheta 1)^2 - A\, \lambda\, (\vartheta_1 - \vartheta_2)/\vartheta_1 \\ \text{production (Nm/s)}\end{array}$$

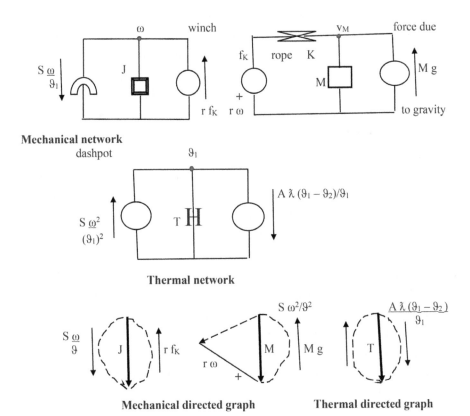

Figure 6.18. Networks and directed graphs of 'lifeboat' scenario

Multiplying each equation in eq 6.1. by the corresponding independent variable i.e. the first by ω and so on we obtain

$$M\, g\, v_M = A\,\lambda\,(\vartheta_1 - \vartheta_2) \qquad\qquad \text{eq 6.2.}$$

which says that the mechanical input power due to the pull of gravity, equals the thermal output power. Also, when the rates of changes on the left side of eq 6.1. are zero and the parameters are: $\lambda = 52.2$ (N/m s °C, $A = 1.1$ m^2, the steady state equations from eq 6.1. yield eq 6.2. from which the temperature rise is 27 °C or there is no overheating.

Remark &&&

The semantic diagram or static, linguistic network displays the basic structure of the scenario as far as the 'story' captures it. It is then possible to inquire further into details such as quantify qualifiers at object level, add more elaborate certainty factors. Here we can say by considering the acquired property, ap(12,12), that 'people' lands on the 'sea surface' with certainty of .68 or .46 which mean from Figure 5.18. in section 5.4., 'probably' or 'may be' respectively. The uncertainty has arisen because there is doubt about the 'duty of the sailor, dp(1,1). The semantic diagram is not clear about whether the landing speed of the 'lifeboat' is exceeds 0.5 m/s or not.

The mathematical model of the quantitative aspects of a scenario shows how restrictive but precise such a model is when compared with the linguistic model. It also shows that the temperature rise of the dashpot does not exceed 30 °C for 0.5 m/s so the 'speed limit' is kept.

This example has introduced the term 'functional properties' for the qualifiers carried by 'objects or agents' in the semantic diagram and has shown how to use exp 1.1. in section 1.3. It has demonstrated how to implement the scheme in Figure 3.1. but has left further elaboration of both Parts A. and B. open. We have seen the application of 'systems theory' or the scheme in Figure 3.1. in *mechanical engineering*, how to devise structures for the realisation of purposive activity involving human components.

End of **Remark &&&**

Generality of the scheme in Figure 3.1.

We have seen the application of the scheme in Figure 3.1. in five diverse examples, all representing Utilising systems as introduced in section 3.2. The applications have been successful in demonstrating the applicability of the scheme to a diversity of instances. The opinion of applicability is based on that *it looks right*, it would have been stronger had we taken one or more of the examples to their operational level as suggested in the Remarks &&& of the 'householder' example. In this case, the 1st and 3rd criteria in section 1.3.

We now intend to extend the application of the scheme in Figure 3.1. to scenarios described as 'living systems' [Miller, 1978]. This reference is an extensive piece of work and may be regarded as fundamental. We use this reference as a basis for further discussion.

Miller views living things to exist at *eight levels* of hierarchical, nested development as suggested by the 1st Hypothesis in section 3.1. The lowest level is 'cells', followed by 'organs' to 'society' etc through 'organisations'. Living things at each level are operated by 'twenty, interacting subsystems' like 'ingestors' like 'mouth at organism level' or 'output transducer' like 'spokesman at organisation level'.

Living systems are 'open systems', they input, throughput and output diverse kinds of matter, energy and information. Processing these all they do, possibly in order to *survive*.

The problem with this view based on a superficial study, is that it is 'descriptive', does not appear to show the 'interaction aspect', it fails the criteria discussed in section 3.1. except perhaps the second, lacks the analytical flavour. However, this work gives an overall view of how living things appear to operate

We now examine the operation of a *component of a plant*, a leaf, which fit into the level 'organism (plant)' as 'subsystem' or 'ingestor (leaf)' according to Miller's terminology. The function of leaves as part of a plant is 'to use the energy from light to convert carbon dioxide from the air and water from rain and soil, presumably, into glucose and oxygen'. This description or 'story' can be expressed as a *chemical reaction* as follows

$$6 CO_2 + 6 H_2O \rightarrow C_6H_{12}O_6 + O_6 \qquad\qquad \textbf{exp 6.3.}$$

which is performed by the 'chlorophyl molecules' of the leaf and is called *photosynthesis.* The arrow indicates 'energy input' from light.

From the point of view of the scheme in Figure 3.1., exp 6.3. may be seen as follows

Left hand side = = Chemical reaction or User/Producer [2] needing matter, energy and/or information *input* which produces the *output* ---

exp 6.4.

Right hand side = = Product [3] which then generates the kind of *interaction* needed by and transmitted to '*another component*' to exert the 'interaction'.

In this particular case, the 'chlorophyl molecules' in the leaves perform the 'left hand side' using the *input* energy from light, carbon dioxide and water resulting in the 'right hand side' which is the product [3] or glucose to be used by 'another components' of the plant such as branches or the trunk and oxygen which is breathed in by air breathing living things like the large variety of mammals [lions, hens, humans etc]. When the product [3] reaches the appropriate part of the 'another component' the *material interaction,* the '*output*', which it carries, becomes effective to change the state of the appropriate part of the 'another component'.

Observation of other organisms or, in fact, entities at *all levels* of Miller's classification can be seen to lead to similar result. For example, the organ or component or subsystem 'pancreas' in the organism of the 'human body' functions as follows

Input = Blood, lymphatic fluid [matter], nerve messages [information],
Output = Peptides, insulin [Material interaction carried by product [3]]

The transformation and transport to 'another component' is carried out by complex chemical reactions. In this case, 'peptides are carried to the stomach [another component] where they 'aid digestion' [change of state of nutrients]'.

Also, 'insulin is carried to the blood [another component] where it shifts glucose to the cells [change of state].

Thus, exp 6.4. is proposed to be generalised as follows:

111.---- 'The statements in exp 6.4. describe an *'input to output transformation'* of matter, energy or information by User/Producer [2] to fit into product [3] so that the latter can exert *interaction* in dynamic state or become related to in static state to change or to maintain the state in 'another component' carrying an OPI [5 -6]'. This latter case is likely to occur in the course of cell multiplication when the genetic material becomes related or when a pair of shoes is a good fit and creates the feeling of satisfaction in the wearer. ----

The generalisation can be expressed as the diagram in Figure 6.19. which also fits the scheme in Figure 3.1.

In case of the 'small intestine' in Figure 6.19., we have

Input = Enzymes, bile, blood [matter], nerve messages [information]
Output = Food residue [matter]

The diagram in Figure 6.19. also indicates the inevitable production of 'waste matter' in the course of dynamic operation such as 'heat generation' [Korn, 2009], 'free radicals in chemical processes', 'packaging in storing, transporting and selling goods', 'applying material such as mortar when building a wall' and so on.

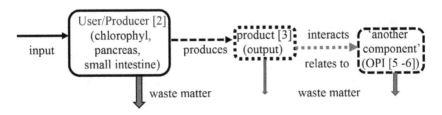

Figure 6.19. General 'input/output/OPI' relation

Remarks &&&

We have looked at examples of human activity scenarios of Utilising systems before extending the application of the scheme in Figure 3.1. to the chemistry of living things which have turned out to be instances of Producing systems as introduced in section 3.2.

1. Consideration of operation of organs or subsystems has shown that they can be viewed as creators of 'input – output relations' consisting of a 'whole' enclosed by the rectangular contour which creates the 'interrelations' as considered in section 4.2. or 'input – output' which enables a whole to be connected to other wholes.

This is a very general notion which, in fact, is universal as far as the generality of the notion of *system or structure* is concerned as stated by the 1st hypothesis in section 3.1. The diagrammatic representation of the operation of the 'whole' + 'input – output' + 'another component' enables the entity to be seen as 'everything in nature and in the artificial world is a *holon* or a 'whole and a part' [Koestler, 1967]. Also, the representation gives Miller's subsystems the means to be joined each others.

Diagrammatical representations similar to that in Figure 6.19. are used in 'transfer function analysis' of linear control theory and in 1 – and 2 – place sentences of 'linguistic modelling' which is introduced in section 5.1. We use the 2 – place sentence again to demonstrate how it conforms to the idea expressed in Figure 6.19., the generalisation **111.** and the scheme in Figure 3.1. This is shown in Figure 6.20.

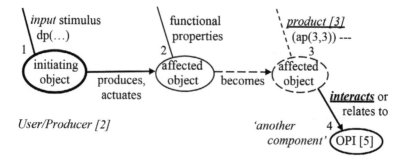

Figure 6.20. 2 – place sentence to fit Figure 3.1.

2. We have now established that the idea *holon* fits into 'systemic or structural thinking' and we have translated the idea into a symbolic model in Figures 6.19. and 6.20. We pursue this notion further by recalling the considerations of 'relationships' in section 4.2. which indicate the existence of

Static and dynamic states signalled by the 'main verb' in a contingent statement.

With reference to Figures 6.19. and 6.20. and to 'interrelations', we can have

Product [3] in 'static state' is described, for example, by:
'One of the legs of a single bed (product [3])
Is fabricated (produces) for sale (input) by the woodworker (initiating object or User/Producer [2]) and
Is intended to support (relation) the bed (OPI [5 – 6] or 'another component')'.

Product [3] in 'dynamic state' is described, for example, by:
'The fisherman (initiating object or User/Producer [2]) needed something to eat (input stimulus as dp(...)) so he caught (produced) a fish (product [3]) which he cooked (material interaction or skilled power) for his lunch (OPI [5 – 6] or 'another component')'.

This shows that 1 – and 2 – place sentences or elcons fit in the scheme in Figure 3.1. and the notion of 'holon' can be applied to them.

3. We note that exp 6.4. and all subsequent developments needed an *input stimulus* of one form or another. This is a state of affairs which prevails throughout the 'systemic or structural view' so as to satisfy the idea that 'no change of equilibrium state can change by itself unless disturbed by an agent'. However, thinking about how change takes place in the subatomic, celestial sphere and in the brain/mind, this state of affairs may no longer required.

4. If the superficial considerations of the nature of chemical reactions in living things and perhaps beyond, stands up to further investigations then the discipline of *chemistry* may be seen as part of the 'systemic or structural view'.

End of **Remarks &&&**

CONCLUSIONS

The intention of the current work inclusive of this book is stated in section 1.2. as 'The development of an integrated theory of 'problem solving thinking' and the 'systemic or structural view' of parts of the world'. This is an *empirical* theory which:

=Tells us about aspects of parts of the world i.e. has *cognitive value*, not about discussing abstract concepts per se, as referred to in APPENDIX 1., 2., 3. and 4.

=Gives a content which can be learnt [hypotheses and linguistic modelling plus the knowledge base such as network theory, mathematics] and a method which can be used [scheme in Figure 3.1. implemented by examples in CHAPTER 6.].

We can say that we have made a start towards achieving this aim through proposing the scheme in Figure 3.1. This scheme combines the scope of creativity, invention, ingenuity of 'living things', in particular humans, in Part A. which leads to a methodical design of systems or structures in Part B. stipulated by the former by means of the 'product and system design parameters' in section 4.3. This process if acceptable, results in a general, design methodology of products and systems.

The 'problematic issues' addressed by the material of this book is discussed in CHAPTER 2. with added remarks in APPENDIX 1., 2., 3. and 4. This material attempts to treat the subject matter of 'systemic or structural view' of aspects [concrete, abstract, symbolic and imaginary] of parts of the world in a more *rigorous manner* as far as admitted by vague, emotive properties and uncertainties prevailing in scenarios with living, in particular human 'holons'. The influence exerted by such 'holons' in User/Producer [2] and transmitted to the production of *interaction* by product [3], on 'objects or agents' carrying the 'problematic issue', OPI [5], can be assessed or worked out.

However, the material offers only the beginning which need to be evaluated by peer scrutiny. Examination of the soundness of the concepts suggested, further developments in linguistics, applications to more practical problems and working out by experts of details of 'design parameters' put forward in section 4.3. together with subsequent detailed designs of 'products and systems'. Scenarios involving the logical OR function have not been considered. More applications of the 'cp property' using eqs.5.42-5.44. in section 5.4. in improving certainty of occurrence of outcomes, have not been shown. Only simple examples resulting in diagrams which fit an A4 page, have been given. The MARKET [4] in Figure 3.1. has not been given sufficient attention because scenarios involving assembly, sale and delivery of products have not been shown.

C1. The intention of this section and the rest of the CONCLUSIONS is:

To give more points considered relevant to the subject matter of the book.

1. First, the difference between Conventional and Systems science is described as:

Conventional science --- The qualitative, quantitative branch of Figure 2.1. has produced many different kinds of intellectual products. Conventional science of physics, the product of observation which is turned into symbolic usually quantitative models by ingenious persons with varying talent, is one with the function of producing 'reliable, empirical knowledge' of aspects of parts of the world which can be used for *explanations* and *predictions* of existence of states and occurrence of events. This intellectual product is able to produce such knowledge because it:
= Satisfies all 4 criteria discussed in section 1.3.,
= Uses mathematical models which can lead to precise comparison of symbolic models, the invention by imagination, with the results of tests or observations.

Systems science --- The function of intellectual products i.e. 'systemic or structural theories' as indicated in the structural branch in Figure 2.1. is to produce such products which generate *interactions* capable of changing equilibrium states of objects or agents carrying 'problematic issues' as shown in Figure 3.1. to the satisfaction of 'expectations'. Once such science comes into existence, it can accomplish this because it:

= Satisfies all 4 criteria discussed in section 1.3.,

= Uses linguistic modelling supplemented by mathematical models and instances of other disciplines such as physics and social science which can carry the symbolism to 'operational level'.

Second, 'systemic or structural view' of parts of the world is hierarchical in a 'nested' way which means that holons at any level of the hierarchy contain holons at all other levels below. For example, the common salt crystal contains salt molecules called sodium chloride, NCl, arranged in a structure, each consists of sodium, Na, and chloride atom, Cl, in specific relation each of which in turn is constructed of electrons and a nucleus of elementary particles arranged in specific configuration.

2. Relationship to instance of current 'systems thinking':

First, Part A. in the scheme in Figure 3.1. may be seen as a mental activity described as *2nd order cybernetics* and Part B. corresponds to that of *1st order cybernetics*, the former 'directing' the latter through the 'product and system design parameters' as described in section 4.3.

Second, The predicate, logic conditionals produced by 'linguistic modelling' as introduced in section 5.1., resemble the 'rules' of Artificial Intelligence and the differential equations of Systems Dynamics, a point which needs to be explored. However, linguistic modelling operates in 'organised', linguistic terms, AI and Systems Dynamics begins to operate with linguistic terms followed by quantification of abstract terms to fit into their computing software. Lack of comprehensive *'quantification method'* is a problem.

3. Matters outstanding:

First, the proposed 'systems theory' as described in this book, is intended to deal with what may be referred to as the *fundamental notions* of the 'systemic or structural view' of parts of the world. To cover topics like 'adaptive systems', 'learning systems', 'more about purposive systems' or 'cybernetics', application to 'service systems', scenarios involving 'markets' and mental changes of state etc. needs to be developed.

Second, the relationship between 'product and system design parameters' which are produced by Part A. of Figure 3.1., and the design of product [3] and User/Producer [2] needs to be examined and put into practice by professional, component or product designers. Basically, Part A. requires a product [3] to develop interaction capable of changing the state of OPI [5] into OPI [6] and the task of a *product design designer* is to design the detailed elements of a product so as to satisfy this requirement. This is called *top down design*. Similar considerations apply to 'system design parameters'. A more complete *description* of 'product [3]' in Figure 3.1. is given below:

'The function of product [3] is to produce, in response to a stimulus, an *interaction* as considered in section 4.2., which is capable of changing the state of OPI [5] into OPI [6] so as to satisfy '*expectations*'. Hence a product [3] is designed i.e. is imparted and arranged in a *static structure*, the appropriate structural and qualitative, quantitative properties so as
= To deliver interaction, to withstand and to satisfy environmental conditions [physical conditions, waste disposal, conform to stakeholders expectations, display selling points [to fashion, convenience, performance and so on]]. In addition, product [3] needs to pass *tests* of experience'.

In living things 'problem solving' is 'innate' and carried out 'instinctively' in accordance with a *purpose* as outlined in Figure 3.1. so a product [3] is already available when, for example, 'fingers' are used to tie a shoelace or 'bile' is delivered to the stomach to aid digestion. Alternatively, product [3] is constructed in accordance with a *purpose* i.e. there is a '*plan*' showing an envisaged *complex product* [a car engine, for example] or an '*objective*' showing the envisaged *simple* product [desired speed in a speed control system, Nise, 2008]. A 'complex product' is one that can be seen to consist of more than one property arranged in a specific configuration so as to be capable of performing its function like a 'ruler with units of measurement engraved along its edge' for drawing straight lines which consists of geometrical [length, width…] and material [plastic] properties. A 'simple product' consists of one property such as 'temperature of air in a room'. A generalisation:

200. --- 'In a purposive configuration or system exercised by living things or by control, computer systems, only two properties can be *compared* at a time

= One being produced and delivered by a feedback loop to the comparator, and

= The other is part of a plan or is the objective to be achieved.

Therefore, delivery and arrangement in the structure of a product each property requires a purposive system or

= The number of properties in a product [3] equals the number of purposive systems in User/Producer [2],

Or any system operating in the inanimate world.' ---

This generalisation shows the relationship between User/Production [2] and product [3] in Figure 3.1. and can be seen in the examples in CHAPTER 6.

Third, the dotted, directed lines in the semantic diagrams designate 'change in time', the dynamics of scenarios which need computational facility or software as exists in Systems Dynamics. This deficiency needs to be remedied.

4. Problematic situations:

Perhaps what distinguishes 'living things' from inanimate ones is that the former can display the 'mental state of *awareness* or being conscious of state of self and surrounding in general and 'problematic states' in particular (added by the author) [Searle, 1984]'. They are then called on to resolve the 'problematic issues' urged by the need to survive or to strive for achieving ambitions. Thus, any living thing as soon as it makes an appearance in a surrounding outside its 'mother' or any other protective environment, faces a 'problem' = = The 'problem' of how to stay alive or *to survive* or succeed by *achieving* ambitions, if any, as discussed in section 3.2.

There are 'two concepts' which need to be described:

1. A *thing* is considered 'living' when it is observed performing *specific functions* like 'inputting and outputting matter and energy', 'responding to and outputting stimuli coming from and emitted to an environment including own body which together are interactions considered in section 4.2. They are also 'capable of reproduction, growth, metabolism, disposing of waste' and so on taking place at all levels of Miller's classification of 'living systems'. All the functions are performed by 'objects or agents' organised in a *specific structure or system*.

2. A *problem* is a situation 'subjectively' regarded as undesirable or harmful by an observer which can be ignored or may need to be dealt with and overcome if possible.

For example, we have a 'story' = = 'There is a person who feels hungry [a stimulus from own body creating a mental state which judges the signal to indicate a 'problematic' or undesirable state] so h/she responds by booking a table in and proceeding to a restaurant to alleviate the feeling of hunger [the system to resolve the problem]'.

From the brief description, '*two topics*' have emerged, A. and B.:
A. *Situations* which may be described as changes ---
= From one equilibrium state [with the undesirable or 'problematic issue'],
= To another [envisaged, the one that is acceptable to an agent], or
The change of state as introduced by the 2nd hypothesis in section 3.1.,
B. *Structures or systems* which are the means of attempting resolution of the 'problematic issue' by accomplishing the change of equilibrium states.

Currently the two topics by and large are discussed separately, however, they are connected: 'Perception of a 'problematic issue' by an observer or 'interested party' and the subsequent 'thoughts' in Part A. of Figure 3.1. appear *to cause* the bringing into existence and operating the 'structure or system' in Part B [or vice versa]. This mental work is conducted by creative *imagination* and inspiration of the human being in particular and by the innate ability of living things in general.

The *basic aim* of this book is to present a 'systems theory' which is the symbolic model for the representation of these *topics* as an '*integrated whole*'. Hopefully there will be constructive comments towards acceptance, or not, leading to application, teaching and further research.

There are consequences of the above discussion as follows:

1. As mentioned in section 2.1. conducting 'problem solving' is **innate** in 'objects or agents' in the living sphere at all levels of Miller's classification. It is done by systems in *purposive configuration* as discussed above and in section 3.1. [Brown, Campbell, 1948, Nise, 2008, Korn, 2018],

2. We have connected 'problem solving' to the concept of '*change of equilibrium states*' which is a very general concept. Since we suggest that this change is 'caused' by systems or structures, the view of parts of the world as 'systems or structures' is also very general as suggested by the 1st hypothesis in section 3.1. It is applicable when observing and interpreting the results of observation of aspects of inanimate and animate natural and artificial things, **3.** Figure 2.1. which is a brief presentation of paradigm changes over the not too distant past evolution of human thought, displays *two branches* of means or raw material for turning these thoughts into symbolic models for the resolution of 'problematic issues', they are

The 'qualitative/quantitative' *properties* [qq], and
The 'structural or systemic' *properties* [ss].

We note that practically all intellectual endeavours have been achieved along the qq branch, there is a scarcity of such endeavours along the ss branch.

The following reasons may be seen to account for this:
1. Any symbolic model constructed from qq properties is of immediate interest to people (appearance, colour, size, explanations and predictions of phenomena of interest), symbolic models using ss properties are of interest mostly to manufacturers and constructors of products [3] like plans for 'building a house'.
2. Symbolic models of qq properties are used for constructing 'intellectual products [3]' for changing the mental state of curiosity to its satisfaction by answer the question 'why'. These models can be expressed in *mathematical terms* of great precision, predictive power, falsifiability and application in practical projects. These models usually satisfy the four criteria discussed in section 1.3.

The first organised, theoretical approach to the 'systemic or structural view' was the 'control theory' during and after the 2nd WWar together with OR [Blackett, 1948, Brown, Campbell, 1948]. This was followed by the development of what may be described as 'systems thinking' defined in section 3.2. which recognised the generality of the 'systemic view' and has encouraged discussion of a wide range of topics. However, its efforts to contribute to the ss branch have:

= Remained at the 'speculative, discussion level' usually of highly abstract topics without appreciable effort to relate them to parts of the *empirical* world,
= Furthered inadequate, particular approaches as discussed in CHAPTER 2. which perhaps emerged due to inability to come up with a general approach matching the generality of the 'systemic or structural view' which resulted in 'fragmentation of the subject matter of 'systems thinking",
= Considered 'systems thinking as some kind of 'super science',
= Led to no 'significant effort to encourage debate and to admitting critical contribution',
= Not succeeded in finding although tried [Klir, 1969] an acceptable 'general systems theory' to match the generality of the 'systemic view', and
= Not succeeded in finding a generally applicable 'systems and product' design method.

On the other hand, since its inception 'systems thinking' has been active in encouraging discussion of wide ranging and stimulating ideas which perhaps bore many other interesting ideas.

This point is discussed in section 2.2. in detail but repeated here because of its great importance and because it fits into the discussion here.

The qq branch has succeeded in producing an abundance of diverse intellectual achievements ranging from simple, mathematical models such as representing the relation between speed and friction force, to great theoretical structures of science and brilliant works of art. These great achievements can be due to its having managed to find the appropriate 'elementary constituents [elcon]' for the construction of diverse symbolic models which are:

The concept of **qualitative** and/or **quantitative property** leading to models which satisfy the criteria in section 1.3. [Korn, 2012]. The proposed 'systems theory' follows this trend by using 1 – and 2 – place sentences of processed, natural language, the *minimal, linguistic unit that makes complete sense,* as the elcon or **structural property** in the ss branch. The 'systems theory' also satisfies the four criteria. Use of *qualitative* properties in the ss branch includes *emotive* properties for the exploration of their effect or influence on action by individuals and their groups.

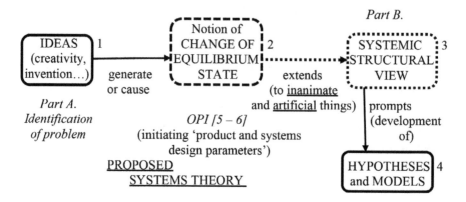

Figure C1. A diagrammatic view of 'systems theory'

The approach to the development of a symbolic model proposed here is shown diagrammatically in Figure C1. The diagram is related to Figure 3.1. as indicated by the italicised terms next to the relevant contours.

The 'systems theory' in this book like theories in physics like Newton's laws and the laws of thermodynamics, consists of TWO parts as pointed out in the introduction to CHAPTER 5.: =The *hypotheses* as suggested in section 3.1. and the symbolic model of *linguistic modelling* which is introduced in section 5.1. [Korn, 2009]. Here we intend to add a number of general points to this introduction and its application in CHAPTER 6. as demonstrated in Figure C2.

C2. Remarks concerning linguistic modelling

The diagrammatic representation of the procedure of 'linguistic modelling' is shown in Figure C2. with details enclosed in the contours and the steps between contours are written alongside the directed lines. Further to this figure, we can say:

The *first* point is that, in general, creating a model means creating a symbolic image produced by an *observer* along the lines of Figure 1.1. based on 'perception' which is the only connection between awareness of parts of the world and the world itself or produced by 'imagination'. There is a large variety of such models, by far the most immediately available with powerful expressive power, is natural language.

The *second* point is that natural language is the *primary model* usually first created in the mental process of modelling, deliberately or not. Other models are produced following natural language and usually can be expressed in

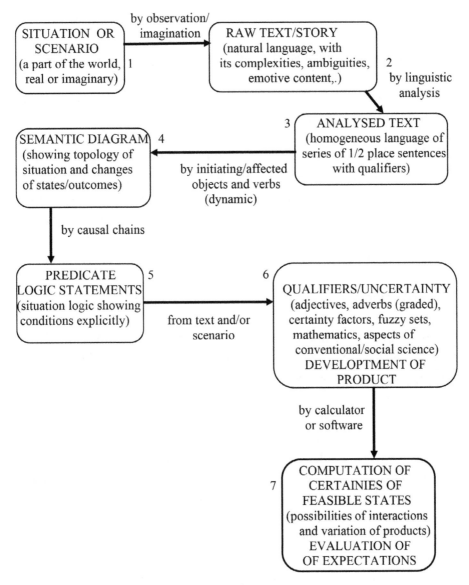

Figure C2. Scheme of linguistic modelling of scenarios

terms of this language. Models other than natural language are produced for emphasizing a specific aspect of a part of the world such as a painting which strongly exposes colour and shape. Mathematical models as demonstrated in the '5th example [people-lifeboat]' in section 6.2., are another example which emphasize the quantitative aspect.

The *third* point is that 'linguistic modelling' is a *'transformation'*. It transforms a 'story' in natural language of a scenario into a reasoning scheme of sequences of *'if... then'* statements.

The advantage of *conditional statements* is that they explicitly exhibit the conditions [antecedent] on which the occurrence of the outcome [consequent] depends. It is the conditions being expressed in operational terms, their reliability and certainty which can affect the *occurrence* of the outcome.

Furthermore, the linguistic model provides the basic, reasoning structure of a scenario on which aspects of conventional science and mathematical models can be superimposed at the object or agent level for detailed evaluation of outcome. However, doing this requires the break down of *abstract qualifiers* into their *operational elements* as demonstrated by the generalization **101.** in point 1. of the Remarks after the '1st example [householder]' in section 6.2.

C3. Further remarks to problem solving and modelling

The exercise of 'problem solving' is *'innate'* in the living sphere. Attempts have been made at creating symbolic models designed intended to be 'problem solving' [Checkland, 1982, Anon., 2014]. The advantages of 'artificial problem solving' is that:

1. It deliberately identifies and makes the 'problematic issue' and the procedure of 'problem solving' explicit,
2. The proposed resolution of a problematic issue may be seen by an individual or organization as a designed or intentional *intervention* into the prevailing order of activities of an organization such an individual, a family or a manufacturing company,
3. The effect of the intervention i.e. the resolved problematic situation, can be *evaluated*,
4. The proposed 'systems theory' is suitable for constructing 'planning schemes' as used in military operations or planning a holiday by providing

a means for methodical thinking and showing explicitly the *conditions* on which the occurrence of events depends. The method could be widely used when software becomes available. It can also be used as an aid in exercising *imagination* in dreaming up 'future, not yet existing states' such as novel buildings, towns or societies.

The inadequacy of available 'problem solving' methods is discussed in CHAPTER 2. The proposed 'systems theory' is an attempt at an improvement.

To operate its 'dynamics of scenarios', the proposed 'systems theory' needs 'software development' and further developments such as how to ensure or to organise the 'cooperation of experts' in assembling diverse products as demanded by the 'process of vaccination'. This will make the 'system theory' a means of application to larger scale problem situations. There is much to discuss concerning the validity of the suggested concepts, especially in the disciplines of linguistics and logic. However, the 'systems theory' is based on branches of existing knowledge such as linguistics, logic, conventional science like chemistry, physics and social science and mathematical modelling. It can be eminently teachable at school and university levels if found acceptable and introduces linguistics as well mathematics as symbolic models. It introduces comprehensive *design thinking* which follows when the inspirational, creative stage of Part A. in Figure 3.1. changes to Part B. which aims at the actual design of static and dynamic structures or 'product [3] and User/Producer [2]' as demonstrated by the examples in CHAPTER 6.

Only simple problems with diagrams which could be accommodated on a single page, are presented for demonstrating the general ideas of 'systems theory'. Teamwork is required for discussion and decision making for agreeing on ideas such as 'what is the problem', 'who is involved', 'feasible and acceptable systems or structures of 'product [3] and User/Producer [2]' and so on. Some of the material in this book has been taken from other publications of the author which is acknowledged.

People especially politicians who are anxious to show their competence and willingness to help, are in the habit of offering 'remedial, usually helpful courses of action' when concerned with a 'problematic issue' presented by others. The proposed 'systems theory' offers the structure of:

First, considering, investigating what is thought to be 'wrong, unacceptable or harmful' in a situation or with an object or agent (Initial state, OPI [5]),

Second, suggesting, offering consistent, envisaged ideas for what is thought to be 'right, desirable or harmless' to satisfy *expectations* (Final state, OPI [6]),

Third, THEN seeking the means which appear to be capable of turning the 'First into the Second' (product [3], User/Producer [2] == *The system or structure*),

Fourth, '*evaluating the effectiveness of the intervention*' or of the resolved problem.

This structure together with the one described in point 4. of section C1. may be seen as an instance of the idea of '*thesis, antithesis and synthesis*' [disregarding the 'Fourth point'] of Hegel followed by Karl Marx. In words:

THESIS = [First point and 1st STEP in 'Implementation of Part A.'] Presents the status quo, the viewpoint that is currently accepted and widely held and articulates the perceived problems,

ANTITHESIS = [Second point and 3rd STEP in 'Implementation of Part A.'] Shows a new viewpoint that is seen to resolve the problems,

SYNTHESIS = [Third point and 'Implementation of Part B.'] Offers the means which can bring about the new viewpoint.

Or thesis is the 'starting point', antithesis is the 'reaction to it' and synthesis is the 'outcome'.

Remark &&&

We conclude that

X. CHAPTER 2. discusses the currently accepted and widely held view in 'systems thinking',

Y. Point 4. in section C1. articulates the problems'

Z. The scheme in Figure 3.1. succinctly presents the new viewpoint.

Accordingly, the notion of 'thesis, antithesis, synthesis' appears to be equivalent to the idea of 'problem solving'. As such this notion is then perhaps the description of the fundamental feature of HOW *progress* is made through the emergence of *new properties* necessitating the emergence of *new systems or structures.* The pursuit of this novelty appears to be propelled by the inventiveness and creativity of the *human mind* along the path of increasing *complexity* as the new properties represent more complex problematic issues to be resolved. The increase of 'convenience' or the changing features of 'travel' demonstrate this idea.

Natural *evolution* of living things along the path of increasing complexity may be seen to take place by living things exploit the prevailing *opportunity* or *conditions*. Thus, we note that 'water was available so fish evolved', 'soil was available so plants evolved', 'plants were available so herbivores evolved', 'herbivores were available so mean eaters evolved'. However, the idea does not explain the appearance of variety, perhaps more thought can come up with an explanation ???

End of **Remark &&&**

C4. Comments on 'models'

Another point concerns the *difference* between 'modelling' in general and 'linguistic modelling' in particular = = =

We repeat in an expanded form the *second* point under remarks concerning Figure C2. because of its importance. Natural language may be called the 'primary model': It is accessible to all who speaks a given language and can be used by the brain/mind to turn thoughts into symbolic model when a text is written on a piece of paper or it is audible. However, when we want to *emphasise* a 'particular aspect' of a part of the world or a particular way of viewing it, we devise and use another kind of model. For example, 'a gesture by hand can be interpreted to say: 'I cannot help it, I am sorry", 'artistic models like ballet can be seen to say by the dancer when he bows in front of another: 'I salute you" or 'a smoke signal can be interpreted by its receiver: 'enemy approaching".

All models carry *information* which carries 'meaning', they say something which is, thus, meaningful and can be interpreted or misinterpreted and their content can be *informative* or *emotive*. Thus, the 'function' of models is to *inform* about the state of a part of the world, real or imaginary. 'Linguistic modelling' is no exception. However, it is not 'another kind of model', it is a modification of a 'story' in natural language into a *reasoning scheme* of logical conditionals. Models of the 'other kind' such as mathematical models are restricted to representation and communication of a particular aspect of a part of the world which the author of the model wants to emphasise, the quantifiable aspect in case of a mathematical model. Natural language in its expressive power is restricted only by the *human imagination*. Accordingly, it is the most suitable model, when modified by 'linguistic modelling', to represent the 'systemic or structural view' in its generality as suggested by the 1st hypothesis in section 3.1.

The concept of 'model' is defined by the generalisation **VWX.** in section 2.2. A more operational kind of description is: 'The term 'model' refers to a symbolic structure originated from and constructed by the *imagination* of the brain/mind to express 'thoughts' for their representation, communication, manipulation and perhaps as the means of memorising. When such a structure is embedded in a 'medium' we have a model which can impinge on the senses'.

This description implies that for a 'model' to be constructed there must be a 'thought' which is to be implemented by the model. *It is the appropriate 'thought' that appears to be missing in current 'system thinking' discussions* as discussed in CHAPTER 2. and in [Korn, 2018b]. The question 'appropriate for what' does not arise. It is likely that all living things with a kind of central nervous system can generate 'thoughts' in response to sensory input which control all activities but only animals at a higher stage of development like chimpanzees, can generate models. This ability culminates with humans who devised 'natural language' with its immense expressive power.

The following points are relevant to the notion of 'model':

1. 'Model' is seen as a *transformation* of 'thoughts', a mental construct, into a physical structure carrying 'information' to be ignored or picked up by the senses of a recipient. A 'thought' or the 'mental state' is created by the chemistry of the brain or seen as an 'emergent property' of the large number of molecular activity like the notion of 'density' is the result of molecular activity of matter [Searle, 1984],

2. 'Model' is a symbolic structure which, as such, needs to satisfy the criteria suggested in section 1.3. The 2nd criterion as given by exp 1.1. perhaps especially important because it gives a model its *applicability*. Otherwise a model is just an intellectual achievement or product. An instant of illustration of this idea is the 'horoscope'.

3. 'Model' is constructed for a 'purpose' or use by a recipient who appreciates it if it can explain, predict, aids design and application and carries *novelty*. Conventional science supplies this kind of models but there are others such as 'road signs' which are of use. Speculative models usually expressed in terms of natural language or works of art, are useful for those with shared interest as sources of emotional and intellectual pleasure.

C5. Other comments

The *first* comment concerns Figure 3.1. which is the diagrammatic representation of the idea of integrated discussion of 'problem solving and systems or structures'. This figure is the most general representation of this idea 'innate' in living things but used by human beings in its full extent, Parts A. and B. For example, a monkey can use a stone [product [3]] to break a nut [skilled power interaction] or whistle [product [3]] when perceives danger [influence interaction] but it is unlikely that creative and innovative thinking is involved. More likely these activities evolved by chance. However, the scheme is applicable to 'natural, inanimate things' when Part A. is zero.

Accordingly, with reference to exp 1.1. in section 1.3., it is possible to apply Part B. to phenomena like a 'volcano' seen as an interacting entity or whole consisting of moving parts of earth driven by geological forces with 'lava' as 'product [3]'. Other phenomena like an 'atom' or 'molecule' or a 'galaxy' can also be considered as 'interacting wholes' with subatomic particles held together by nuclear or gravitational forces but it is harder to identify the part which functions as 'product [3]'.

The implication of this discussion to 'systems thinking' is the change of point of view of classical sciences like physics and chemistry from the purely 'physics' standpoint to the 'systemic or structural view'.

The *second* comment concerns a feature of *properties* considered in section 3.2. which are the 'qualitative, quantitative, qq' and 'systemic or structural, ss'. Qq properties are applied to an 'object or agent', they can be added or removed, they are *incidental*. Ss properties, on the other hand, when they comprise a 'tree' as considered in section 5.3., cannot be disturbed as removal of any alters the structure or adding any introduces redundancy, they are *defying*.

The *third* comment concerns drawing attention to 'products [3]' at the 1st level are constructed by *assembling* 'acquired properties' each one of which is produced by an 'elementary constituent, elcon' as considered in sections 5.1. and 5.6. and in CHAPTER 6. In its turn, 'products' at a higher level are *assembled* from 'products' at the 1st level. For example, a bicycle which is a 'product' to be identified as or called a 'bicycle' is assembled from a combination of 'products' of the 1st and higher levels. The 'horizontal tube of the frame' is a 'product' of the 1st level and the 'frame' itself is a 'product' of higher level.

This description needing further development, corresponds to the idea of *subsystems* which is a term generally used in 'systems thinking'.

The *final* comment points out that this book is regarded as the subject of further development assuming it passes peers' scrutiny, towards application by individuals and organisations to handle physical, intellectual and emotional effects, it is not the end.

APPENDIX 1

This APPENDIX has been produced to contribute to the discussion of the Holistic SIG of the International Society of Systems Science. It is offered here to provide further justification supporting the production of the subject matter of this book which draws more material from other publications by the author.

RESPONSE TO A PRESENTATION delivered at a Holistic SIG meeting of ISSS:

Systems type modelling: A path forward

March 2022

The presentation raises the question of a 'Great challenge for humans, not currently met', 'There is a need for a new approach, better tool' and 'Coherent modelling provides a better approach and a viable path forward'.
The author's immediate comment: 'There is a legitimate point here, all rather vaguely put'.

First point concerns part of the title: 'A path forward'. The direction of advance 'forward' is not clear together with the end point or how we know we have arrived. Also, there must be a starting point or state of affairs which is not discussed. If we want to proceed from somewhere there is usually a reason for making a change. The presenter says there is a 'Great challenge [presumably arising from 'A system can only be understood as a whole] which is not being met'. There is a 'Need for a new approach, a better tool' which is 'Coherent modelling which provides a better approach and a viable path forward' [Which is the suggested 'path forward' !!!!!!!!!].

The thinking in the presentation fits the topic of 'problem solving':
'There is an 'Initial state' of an object or agent which is regarded by an observer as unsatisfactory for whatever reason and called the 'problematic issue',

'There is a consistent, envisaged 'Final state' of the same object or agent which has to satisfy a User/consumer', and

'There is a 'system or structure' consisting of a 'Product and a User/Producer', the *means* which is designed by man or intended by nature to accomplish the change of state'.

A CORRECTION: The connection between 'problem solving', usually the 'initiator of a change of an equilibrium state' AND the 'system or structure', the *means* or resolver of the problem if possible, has been noticed and an attempt which might meet the 'great challenge', is available for consideration by interested parties if any. The notion of 'problem solving' which is a particular case of change of equilibrium state, is, thus, general, therefore, the 'systemic or structural view' is general.

Second point concerns the 'problematic issue' which is:

'The 'systemic or structural view' or 'systems thinking' of parts of the world is an *empirical view*, along with the 'qualitative, quantitative view' of conventional science of physics, conventional engineering, the arts, every day life, the beauty of nature. We can perceive or observe *structures* as 'wholes' or 'holons' and/or their 'structural elements' and we can abstract concepts suitable for creating *symbolic models* for generating *knowledge of the empirical world*.

Simple and complex symbolic models of a great variety have been created over the centuries using the appropriate elements of the 'qualitative, quantitative view' resulting in paradigm changes. However, 'not' known, adequate, comprehensive, sufficiently general symbolic models have been produced to match the generality of the 'systemic or structural view'. [Which agrees with the statement under Rationale].

Third point is about suggesting reasons why the state of affairs put forward in the 'Second point' exists. The following ideas may serve as 'reason':

1. Researchers and thinkers in the 1950's [Bertalanffy, Boulding….] recognised the generality of the 'systemic or structural view' of parts of the world and floated the notion of General Systems Theory,

2. They discarded the relevance and methodology of conventional science of physics to the 'systemic or structural view' and misjudged reductionism in relation to the concept of model,

3. They regarded GST as some kind of a super intellectual product unifying the diverse disciplines of conventional science perhaps through discovering 'isomorphisms'. A new approach is needed,

4. They and the followers to the present time are engaged in discourse of 'highly abstract terms' like 'darkness principle', 'system', 'emergence' and so on and trying to define others. Stimulating ideas are put forward and on occasions presented in diagrammatic form of contours with linguistically indiscriminate terms inside joined by mostly unlabelled directed lines. Definition or appreciation of 'abstract terms' usually emerges from a theory as witnessed from instances of conventional science like 'energy', 'voltage'.... the presentation belongs to this category. The result is 'speculative practice', few attempts at trying to relate to the empirical world. There are universities where practical application of vague systemic terms is practiced,

5. Researchers in 'systems thinking' rarely practice observation of aspects of parts of the world and attempt to abstract 'suitable [?????] empirical concepts',

6. It is not generally recognised that symbolic structures need to satisfy 4 criteria, one of which being the recognition that any such structure [like all other kinds: concrete, abstract, imaginary] consists of 'elementary constituents [elcon]'. Perhaps the success in generating far reaching theoretical structures for explanation, problem solving and application in teaching, research and technology by conventional science is due to its recognition [instinctively ?????] of appropriate elcons [physical, quantifiable, properties],

7. Attempts at 'systems theory' 50 – 60 years ago such as SSM, VSM, systems dynamics do not explicitly recognise elcons, they are difficult to relate to experience, not easily and generally applicable, create fragmentation of the universal 'systemic or structural view' and are not rooted in accepted branches of knowledge. However, SSM is recognised as perhaps the first attempt at methodical problem solving from the systemic point of view,

8. The generality and connection to the 'systemic or structural view' of the idea of 'problem solving' has not been recognised [It is now].

Fourth point shows an 'Abstract' to introduce a 'systems theory' which is a symbolic model and claims 'to describe an integrated approach to 'problem solving' AND 'system or structure' to act as the means of 'resolution of the 'problematic issue''. Whether such a claim is justified is subject to peer review.

The Abstract: DESCRIPTION OF A PROBLEM DRIVEN SYSTEMS THEORY AND DESIGN

janos korn

Living things, in particular humans, are aware of their surrounding including own body, by means of their sense organs which transmit their input signals into the brain/mind apparatus for processing into 'thoughts'. Thoughts resulting from sense input and imagination may be turned into 'symbolic structures or models' for internal and external consumption. The basic raw material of symbolic structures are the 'concepts of qualitative, quantitative [qq] AND/OR structural, relational [sr] properties abstracted from parts of the *empirical* world' carried by statements.

Examination of paradigm changes over the past shows that the vast majority of human, intellectual endeavour has been achieved using 'qq' properties as in mathematical, geometrical, artistic models etc. This could be due to people's predominant interest in material (density, shape, colour...), numerical and energetic (force, current...) properties. 'Sr' properties such as elements of *static structures* describing parts of the world are of interest mostly to manufacturers of artifacts, architects etc. *Dynamic structures* are involved in 'problem solving' for survival and achievement of ambitions which is an ability *innate* in living things and is of their universal activity executed instinctively in purposive configuration. In general, 'sr' properties are *universal* throughout existence. There is no comprehensive symbolic structure describing parts of the *empirical world* commensurate with the generality of the 'systemic or structural view' of parts of the world.

'Control systems theory' developed during the 2nd WWar was the first organised symbolic structure of a 'systems theory' followed by 'systems thinking' evolved in the 1950's by von Bertalanffy and others. These researchers recognised the generality of the 'systemic or structural view' of parts of the world but their approach has remained at the level of speculative discourse about abstract concepts rather than abstracting empirical concepts by *observing* parts of the world. Sporadic, inadequate analytical approaches had been developed 50 – 60 years ago.

The intention is to elaborate the points made and to present a symbolic model of an *empirical* 'systems theory' which considers 'problem solving' AND 'static and dynamic systems' in an integrated manner. Methodical 'problem solving' thinking which involves creativity, inventiveness etc, generates 'product and system design parameters'. Three hypotheses are described: 1. Generality, hierarchy [nested], empirical character and indivisibility of the 'systems or structural view', 2. The notion of equilibrium and its change which is the background motive behind the operation of systems, 3. The idea of 'problem solving' which is a *particular kind* of change of equilibrium states.

'Linguistic modelling of scenarios', the language of 'systems theory', based on processed natural language and derived from a 'story' or narrative in natural language leading to *'elementary constituents'* of 1 or 2 – place sentences, results in predicate logic, conditional statements of the propagation of state in time or 'algorithm'. Linguistic modelling is supplemented by aspects of:
1.   Mathematics such as uncertainty theory and others as required,
2.   Aspects of conventional science etc.

The proposed 'systems theory' is based on accepted branches of knowledge, eminently teachable, encourages methodical thinking, introduces linguistics as a symbolic structure alongside mathematics in teaching curricula. Possible connection to AI needs to be explored. However, it needs peer evaluation, debate, software development, more extensive applications, more scrutiny of its concepts and further research.

Conclusions

This writing is intended to be a response to the thought provoking presentation. In particular, to the clear call for some kind of a change and it is hoped this contribution has expressed this call in more concrete form which is amenable to further critical peer review. However, the justification of the call depends on the *intention, purpose or objective* of the 'systems thinking' community:
'The first version is to engage in generating and discussing intellectual products of the imagination to maintain interest'. In this case the 4th item under the Fourth point is unjustified, in fact most of the items are unjustified. 'The second version is about inventing an empirical systems theory along the lines similar to those existing in conventional science but with 'systemic

content' and to aid 'product and systems design'. The proposal of 'Description of a problem driven systems theory and design' goes further than that: It tries to connect the two aspects of existence which are 'problem solving' and 'existence and operation of systems or structures in static and dynamic states'. In this case, Tom's paper is very relevant and the critical comments in this paper are perhaps justified.

These two versions are not exclusive, there are other possibilities to be considered and decided on by those interested.

Perhaps we can say that the presentation [and I] advocate another paradigm change in the interest of increasing the *cognitive value* of symbolic models or the knowledge of the empirical world. In making these comments only the slides but not the actual presentation were used so the comments are not quite justified. 'Linguistic modelling' operates through expressions of logical conditionals which are similar to the 'rules' of Artificial Intelligence and to the differential equations of Systems Dynamics. So there may be a possibility to establish a connection.

Further to the dichotomy in Figure 3.1. a point for a possible debate has emerged concerning what came into being first: The 'system or structure', Part B., or the 'problematic issue', Part A. The possibilities seen at the moment are:
1. In the living sphere with suitable brain/mind apparatus =
A. It is likely that a 'problematic issue' is detected first incidentally or by *chance* followed by efforts for its resolution unless it is ignored. For example, 'A shoelace is undone which was noticed when the person stepped on it followed by tying it'.
B. Alternatively, it is the imagination of the living or human intellect which generates the 'disequilibrium' by *chance* or deliberately by *purpose* by envisaging future, not-yet-existing states or ambitions to be achieved or dangers to become protected from. For example, 'The four legged animal was hungry and happened to stretch out h/her neck to reach the edible leaves on a tree rather than eating the grass.' or 'The commercial director decided to become the managing director by working for promotion'.

Hopefully the comments are regarded as constructive and, together with the proposal of a 'systems theory', turn out to be worthy of consideration.

Through debate progress can be made and mistakes, misconceptions uncovered in developing symbolic structures representing a 'systems theory'. The more debate and application a symbolic model passes successfully the more trustworthy the knowledge it can deliver, is.

APPENDIX 2

This is a paper produced to present a summary and a few modifications of this book

PROBLEM DRIVEN SYSTEMS THEORY AND DESIGN

Abstract

Details of 'human intellectual endeavour' are interpreted including innate purpose and design using qualitative, quantitative, systemic properties of '1 – and 2 – place' and simple/complex sentences. The inadequacies of current, systemic or structural view is discussed. The incompatibility between Conventional Disciplines such as physics, chemistry and Modern Disciplines such as control theory, systems thinking, design, operational research, is exposed. A proposed 'systems theory' is outlined aiming to treat problem solving and systems thinking joined by design thinking, as an integrated whole. Three hypotheses : 1. Generality, empirical nature, nested hierarchy, 2. State and change of equilibrium, 3. Purposive activity in problem solving, are the basis of the Modern Disciplines with 'linguistic modelling' serving as the symbolic structure resulting as an alternative symbolism to teaching mathematics. This modelling is general enough to cope with Modern Disciplines and provides the static linguistic networks of products and dynamic structures of producers using predicate logic conditionals. Mathematical models such as uncertainties and the required knowledge from Conventional Disciplines can be incorporated at the object, agent and interaction levels. The proposed 'systems theory' is teachable, rooted in accepted branches of knowledge, leads to operational level, needs peer evaluation, software development for working out the dynamics and stability of operation of scenarios and more extensive applications.

This additional writing is introduced because it gives a summary of the extensive content of the book and a somewhat modified version of 'Implementation of Part A.' in section 4.3.

INTRODUCTION

In this paper we are going to discuss the topic of the

'Systemic or structural view of parts of the world'
and its *relation* to a
'Method of problem solving'

from the point of view of developing a *'systems theory'* which treats the two topics joined by *'design thinking'* as an integrated whole. This topic is offered as an *alternative* to the current speculative, fragmented practice which appears to be inadequate to deal with the Modern Disciplines of control, systems thinking, design, problem solving, operational research, management etc. A paradigm change is introduced with reference to these Disciplines [Kuhn, 1996, Korn, 2009, 2013, 2016, 2018, 2020a, 2020b, 2022].

We begin with the basic idea or concept of 'system' or 'structure' or 'complexity' because they can all be seen as the characteristic or descriptive feature or *property* which can be assigned to an aspect of entities, concrete, symbolic, abstract or imaginary by an observer who happens to be interested. This common meaning or representation of these terms may be expressed by the sentence 'They refer to a set of related things or objects or agents natural or artificial, alive or inanimate in their static or dynamic state'. In this sentence 'related' stands for 'being connected physically [chained to, driven by, electrocuted by, below or next to], informatically [listened to], formally [married to], emotionally [angry with] and so on'. Things or objects or agents refer to selected, observed or imagined *'parts of the world'*.

People have no difficulty in describing a thing or a situation in terms of 'related objects' expressed as one or more sentences. For example, 'There are [six] *ribs joined to the* [spinal] *cord* [firmly, at their ends] which [is an arrangement or 'structure' known as the 'chest cavity']. The expression 'chest cavity' is the property of the whole, it does not apply to any of the parts, it is, thus, an *emergent property* [Checkland, 1982]. In this sentence we have two adjectival and two adverbial qualifiers and a subordinate clause in the brackets [Burton, 1984].

First, sentences understood to refer to *static states*

To generalise from this example, we can say we have *three ways of describing* a part of the world using sentences in natural language :

1. Sentences with qualitative, quantitative' properties (qq)
We can describe things in terms of their material properties [weight, colour, size], energetic properties [speed, voltage, temperature], mental properties [clever, IQ], emotive properties [angry, loving], social properties [priest, prince, dustman, rich] and so on which function in a sentence as 'adjectival phrases' adding meaning to noun phrases and 'adverbial phrases' which qualify verbs. In this example, we can say : 'There are six ribs'. or 'An arrangement of ribs and spinal cord is called 'chest cavity''. or 'Ribs are joined firmly'.

2. Sentences with systemic or structural' properties (ss)
The term 'system' or 'complexity' or 'structure' is commonly applied to description of parts of the world in the course of professional and everyday lives of people such as 'solar system', 'transport system', 'molecular system', 'healing system', 'library system', 'management system', 'complex machinery', 'structure of sentence' and so on. In this example, we can say 'The chest cavity consists of [ribs which are joined to the spinal cord]'.

3. Simple or complex sentences (cc)
Natural language is one of the large number of *symbolic structures* or models which humans have invented for representing and communicating their thoughts about aspects of parts of the world but it has by far the greatest expressive power. Simple sentences have a single verb which can attract one or more noun phrases called 'cases' such as the 'dative case', the case of the 'affected noun' which perform specific functions in a sentence. For example, 'Ribs and the spinal cord form an organised arrangement' [Fillmore, 1968, Korn, Huss, Cumbers, 1988].

A complex sentence is recognised by having 'linguistic complexities' such as a 'subordinate clause' which provide additional informatic content to and enriches the expression of a sentence [Burton, 1984]. In this example, we can say: 'Ribs and the spinal cord is an arrangement or 'structure' which [is recognised as the 'chest cavity]'.

We conclude =
Sentences describing static states are used for *description* or *identification* of entities, real or imaginary. Sentences with systemic or structural properties are no different.

Second, sentences understood to refer to *dynamic states*

Sentences express 'dynamic state' through their use of *dynamic verbs*. Referring to the example above, we can say 'Six ribs joined the spinal cord at their ends firmly so as to form the 'chest cavity'. Or 'The wild horse kicked the puma to stop it attacking h/him'. Also, when we refer to a part of the world as 'transport system' we can say a 'transport system operates so as to carry people and goods' or the 'sunflower turns towards the sun to absorb light', the 'volcano erupted which leads to production of lava', 'solar system exists because the planets revolve around the sun'.

We conclude =
Sentences describing dynamic states refer to *purpose* or *goal* or *cause* or *result* or may be interpreted *to resolve a problem*.

In general, we have made statements of the 'subject – predicate' form which 'make complete sense' such as 'John gave money to charity' in which 'John gave' does not because it feels that something is missing. In these statements the 'subject' locates the part of the world of interest and the 'predicate' asserts a view, opinion or belief about the 'subject'. These remarks can refer to both 'context – free' and 'context – dependent' sentences : In the former the noun and verb constituents are not qualified whereas in the latter they are as in '[Six] ribs are joined [firmly] to the [spinal] cord'. Depending on the *precision* of the qualifiers, 'context – dependent' sentences can be expressed in 'operational terms and can be exposed to *falsification* through experiment or observation [Popper, 1972].

We remark as follows :

A. Points 1., 2. and 3. identify three ways of *inquiry* or creating instances of the 'human intellectual endeavour' as shown in Figure 2.1. [Korn, 2022]. The description in Point 1. is exercised in the branch beginning with contour 3 and leading on to contour 10, in particular to 'Conventional science of physics or the natural sciences'. Point 2. begins with contour 4 and ends with contour 13 covering the 'Systems topics'. Point 3. is of interest in contours 8 and 9, in 'social sciences' and in everyday communications. This figure also draws attention to recent paradigm changes shown by the horizontal, continuous arrows. The 3rd paradigm change is of concern here.

B. We note that using

Inquiry 1. imparts *characteristic features to a chosen part of the world*,

Inquiry 2. contributes to the *structural features of a chosen part of the world*, as a 'whole' or holon [Koestler, 1967].

Inquiry 3. results in *stories* or narratives as a means of 'professional and social communication' or the first stage in generating *symbolic structures* or models by the brain/mind towards *representation* [generation of knowledge] or *communication* [generation of information] and *design thinking* in contour 6. Natural language is the *primary model*.

C. Along the branch of following contour 3 in Figure 2.1. the human intellectual endeavour has produced a much higher *quantity* of intellectual products and in many cases they are of great significance, than along that following contour 4. This may have happened because

X. Qualitative, quantitative properties are of more immediate interest to people than structural ones. Structural properties are usually of primary interest to manufacturers of artefacts.

Y. Construction of an intellectual product or a *symbolic structure* or model requires a 'recognised, elementary constituent' like the concept of 'atom' or 'classification of variables' of which more complex structures can be constructed. This requirement is one of four needed for the construction of empirical, symbolic structures and has been lacking in the field of *systems thinking* until now [Korn, 2012].

D. Figure 2.1. also shows the 'problem solving' activity as part of human intellectual endeavour in contour 6 together with *design* thinking. 'Problem solving' activity is *innate* in living things with design thinking peculiar to humans.

The subject matter of 'problem solving' is vast and may involve 'psychology, cognitive science, computer science, engineering etc.' and more recently the notion of 'problem structuring methods' [Lewin, 1981, Mingers, Rosenhead, 2004, Anon., Wikipedia, 2018].

A few suggestions for what is understood by the term 'problem' and 'problem solving' are

1. 'Problem' is a source of perplexity,
2. 'Problem solving behaviour' is the use of various strategies to overcome difficulties in attaining a goal or resolution of the 'problem'.
3. A 'problem' is the distance between how things currently are and the way they should be,
4. 'Problem solving' forms the 'bridge' between the two elements in points 2. and 3. In order to close the gap, we need to understand the ways things are (problem) and the way they ought to be (resolution) [Anon., 2014].

The suggestions seem to imply that the mental process of 'problem solving' consists of *two parts* :

A. Identification of and agreement on what constitutes a 'problematic issue' or *initial state* of affairs regarded as unsatisfactory for some reason and an envisaged, satisfactory, *final state* of affairs which satisfies 'expectations' of a beneficiary,

B. The means or *dynamic structure* or system that is seen to bring about the change from the initial to the final state.

In general :

a. In 'problem solving' we are concerned with changes of *equilibrium* from an unaccepted state of affairs to an envisaged, acceptable one.

b. Both parts acting together, are concerned with *creating, physical and mental things* that satisfy _expectations_ which did not exist before the human interference had taken place. Much analysis, discussion, creative effort and agreement are needed before the results can be finalised if at all.

c. The mental activity of 'problem solving' is *innate* in living things and is operated 'instinctively'.

We conclude that the preceding discussion suggests a _**need**_ for the production of an *empirical systems theory* to :

1. Use 'conscious, deliberate, purposive' *activities* to supplement the instinctive activity of 'problem solving' in humans,

2. Integrate the two aspects of 'problem solving', Parts A. and B., by regarding Part A. as the driver or initiator or motivation of *progress* and Part B. as the necessary *executor* of progress which gives systems or structures a 'reason for existence',

3. Enable Part A., the creative, inspirational part, to generate the *design parameters* for the detailed design of the constituents of Part B., the innovative, systemic or structural part.

The overall intention is the development of a symbolic structure that is capable of generating knowledge of parts of the world from the point of view of 'systems or structures engaged in problem solving'.

BRIEF HISTORICAL DEVELOPMENT OF SYSTEMS THINKING

This topic is introduced here to support further the need for development of an *empirical systems theory* to be part of the 'Structural interest', contour 4, branch in Figure 2.1. The need is discussed in more detail in [Korn, 2009, 2022]. To clarify, we are engaged in the intellectual activity of 'systems thinking' when using 'Inquiry 2.' in the INTRODUCTION.

The 'systems thinking' industry has expanded hugely since its first organised theoretical treatment appeared before, during and long after the 2nd WW, called 'control systems theory'.

This theory exerted immense influence on higher education teaching, industrial practices and invention of new devices. However, perhaps with the enormous development of computers, digital devices, AI etc., the use of this theory had declined. Operational Research, another new discipline, was also invented during this period. In the 1950's researchers hit on the idea of the *'generality* of the concept of system' mostly associated with von Bertalanffy, which was the beginning of the 'huge expansion of systems thinking' and related topics and continues to be so.

Although a vast amount of publications, meetings, sporadic teaching at university level have been produced, researchers in the 1950's and after have been unable or uninterested in the development of an *empirical theory* of 'systems or structures' to fit in the 'structural interest', contour 4, branch of Figure 1. comparable to those in the 'qualitative, quantitative interest', contour

3, branch. A reason for this is suggested in point Y. in the INTRODUCTION.

This has resulted in :

I. A vast amount of diverse speculative output,

II. Workers in the field are engaged in development of theories about *systems themselves* but unrelated to aspects of parts of the world. For example, 'system of systems', 'system literacy', 'nested levels of systems...' and so on using Inquiry 3. or *verbosity* illustrated with diagrams [Ackoff, 1971]. These efforts are similar to those of the ancient Greek philosophers who propounded wide ranging ideas such as 'water being the prime substance' without reference to empirical evidence [Levene, 2010]. This novel methodology was introduced by the Renaissance science. However, inspiring and stimulating ideas have and do emerge.

III. Thinking and expecting that a General Systems Theory is a 'super science' or a 'unification of scientific disciplines' which can be constructed by seeking out 'isomorphisms',

IV. Using concepts from physical sciences in discussions like 'open and closed systems', 'entropy',

V. Producing inadequate approaches as far as the 'four criteria' for constructing an 'empirical theory' are concerned [Korn, 2022]. For example, 'causal mapping', 'viable systems model', 'soft systems methodology', 'evolutionary, learning laboratory' and so on. This effort has resulted in *fragmentation* of the unique 'systemic or structural view' of parts of the world.

VI. Continued production of symbolic structures mostly mathematical models or intellectual products for the satisfaction of *human curiosity* rather than being concerned with 'problem solving' [Anon., 2022].

Although the application of 'design thinking' goes back to when humans had started to use artefacts and had continued with the invention of appliances and construction of monuments and large buildings, the question of the nature and application of 'design thinking' were raised only around the 1960's and 1970's at least in higher educational circles and is still unresolved, its application owes much to human instinct. The lack of comprehensive design method felt in 'systems engineering' as well [Blackett, 1948, Brown, Campbell, 1948, Bertalanffy, 1962, Feilden, 1963, Robbins, 1963, Pahl, Beitz, 1984, Finniston, 1980, Jones, 1980, Lewin, 1981, Hubka, Eder, 1996, Cross, 1989, Korn, 1981, 1989].

With reference to Figure 2.1., we note that further to 'structural interest', contour 4, branch of human intellectual endeavours : 'Control Systems, OR, General Systems including systems engineering, social and management sciences and Design Thinking' [called here Modern Disciplines] were developed more or less around the same time. The appearance of these Disciplines had raised **questions** against the well known, accepted 'Conventional science of physics, chemistry, product engineering etc. and the Arts' [called here Conventional Disciplines] which have been hugely successful in application in technology and society.

A proposed *answer* is :

'The Modern Disciplines are concerned with the SINGLE activity of *problem solving*, the concern of Conventional Disciplines is the production of a VARIETY of *intellectual products* for the satisfaction of human curiosity and use'.
The two Disciplines are *incompatible* but aspects of the Conventional Disciplines can be integrated at object or agent or interaction level into the linguistic framework of the proposed 'systems theory'.

This was noticeable in engineering education by the great difficulties in fitting Modern Disciplines into the curricula based on the philosophy of Conventional Disciplines which was the only one available with teachable knowledge. In constructing *symbolic models* this philosophy primarily fits into explanatory arguments and is based on Inquiry 1., there was no comparable *symbolic model* of 'systems theory and problem solving'. Although the 'engineering philosophy' is 'problem solving' including 'design thinking' this idea was difficult to fit into teaching schemes of engineering courses [Lewin, 1981]. The symbolic models of the Conventional Disciplines are 'intellectual products' intended to 'represent aspects of parts of the world' and 'to explain the existence and happenings of phenomena' so as to satisfy *curiosity* i.e. to change this particular mental state.

We conclude =
This is the kind of 'problem solving' in which human intellectual endeavour is engaged using Inquiry 1. It does not fit into 'problem solving' of interest to the Modern Disciplines which is about problems of creating and designing *novelty*

concerning aspects of 'parts of the world' in nature, technology, organisations and society. This contradiction raised the questions in engineering degree courses with curricula based on symbolic models generated mostly by the philosophy of Conventional Disciplines. The contradiction can only be resolved by an acceptable *systems theory* to satisfy the 'need' as suggested in the INTRODUCTION subject to peer scrutiny, software development to work out the dynamics of scenarios and further development for handling large, practical problem situations.

The chasm between the Conventional and Modern Disciplines is emphasised in Figure 2.1. Accordingly, there is a further need for an *empirical systems theory* which can help to reconcile the fundamental difference between the two Disciplines. This difference has not been resolved over the past decades, only masked by the immense development and application of computers and the application of available knowledge in teaching and practice.

Although the Modern Disciplines are concerned with 'problem solving' as their *common theme*, they are not 'homogeneous'. We now elaborate the relevant, distinguishing features in the various branches constituting these Disciplines in Figure 2.1. :

Contour 6 ---
First, includes the *innate, instinctive* problem solving activity common in all living things.
Second, indicates problem solving activity in *conventional engineering, architecture etc* making use of qualitative, quantitative properties of Conventional Disciplines in contour 10 and *product design* but no comprehensive approach [Cross, 1989]. This is reflected in university teaching programmes.
Contour 4 ---
First, engineering control theory in contour 11 developed the structural symbolism or model of *transfer function analysis* and other approaches with problematic issues like being signal based, restricted to isothermal operations etc. There is a limited use of design thinking based on identifying a desired outcome [Nise, 2008, Korn, 2009, 2012]. This theory satisfies all 4 criteria for constructing symbolic structures as discussed in section 1.3. However, the 'elementary constituents' are not identified.

Second, operational research (OR) in contour 12 is engaged in using rigorous, mathematical models along the lines as in Conventional Disciplines applied to issues of current interest [Anon., 2022]. These are intellectual product for the satisfaction of curiosity. There is a need for a Problem Structuring Method along the lines of Figure 3.1.

Third, current systemic views in contour 13 with a number of problematic issues discussed

in this section and in [Korn, 2018b]. Many novel and stimulating ideas have been produced but with inadequate attention to the development of a satisfactory empirical theory.

The *intention* of the proposed 'systems theory' is to produce a symbolic structure which reflects the underlying *common theme* of 'problem solving'.

A way to satisfy the identified *need* is also suggested by the diagram in Figure 2.1. and by the discussion so far :

First, to create a 'systems theory' as suggested in contour 14 next to the 3rd paradigm change to satisfy the 'generality condition' of the systemic or structural view and to integrate the 'systemic or structural view of parts of the world' with 'problem solving' in contour 6,

Second, to utilise 'processed natural language' or 'linguistic modelling' as the symbolic structure of the proposed 'systems theory' which is capable of presenting the *inquiries* discussed in the INTRODUCTION in an integrated whole.

ONE : Inquiry 1. is the language of 'natural sciences',

TWO : Inquiry 3. is the language of 'social sciences' and of professional and everyday use,

THREE : Inquiry 2. is the language of 'systems science' utilising ONE and TWO by converting TWO into its structure of 1 – and 2 – place, simple sentences and using the knowledge generated by ONE at the object or agent or interaction level, especially its mathematical models.

PROPOSED RESOLUTION OF THE PROBLEM

By and large in the field of Modern Disciplines the current practice is to consider 'systems thinking', 'problem solving' and 'design thinking' as separate subject matters as discussed in the INTRODUCTION. This is considered to

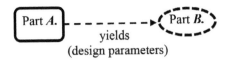

Figure A2.1. Basic idea of integrated 'systems theory'

be the 'problem' and the currently available methods offer no satisfactory resolution as described in the BRIEF HISTORICAL DEVELOPMENT OF SYSTEMS THINKING. Accordingly, a 'systems theory' is suggested as its possible resolution which can also resolve the anomaly between Modern and Conventional Disciplines. We now give an outline of this theory with the basic idea diagrammed in Figure A2.1. with details in this book.

With reference to the INTRODUCTION, Part A. represents the thoughts in the brain/mind or in the 'central nervous system' of an *observer* or an individual living thing which identify or raise a *'problem situation'*, suggest a resolution if any can be found and agreed on by the interested parties so as to satisfy the 'expectations' of a person or an organisation involved. In this part creativity, innovation, intuition govern the thoughts where the new ideas are born to fuel progress towards survival, convenience, higher productivity and efficiency, better appearance and so on. This part also yields the *design parameters* which are to be satisfied by the construction of the constituent elements of Part B. which ensures that the innovations introduced in Part A. are fulfilled.

These considerations suggest :
1. Part B. or the 'systemic or structural part' comes into existence in accordance with purpose or by chance i.e. designed to satisfy expectations or evolved by trial and error arising from exposure to the *surrounding*, and
2. The scheme in Figure A2.1. locates and *justifies* the existence and operation of the structures in Part B.

Introducing the basis of 'systems theory'

Humans can have : *Ambitions* or *objectives* or *expectations* to achieve = Survival, convenience, power, influence, improvements in physical and mental well being [own and of others], feelings, emotions, desires, wishes etc.,

Animals can have : *Objectives* to achieve = Survival including overcoming harmful agents,

Structures of controls and computers can have : *Objectives* to achieve = Set targets,

Plants can have : *Instinct* [?] to achieve = Aiding survival such as 'turning towards the sun',

Inanimate things can have : *Changes* driven by 'chance'.

Ambitions, objectives and instincts are driven by *imagination* in a decreasing extent in humans, animals and plants. *All changes* are driven by 'change of equilibrium states'.

The results of execution of 'ambitions' and 'objectives' are *accessible* in the first place by means of the 'senses' and instruments through qualitative/ quantitative properties. These are then interpreted by the brain/mind as 'thoughts' and can be formulated in terms of a suitable *symbolic model* such as language, writing, mathematics, painting etc. and their effect can be *evaluated*. Construction of a *symbolic model* 'in the first place' enables pre – evaluation.

Any **ambition** is realised by means of **achievement** as shown :

For example, | **Ambition** | **Process of achievement** |
| --- | --- |
| To survive | Seeking to *have food, drink and shelter* |
| To have convenience | Ensuring to *use transport* instead of walking |
| To have power | Conspiring to *depose the government* |
| To have mental well being | Going to a museum to *look at paintings* |

where the words in italic designate the *achievement* which can convert a deficient state into a 'state of ambition'. The present participle of dynamic verbs indicate *action* to produce the 'new state'.

Consideration of the notion of **ACHIEVEMENT** in its widest sense leads to the following points and its representation in Figure 3.1. :

I. The concept of *achievement* is 'identified' with the notion of intellectual and material *product* as an artefact. Both concepts have a common meaning as 'that created by an agent'. The term 'achievement' usually means : Created by self,

The term 'product' means : Produced by a third party.

PRODUCT is the central, pivoting point in the accomplishment of any change: It is the subject of *invention*,

It is the generator of *interaction* for the accomplishment of change,

It is the *interface* between the 'changing object, in Part A. and the 'system or structure' in Part B.

II. The function of the *product* is to change the state of an object or agent which carries a 'problematic issue', designated as *OPI*, which arises in a 'problematic situation' described by a 'story',

III. The 'product' can do this by being manufactured, assembled and/ or delivered by a *producer* to a 'notional' or 'actual' 'market' according to 'specifications' which should satisfy the 'requirements' of an OPI and other objects involved in a scenario such as 'stakeholders' or 'environmental objects',

IV. The 'producer' in producing a product operates according to a plan as directed by a *brain/mind*,

V. The 'brain/mind' directs the 'producer' so as to result in a 'product' that can change the state of 'OPI' to lead to *satisfaction* of expectations of another object or agent referred to as *User/consumer* which is also monitored by the brain/mind. The cycle can go round until the User/consumer is satisfied.

Points I. to V. describe the mental process of 'problem solving' operating as a 'purposive activity' the structure of which is shown as a diagram in Figure 3.1.

For example, the story : 'People in a village would like to cross the river more easily than at present'. We interpret the terms in the 'story language' to fit into those in the 'model language' as suggested by the 2nd Criterion in section 1.3. as follows :

'People' identify or see the 'uncrossed river [OPI]' as the carrier of the 'problematic issue' which is the IS [initial (problematic) state] of this object at contour 5,

The 'not yet existing means of crossing' is seen as the 'product' at contour 3,

The 'product' is produced by 'producers' or 'designers and manufacturers' at contour 2 in accordance with a *'plan'* or *'design'*. Its stage of execution is monitored by the 'product feedback' and acts as reference generally known as 'objective' or 'ambition' of the brain/mind at contour 1,

The 'people' also play the part of the 'User/consumer' with 'expectations' to be satisfied at contour 7-8,

The 'requirements' of OPI, expectations of User/consumer and other interested parties should be met by 'specifications' for the 'product' at a real or notional MARKET at contour 4,

The 'crossed river FS [final state of OPI'] achieved by the chosen product at contour 6 should be such as to satisfy the 'expectations' or 'need' of people,

The state of User/consumer at contour 8 is monitored by the brain/mind at contour 1.

The scheme in Figure 3.1. includes *four* kinds of 'systems or structures' as particular cases:

A. *'Utilising systems'* which are recognised by their use of 'existing products'.

B. *'Producing systems'* which are recognised by their activity such as designing, manufacturing, assembling, delivering, selling 'products' to 'Market'.

C. *'Trouble shooting systems'* existing through perception of a 'OPI [5-6]' through 'symptoms' manifested by a breakdown [of a car] caused by lack of fuel, anaemia [of a child] caused by deficiency of iron, difficult to climb [up stairs] caused by weak heart and seeking *product [3]*, *producers [2]* to 'restore fuel supply', 'supply of iron' etc. to eliminate cause so as to satisfy a User/consumer [7-8], once a cause can be found.

D. *'Inanimate systems'* which are recognised by the presence of producers [2] (with no management) producing product [3] and possibly affecting a User/consumer [7-8] such as a volcano producing 'lava' and 'ashes' can affect the surrounding countryside and people living nearby. No brain/mind [1] and OPI [5-6].

Introducing the details of 'systems theory'

Figures A2.1. and 3.1. show the basic ideas of the 'systems theory' as a whole. In order to apply it, it needs to be implemented into a procedure which can be used in practice. This section deals with :

Implementation of Part A. of Figure 3.1.

1ˢᵗ STEP

Having read and digested the 'story' of a 'problematic situation', the *observer* or *investigator* exercises 'perception, imagination, inspiration or methodical thinking' to obtain consensus of all interested parties regarding identification of the object or agent carrying the 'problematic issue' and the subjective beliefs of what is 'wrong', 'undesirable', 'harmful' and so on.

This 'step' deals with the identification of OPI [5] in Figure 3.1. which, as all other terms, is based on consideration of the *meaning* of the wording of the text of the 'story' or the relations of symbols to their *perceived, existing or imaginary impression* or the intention is

'"To identify the Object with 'Problematic Issue' or the 'Initial state [IS] of OPI [5]'",

2ⁿᵈ STEP

Having investigated the problematic situation involving the 'User/consumer', the *observer* states

'"The expectations as the 'Initial state [IS] of User/consumer [7]'""

which are formulated by an individual or group of individuals based on what they regard as 'acceptable resolution' of the 'problematic issue' or OPI [5].

3ʳᵈ STEP

The *observer, investigator* produces or invents a *choice* of

'"Possible, desirable, consistent 'Final state(s) [FS] of OPI [6]'",

4ʳᵈ STEP

Investigating how close the 'Final state [FS] of OPI[6]' comes to 'IS of User/consumer [7]' so as to allow the

'""Final state [FS] of User/consumer [8]' to happen'",

If the *observer* is not satisfied then the 3rd STEP is repeated until h/sh is.

Remark &&&

At this stage OPI and User/consumer in contours 6 and 8 are *THEORETICALLY* in acceptable states.

End of **Remarks &&&**

5th **STEP**

The potential 'products [3]' i.e. objects or agents which appear to the *observer* to be capable of converting the 1st STEP to 3rd STEP are found assuming there is a STORE of products in existence or invented if not found in the STORE. Suitability of any of the variety of 'products [3]' is recognised by 'perceiving' its ability to exert the *interaction* in response to *stimulus* from producer [2] seen to be REQUIRED to accomplish the change of state from the 1st STEP to 3rd STEP.

6th **STEP**

Based on *subjective considerations* [Korn, 2022], the *observer* needs to suggest "The 'pertinent, static and dynamic properties or characteristics'" of = = =
1. OPI and User/consumer, and
2. Objects or agents and/or circumstances in the *surrounding* which are judged
to be 'relevant to the 'problem situation" such as environmental objects and others with interest in the 'problematic issue' such as stake holders.

Remark X &&&

The *observer* now has :
X. A selection of products seen to be capable of exerting the appropriate *interaction*, and
Y. The 'static characteristics' expressed by 'contingent statements' including *properties* of
1.   OPI [5] (**O**),
2.   User/consumer [7] (**U**), and

3. Objects, agents or processes perceived as relevant but external to Part A. and B. (**E**). They can affect any constituents of the scheme and can be affected by any of them.

IF the **5th STEP** fails then 'product [3]' has to be invented, designed, manufactured and assembled and the 'Utilising system' has to change to 'Producing or manufacturing system'.

End of **Remark X &&&**

7th STEP
In this STEP the *observer* selects a 'product [3]' by naming its designation on the basis of 'information' summarised in Remark X above.

To arrive at a suitable 'product [3]' the *observer* needs 'to match and to select' objects using the 'information' in Remark X above aided by the Entailment Relation [ER] and the Object Selector Matrix [OSM] shown in Figures A2.2. and A2.3. [Saeed, 1998].

 It is the *meaning of the terms* and their interpretation in the statements which decides if there is the desired relation between the two sets of properties in points A. and C. in Figure A2.2. For example, 'The lady has just had her hair done and it is raining [A], she does not want her hairdo to be spoilt [B], REQUIRES or entails that she carries a waterproof appliance such as an umbrella or any other implement to protect her hair from rain [C]'.

In ER once the second group of qualifiers has been obtained, an object or agent i.e. 'product [3]' presumed to carry these qualifiers needs to be found.

A. There is a **1st set** of qualifiers carried by 'contingent statements' attached to objects O, U and E in Remark X, and
B. There is a sentence or a phrase of commitment to fit, to match or to satisfy or to the contrary, fulfilment of which,
C. REQUIRES that there be a **2nd set** of qualifiers carried by 'contingent statements' which fit or match or satisfy those in point A. and are designated a, b, c, ...

Figure A2.2. Scheme of entailment relation [ER]

This can be helped by OSM shown in Figure A2.3. The top horizontal line carries the qualifiers from point C. in Figure A2.2. in ER, the vertical line shows the selected objects or agents in the 5th STEP. The numeral '1' is inserted against that object or agent which is presumed to have that qualifier, '0' which has not. The object carrying the largest number of '1's is selected.

The practice of ER and OSM takes place at a notional or actual **MARKET** at contour 4.

The *observer* now has

1. After the 4th STEP, OPI and User/consumer are theoretically in 'acceptable states' i.e.
At contour 6 : OPI [6] is in --- Final state [FS], and
At contour 8 : User /consumer [8] is in --- Satisfied [or not] and observed by the Brain/mind at contour 1 and compared with 'what is thought to be desirable' stored by Brain/mind [1],
2. The designation of a *'product [3]'* which is capable of exerting the required *'interaction'* in a Utilising system,
3. The qualifiers of the *'same product [3]'*, a, b, c,..., which *match* the characteristics of O, U and E.

Points *2.* and *3.* are the ***PRODUCT design parameters***. i.e. product [3] must be *selected* or *designed, fabricated, manufactured* or *constructed* so as to exhibit these 'parameters'.

The considerations so far have <u>*completed*</u> Part A. of the scheme in Figure 3.1.

	2nd set of qualifiers			
	a.	b.	c.	and so on ....
objects or agents carrying,	1	0	0	
or not, the qualifiers	1	0	0	
---	0	1	1	
---	1	1	1	

Figure A2.3. Diagram of Object Selector Matrix [OSM]

Remark 1. &&&

The considerations also have

A. Established 'objects or agents' in contours 1, 4, 5, 6, 7, 8, and
B. Resulted in stating the 'product design parameters' for 'product [3]', and

To satisfy the 'Product design parameters' :

I. As a 'Utilising system', the producer [2], when chosen by the *observer* from those available, needs to have *properties and the 'objects or agents' to carry them*, which enable it

1. *to drive, position, process, handle, treat, control (stimulate)* the *recognised* 'product [3]' or its component parts so that, in its/their turn, it/they can produce the correct kind and quantity of *interaction* which can bring about the change of state in OPI [5] to [6],
2. to be able to accommodate the properties a, b, c, ... of product [3] called the *accommodating properties*. For example, 'A contingent statement with property a. is : 'The lady has a new hairdo [product [3]]' and 'A contingent statement with accommodating property is : 'She operates the 'waterproof umbrella' so as 'to protect the new hairdo' [accommodating property of producer [2]]',
3. to cope with *external conditions* by generating *additional properties*. For example, 'A statement with external condition is : 'In a coal mine the atmosphere is dusty" and 'A statement with additional property is : 'The miners wear suitable face mask",
4. to generate *'objects or agents'* with properties to *assemble, deliver and sell* the 'product [3]'.

Following these points a *generalisation* is introduced [Nise, 2008, Korn, 2012]:
222. --- 'Any part of a system or structure of producer [2] operating in *purposive configuration* produces a *single*, property of an object or agent or the actual property, in accordance with an envisaged property or *objective* because only TWO properties can be *compared* at a time to generate an error signal which drives the producer [2]'. The actual property can act as a product [3] as in engineering control systems [Korn, 2012]. ---

The properties in points 2., 3. and 4. are in the 'story' of a scenario or the need for them arises in the course of implementing Part A. and/or B.

II. As a 'Producing system', the producer [2] must be able *to design, fabricate, manufacture, assemble* product [3] so as to satisfy Points *1., 2., 3.* and *4.* including *delivery* to MARKET [4] for eventual sale or give away.

In other words, a Producing system needs to be set up and to operate so as to produce the product [3] which is capable of changing states and fits into its surroundings. These systems produce the 'holons' from 'properties' as shown by the examples in CHAPTER 6. and *assemble them into more complex holons* [Koestler, 1967].

Utilising and Producing systems are particular cases of the scheme in Figure 3.1. having the capability of
Utilising systems : To accomplish Point *I.*, and
Producing systems : To accomplish Point *II.*

which are the **_SYSTEMS design parameters_**. Any additional components like waste removal, supply of consumables, accountancy, management, personnel department etc arise from needs of operation.

A point concerning 'Systems design parameters' : The implementation of any *property* and *capability* suggested in this Remark 1. requires the construction of a 'story' as shown in the examples in CHAPTER 6.

End of **Remark 1. &&&**

Further to Figure A2.1., Part A. and the 'design parameters' have now been done. We introduce an example in sections 2.2., 6.2. to demonstrate the 'Implementation of both Parts A. and B.'

Points concerning the *Implementation Part B.* in Figure 3.1. :

Structurally Part B. of the 'systems theory' consists of product [3], producer [2] and brain/mind [1]. Following theories in physics like the 'laws of thermodynamics' and 'Newton's laws', this part is based on

I. Hypotheses

Based on the preceding discussion regarding parts of the *empirical world* and previous work, we introduce the following **_hypotheses_** or *principles of systems* which are the intuitive, speculative part of the proposed 'systems theory' [Korn, 2018]

1. The nature of the world : The systemic or structural view of parts of the world is *general, empirical, nested hierarchical and indivisible* and 'there is no alternative',

2. There is no change by itself : Systems or structures emerge so as to *change equilibrium* states from initial to final by **chance** or in accordance with **purpose** or the change of equilibrium state calls for the creation of a system or structure as suggested by Figure 3.1.,

3. The purpose of change is problem solving : The concept of *change of equilibrium* from initial, unsatisfactory to final, satisfactory, is at the basis of *problem solving.* The use of this concept extends the application of the 'systems theory' to describe the operation of 'Inanimate systems' which are particular cases of Figure 3.1.

Inquiry 3. --- Story or narrative of a perceived scenario

        ↓   Meaning Preserving Linguistic Transformations [Korn 2022]

Inquiry 2. --- Linguistic structure of semantic diagram of '1 – and 2 – place sentences'

        ↓   Application of predicate logic

Inquiry 0. --- Sequences of conditional statements

        ↓   Application of mathematical models, instances of conventional sciences

Inquiry 1. --- Qualified objects or agents from the scenario

        ↓   Computation by software to be developed

Inquiry -1. --- Dynamics of scenarios

Figure A2.4. Scheme of implementation of linguistic modelling

II. Linguistic modelling

Linguistic modelling is the executor of the hypotheses. It transforms a 'story' in natural language into *conditional statements* which enable the examination of the strength of alleged 'cause and effect relations' in an envisaged, projected scenario. This is possible because LM uses '1 – and 2 – place, declarative sentences' as *elementary constituents* of which all more complex, symbolic structures are constructed and can be expressed in terms of predicate logic statements [Copi, 1978, Korn, 2009].

The relevance of the 'Inquiries' discussed in the INTRODUCTION to LM is shown in Figure A2.4. which is an alternative to Figure C2.

Inquiry -1. --- Dynamics of scenarios

CONCLUSIONS

The scheme in Figure 2.1. introduces three branches of human intellectual endeavour which currently may be seen as more or less separate disciplines. The lack of a unifying idea has been causing problems certainly in higher education which have not yet been resolved but perhaps masked by the immense development of computers. Current work which is outlined in this paper is aimed at offering a 'systems theory' for discussion which, if passes review, may be suitable to begin to alleviate the problems. The problems have been made concrete by identifying the notion of Conventional and Modern Disciplines with incompatible philosophies and the problematic details of current 'systems thinking'.

Using the concept of 'Inquiries 1., 2., 3.' abstracted from natural language which is regarded as the 'primary model', the relevance of these inquiries to the three branches of human intellectual endeavour is clarified.

The basic idea is for the proposed 'systems theory' to integrate 'problem solving' and 'systems thinking' connected by 'design thinking'. In problem solving the living intellect perceives or driven by imagination, an inadequacy which needs a remedy. This idea in plant, animal or man is then executed either by a naturally occurring or a designed system or structure. These ideas are integrated by the 'systems theory', a generalisation of Newton's first law of motion i.e. no change until there is an interference. The integration also justifies the existence and operation of systems or structures which is to bring about the *change*. Using the notion of state and change of *equilibrium* the basic idea can be extended to inanimate, natural systems or structures which is a particular case of the scheme in Figure 3.1.

Further to Figure 2.1. the proposed 'systems theory' suggests an analytical alternative to 'innate' problem solving with linguistic modelling converting a 'story' as the embodiment of the first idea or perception, into sequences of 'logical conditionals' which enable the strength of *causal connections* to be evaluated and correcting action to be taken if needed. If the 'systems theory' is found acceptable alternatives can be offered for the details like the 'Entailment Relation' or the method of introducing uncertainty. However, the proposed 'systems theory' needs to be discussed for its feasibility and subsequently developed into a working tool for practical use by individuals, manufacturing and other organisation and to be a part of school and higher education.

Further to the particular cases of the 'systems theory' as in Figure 3.1., 'Trouble shooting and Inanimate, natural systems' are not considered in this book.

APPENDIX 3

Appendix 3. has been prepared as slides for presentation at a conference. It shows a condensed version of text of the paper in Appendix 2. some of which has already been described in the book but perhaps worth repeating. The title of slides presented is :

PROBLEM DRIVEN SYSTEMS THEORY AND DESIGN

<u>*WHAT IS ALL THIS ABOUT ????*</u>
In this presentation we are going to discuss the topic of the

'Systemic or structural view of parts of the world'
and its *relation* to
'Methods of problem solving'

from the point of view of developing an empirical *'systems theory'* which treats the two topics joined by *'design thinking'* as an integrated whole. This topic is offered as a *supplement* to the current, largely speculative, fragmented practice which appears to be inadequate to deal with the Modern Disciplines of control, systems thinking, design, problem solving, operational research, management etc. A paradigm change is introduced with reference to these Disciplines [Kuhn, 1996, Korn, 2009, 2013, 2016, 2018a, 2018b].

The objective is to generate knowledge of aspects of the empirical world by constructing models of aspects of parts of this world which are such as to enable us to generate knowledge.

<u>*WHAT IS THE CURRENT STATE ????*</u> [of human intellectual endeavour]
This is shown in Figure 2.1.

<u>*WHAT ARE THE DETAILS OF FIGURE 2.1 ??????*</u>
1. Three or more, separate branches corresponding to
    Qualitative, quantitative properties, contour 3,

Systemic or structural properties, contour 4,
Simple/complex sentences of natural language, contour 6

2. Conventional Disciplines, contour 3, = =
   Variety of intellectual products to satisfy curiosity and use,
   Modern Disciplines, contour 4, = =
   Interest in *single* activity of problem solving,
   Conventional and Modern Disciplines are INCOMPATIBLE !!!!!!!!
3. Disparity of intellectual products
   Branch 3: Qual/quant properties for 'elementary constituents' and mathematical models,
   Branch 4: No universal 'elementary constituent' and underlying principles

4. CONSEQUENCES of Branch 4
A. Speculative output
B. Theorising about systems for its own sake [Ackoff, 1971]
C. General Systems Theory, super science, isomorphisms
D. Concepts from physics, entropy......
E. Inadequate methods, VSM [viable systems method], SSM [soft systems methodology.....]
F. Continuing production of mathematical models for solution of problems

WHAT IS THE PROBLEM ?????
Observation tells us that :
1. The *empirical* world [mental and physical] can be seen as 'systemic or structural' and this view is *universal*, there is NO alternative !!!!!!!!
2. Problem solving is *innate* and *universal* in the living sphere.

Based on the 'CURRENT STATE', Figure 2.1., the Modern Disciplines
A. Are fragmented i.e. deals with a *fraction* of the systemic view,
B. Have no acceptable 'elementary constituents' of which more complex structures can be constructed and most of them do not satisfy the other criteria,
C. Have little reference to concepts regarded as basic,
D. The whole of human intellectual enterprise as shown in Figure 2.1. is *fragmented*,

Humanity have made progress because : 1. Ingenuity, innovation, creativity, 2. Innateness of problem solving, 3. Making use of available knowledge and cumulative experience.

WHAT IS THE RESOLUTION OF THE PROBLEM ???????

In general 'problem solving' or *change of equilibrium* consists of *two parts* :
A. Identification of and agreement on what constitutes a 'problematic issue' or *initial state* of affairs regarded as unsatisfactory for some reason and an envisaged, satisfactory, consistent *final state* of affairs which satisfies 'expectations' of a beneficiary,
B. The means or *dynamic structure* or system that is seen to bring about the change from the initial to the final state.

Points A. and B. in Figure A2.1. shows the basic idea of integrated 'systems theory' with more details of the 'problem structuring scheme' in Figure 3.1.

Part A. is the source of innovation and progress, Part B. is the source of technical novelty.

Figures A2.1. and 3.1. show the 'SYSTEMS THEORY' as a whole, it is put into practice by IMPLEMENTING Part A. and Part B. into a *procedure.*

Implementation begins with a STORY in natural language, the primary model' of a perceived scenario which appears to contain a 'problematic issue'

IMPLEMENTATION of Part A. Consists of 7 steps to arrive at :
OPI [6] final state,
User/consumer [8] with expectation,
Design parameters for product [3] and producer [2]

IMPLEMENTATION of Part B. Consists of :
THREE Principles of systems --- 1. Generality, nested hierarchy
2. State and change of equilibrium
3. Problem solving and purpose
LINGUISTIC MODELLING of scenarios of processed natural language
To provide the *basic linguistic structure* of scenarios consisting of *1 and 2 place sentences*, the 'elementary constituents' of static and dynamic systems

CONCLUSIONS

The proposed 'systems theory' is rooted in accepted knowledge, teachable, can be turned into operational form, handles emotive effects and subjective values, has to be learnt, chemistry, nuclear physics should be part of 'systems'....., needs peer evaluation, software development, practical applications

<u>VERY SIMPLE EXAMPLE OF A *UTILISING SYSTEM*</u>
STORY : 'Using h/her tractor, the farmer's job was to deliver hay from the store to the shed twice a day'.

Implementation of Part A.
1st STEP
Identification and <u>Initial state</u> of OPI [5] = Hay [in the store]
2nd STEP
Expectation or Initial state of User/consumer [7] = Farmer to see hay in front the cows
3rd STEP
Choice of desirable, <u>Final state</u> of OPI [6] = Hay is in the shed from the store twice a day
4th STEP
Investigation of how close Final state of OPI [6] comes to Initial state of User/consumer [7] for User/consumer [8] to happen = Not close enough !!!!!!!!!!

There is a <u>problem</u>: 1. If the 'story' did not mention 'tractor' there would be NO product [3],
2. OPI [6] does NOT match User/cons [7]
3. Note : Choice of 'hay' is not unique, 'farmer' could be selected as OPI [5] !!!!!!!!!!!!

5th STEP
Potential products [3] capable of exerting *interaction* to accomplish change of state of OPI [5] to [6] = Tractor driven by a person
6th STEP
Static, dynamic characteristics of OPI, User/consumer and relevant Environmental Objects which the product [3] has to match =
7th STEP
Selection of properties of product [3] using Entailment Relation and Object Selector Matrix which have to match those in 6th STEP =

Hence, product and systems design parameters leading to linguistic structures consisting of sematic diagrams similar to Figure A3.1. !!!!!!!!!! So, COMPLEX SYSTEMS are constructed from '*elementary constituents*'.

Implementation of Part B.

This means going through STAGES of *linguistic modelling* to arrive at the structure like Figure A3.1.

The verbal form of the *predicate logic conditionals,* NO uncertainties, mathematics, corresponding to the conditionals written next to Figure A3.1.:

IF the farmer wants hay for his cows AND he uses a tractor THEN he delivers hay from the store to the shed twice a day
IF he delivers hay from the store to the shed twice a day AND the hay is nutritious THEN the hay is delivered from the store to the shed twice a day

REMARK: The job of linguistic modelling is 'to transform a STORY in natural language into a set of *logical conditionals*'. The conditionals carry dependence with uncertainties, decisions, mathematical models and so on.

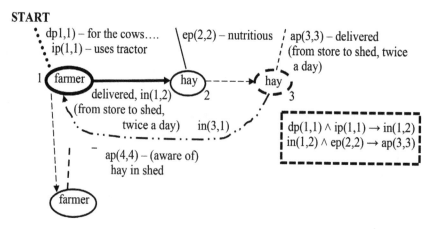

Figure A3.1. Semantic diagram of 'farmer/hay' scenario

NOTES regarding some of the topics which need further attention:

1. Anticipation

To anticipate or to foresee or to realise beforehand can be included in the 'systems theory' by considering the observable or guessed characteristics or properties of objects or agents and from these deduce the possible or feasible consequences. These can be included in a modified linguistic model and then explore what happens as a result of the consequences. This topic is considered in a paper 'Crises and systems thinking' [Brussels conference, 2018, Acta Europeana Systematica, v8, n8].

For example,
'car tyre' --- characteristic = solid rubber   or   inflatable
                consequence   = cannot puncture   can puncture

2. Holon

A holon is something which is simultaneously a whole in itself and part of a larger whole.

Consideration of holons fits into 'systems theory' or in the scheme of Figure 3.1. when the particular case of 'Producer systems [2]' is of concern. This kind of system deals with
'manufacture or fabrication etc AND assembly' of material and symbolic objects or agents or holons of increasing levels and nature of systems.

For example,
'leg of a bed' which is fabricated of material and geometrical properties until the desired holon is reached that fits a larger holon called 'bed' which then fits 'bedroom furniture'.

3. Static linguistic networks

Static linguistic networks are constructed of 'nouns or noun phrases related by *stative* verbs' and can be used to represent products [3] in the scheme of Figure 3.1. This topic is considered in detail in [Korn, 2009].

Identification of 'tree' in a product [3] leads to working out the number of variations of the structure of a product which can be a large number depending on the number of nodes or nouns in a network. The variation can yield useful or useless possibilities of product [3].

APPENDIX 4

HIERARCHY OF STRUCTURES

The examples we considered were intended to demonstrate instances of 'Utilising systems' which is a particular case of the scheme in Figure 3.1. in section 3.2., except the 'Farmer scenario' with semantic diagram in Figure 5.25. and the 1st example in section 6.2. These examples are instances of 'Producing systems', another particular case of this figure which is recognised by its producing a 'product [3]', does not draw it from an existing store. These examples already show the mechanism of how the 'product [3]' itself is created. This appendix is intended to show this mechanism explicitly which is part of the activities of 'Production systems' and leads to recognition of the notion of 'hierarchy'.

Notion of hierarchy

The notion of 'organisational hierarchy' is described as a 'structure of successive concepts arranged in order in which an increase or decrease of a specified concept can be detected'. Instances of the order are : Time as shown by a family tree, Postal addresses like country, town, district, street, house, Subordination like major, lieutenant, sergeant, corporal, private, Organisations like chairman, managing directors, directors, controllers, and so on [Korn, 2013]. However, there is an other kind of 'hierarchy' which is of interest in the *systemic or structural view* of parts of the world and is called *nested hierarchy* [Rose, 2018, Korn, 2018]. By 'nested hierarchy' is meant a 'structure of successive concepts arranged in order in which elements at one level are contained in the elements at the next level organised in a specific manner'. All instances of existence are organised in a vast variety of nested hierarchy as asserted in the 'first hypothesis' in section 3.1., such as atoms, molecules as in the periodic table of Mendeleyev, mixtures or galaxies, constellations, stars, satellites, planets or legs, tables, furniture. All in increasing *complexity*.

Generation of nested hierarchy

In section 3.1. we classified objects or agents or wholes into 'Animate, inanimate and artificial'. Creation of instances of nested hierarchy is accomplished by making *changes in an already existing member of the classification*. This observation prompts a generalisation as follows

793. --- 'The accomplishment of any change of an aspect of a part of the world, concrete, abstract, symbolic or imaginary, presupposes the *existence* of such a part or a change cannot be done from *nothing*, at least in terrestrial circumstances.' ---

In creating a hierarchy, there are two ways of changes :
I. *Fabrication* like change of shape or mental state using a tool, earthquake or a suggestion or force,
II. *Assembly* like change of position, constitution or structure.

Way I. create the *first level* of hierarchy, way II. creates all subsequent levels. Linguistic modelling can be used to represent the process of generating nested hierarchy. For example, there is a 'story' :

'The cook wants to make a sandwich so h/she cuts two slices off a loaf of bread and scoops a lump of butter from a larger lump with a knife. The cook then places the two slices on the table and spreads the butter evenly on them.'

Without going through the STAGES of 'linguistic modelling', the semantic diagram or dynamic linguistic network is shown in Figure A4.1.

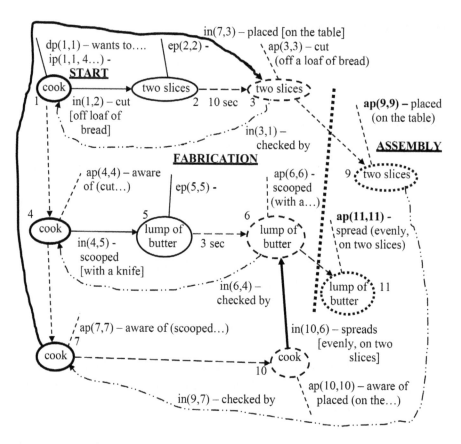

Figure A4.1. A scenario with hierarchy

Figure A4.1. shows the Fabrication, the 0th Level of hierarchy and the Assembly, the 1st Level of hierarchy which correspond to the User/Producer [2] and product [3] in their basic form in Figure 3.1. For example, there is a product [3] called 'cutting axe' consisting of or *assembled* from a 'wood handle' and a 'steel cutting head' which are *fabricated* by a 'wood cutter' and 'black smith'.

The product [3] or 'Assembly' in Figure A4.1. can be expressed in terms 'ordered pairs' as considered in section 5.6.

With reference to ap(9,9) and ap(11,11), we can apply exp 5.68.

$$n_{9,20} = [ep(2,2) \text{ two slices (placed [no adverb]) on the table [no adjective]}$$
$$\text{from } 1^{st} \text{ bracket}$$

exp A4.1.

$n_{11',21}$ = [ep(5,5)] lump of butter (spread [evenly]) on two slices [ep(2,2)]

which are shown as 'static linguistic network' in Figure A4.2.

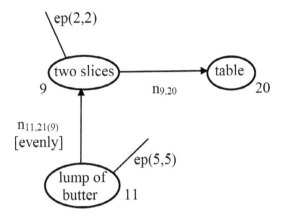

Figure A4.2. Static linguistic network of 'sandwich'

In Figure A4.2. there are 3 objects so when we consider the product [3] from the 'network point of view' as discussed in section 5.3., when we construct the arrays as in eqs.5.19., 5.20. we designate : two slices – 1, lump of butter – 2, table – 3 which lead to

$$
\begin{array}{ccc}
n_{11} & n_{12} & \mathbf{n_{13}} \\
\mathbf{n_{21}} & n_{22} & n_{23} \\
n_{31} & n_{32} & n_{33}
\end{array}
\qquad \textbf{exp A4.2.}
$$

In exp A4.2. the terms in 'bold' correspond to the branches in the network in Figure A4.2. They satisfy Rules 3 and 4 in section 5.3. which means that the network is a 'tree' and can be accepted as a product [3] as such as there are no redundant branches.

Remarks &&&

As in previous examples, reading the semantic diagram in Figure A4.1. begins at contour 1 then following the feedback loop leads to contour 4 with acquired property ap(4,4) which initiates the interaction in(4,5) and so on. This rule is formalised when the logic sequences are derived and can be followed by a computer because of the notation : ap(4,4) → in(4,5).

Remarks are as follows :

1. Contours 1, 2, 3 and 3, 4, 5 represent 'Fabrication' and contours 7, 3, 9 and 10, 6, 11 accomplish 'Assembly' into a product [3] or 'holon' described as 'buttered bread'.

2. The 'two slices' contour 9 and 'lump of butter' contour 11 are the elements which are transmitted into the next level of hierarchy and organised into a new structure by 'Assembly'.

3. The initiator 'cook' has the plan or objective of what h/she wants to achieve. H/she operates in accordance with a *purpose*.

4. We see the operation of generalisation **793.** : The 'loaf of bread' and the 'larger lump of butter' are the background parts of the world from which the change takes place.

5. The operation of 'fertilisation' by *chance* appears to follow the pattern of 'fabrication' and 'assembly' which can be observed in case of animals, for example. Here the egg and sperm are produced by the sex organs of adults and assembled by the same. Growth takes place by cell division which is assembly in the opposite sense.

6. Further to Figure A4.1., in order to develop the 'logic sequences' we use the 'causal chains' which are : 9, 3, 2, 1 and 11, 6, 4, 1 and 10, 7, 4, 1. However, links : 10, 6 and 7, 3 are *prompting* links to accomplish the assembly with 10, 6 taking place before 7,3. Links 3, 1 and 6, 4 and 9, 7 are prompting, *feedback* links to ensure the progression of mental state of agent 'cook'.

7. There are properties missing in the 'story' which shows up in the semantic diagram and obviates the use of 'uncertainties' and estimating the strength of conditions in the sequences of logic expressions. This originates from the sentences in the 'story' being *context – free* and the expression, **exp 5.3.** in section 5.1. called the 'unit of change' as would be used in the linguistic modelling of this example, would become **incomplete**.

8. The last sentence in the 'story' is a 3 – place sentence, the verb 'spread' attracts 3 nouns as considered in section 5.7., it is a *complex sentence*. In the semantic diagram of Figure A4.1. this is dealt with by making the noun phrase 'two slices' an adverb and the noun phrase 'lump of butter' becomes the 'affected object'. The alternative is to make the conversion of a 3 – place to a 2 – place sentence by making the noun phrase 'lump of butter' the adverb.

9. Further to Figure A4.1., construction of a hierarchical structure is done by Producing systems or User/Producer [2], the particular case of the scheme in Figure 3.1. Therefore, such structures satisfy **exp 4.3.** considered in section 4.3. However, the intention of this Appendix 4. is to discuss the question of 'hierarchical structures' so details of the 'systems parameters' such as properties of the 'two slices' are not discussed. Accordingly, Producing systems and hierarchies are related by :

The complexity of a hierarchy is related to the *number of levels* it consists of,
     and   **expA4.3.**
The complexity of User/Producer [2] in Figure 3.1. is related to the *number of instances of fabrications and assemblies* to achieve a hierarchy it consists of.

10. The 'plan' or 'design' or 'objective' designated by the 'dp(x,y)' property in Figure A4.1., for example, contains the details the accomplishment of which is monitored by the *product feedback loop* in Figure 3.1. In Figure A4.1. the 'story' implies that the required *interaction* to change the state of OPI [5 – 6] is produced by the 'sandwich' which is only partially constructed by the hierarchy as shown.

11. The term 'complexity' refers to an *aggregate of many parts*. Any 'level of nested hierarchy' consists of a number of parts except when we deal with single variable control systems like a speed control system [Korn, 2012], it is then a *complex entity*. These parts are embodied in the 'plan' or 'design' of the product [3] or holon anyone of which is *necessary* for regarding the whole as 'planned' or 'labelled' like a 'sandwich', a concept. The presence of all parts is *sufficient* for the recognition of the whole or the product [3]. This description of necessity and sufficiency is not as strict as that in [Copi, 1978] which refers to technical things. For example, 'The presence of fuel in the tank is a necessary condition for the car to run but for sufficiency the conditions are innumerable' or 'The presence of 'oxygen' is a necessary condition for combustion'. In case of the 'sandwich' example in Figure A4.1. the presence of 'bread' is a necessary condition of the whole to be regarded as a 'sandwich' but the presence of a 'lump of butter spread' is questionable to be necessary. We are talking about *empirical necessity* and *sufficiency* i.e. the criterion for a condition to be seen as such is discovered by investigation. The question of necessity and sufficiency may arise in the course of using **exp 5.3.** in section 5.1.

End of **Remarks &&&**

CONCLUSIONS

We have made a number of 'inductive generalisations' in discussing the idea of nested hierarchy and they appear to stand up to the test of thought experiments. As suggested by Part A. in Figure 3.1., progress along nested hierarchy towards increasing complexity is prompted by human ingenuity and creativity. The discussion here, in particular the diagram in Figure A4.1. shows a method of expressing the mechanism of development of nested hierarchy in analytical terms which is generalised by the concepts of 'Fabrication' and 'Assembly'. No more in depth symbolism is offered at this stage. Extension of the method to chemical, biological and nuclear fields is likely to be possible but due to lack of knowledge of details of these fields, it is not attempted here.

The example here and others previously use concrete, physical aspects of parts of the world which are easy to follow. Abstract and mental aspects are not used due to insufficient familiarity but due to the generality of the subject matter, it can be extended by experts. A general statement that sums up what the proposed 'systems theory' is about is given by :

853.--- 'The systemic or structural phenomenon is *empirical* i.e. structures or systems can be perceived by the senses or generated by imagination into 'thoughts', it is *general* and supports 'problem solving. A 'systems theory' is proposed which can cope with the *generality*, can integrate *aspects* of human, intellectual endeavours and analytically is adequate because it satisfies the *4 criteria* for creating empirical, symbolic structures as presented in section 1.3. The objective of this book is to introduce this 'systems theory' which is based on previous work but with new ideas and results'. ---

We add a number of points relevant to the topic discussed in this book :

A. Further to contour 10 in Figure 2.1., the main preoccupation of 'conventional science' is to generate knowledge of the empirical world by creating representations of aspects of parts of the world which are expressed in *elementary constituents* organised into predominantly mathematical models so as to make the representations as generally applicable as possible and testable against observation or experiment. The main preoccupation of 'systems thinking' as defined in section 3.2., is to generate the description of conditions for the occurrence of events expressed in *elementary constituents* organised into linguistic models so as to make the descriptions generally applicable to the resolution of problematic scenarios and amenable to discussions to achieve acceptable resolutions.

B. The production of *artificial*, nested, hierarchical structures towards higher levels of complexity is driven by the *innate human* ingenuity, creativity for novel products by the desire for survival, convenience, power, ambitions, pleasures and so on at the expense of the *natural environment*. The *spontaneous* production of *natural*, nested, hierarchical structures towards higher levels of complexity is driven by the kind of *natural environment*. The former has to happen given the latter.

C. Scenarios with *choices* represented by the logical OR function have not been considered [Copi, 1978]. The scheme in Figure 3.1. gives concrete instances of 1st and 2nd ordered cybernetics i.e. 'cybernetics of observed systems' and 'cybernetics of observing systems' respectively as described by [Foerster, 1974]. The 'product feedback loop' monitoring the state of product [3] and taking correcting action, is 1st order cybernetics and the User/consumer [7 – 8] expecting OPI [6] to conform to expectation, is 2nd order cybernetics.

In general, 1st order cybernetics is concerned with the operation of 'feedback loops' as understood I control theory [Nise, 2008, Korn, 2012] and the subject matter of 2nd order cybernetics appears to be about emotive, irrational states of mind. Both topics involve *purposive* activities and are well understood so the extra term 'cybernetics' is perhaps superficial.

D. The idea of using a 'story' or 'narrative' of a scenario based on a real or imaginary situation, in natural language, the primary model, as the starting point of constructing a symbolic model of 'systems theory', is new. This then leads to the formal, processed natural language of *linguistic modelling*. Linguistic modelling, the converter of a 'story' into *conditionals*, is the basic structure to exhibit the formal model of a scenario to enable :

1. Superimposing mathematical models and further input of mental and physical states of parts of the world for decision making,

2. Studying the conditions for the occurrence of outcomes subject to uncertainties and human emotions,

3. Studying the effects of *interpretation* of information by people on further actions.
4. Opening the study of linguistics and acting as the symbolism in addition to mathematics.

Using natural language by human beings as the starting point for further model construction is universal and more productive than attempts like 'rich pictures' [Checkland, 1982].

E. As has been remarked before, linguistic modelling using the 'logical conditional of predicate logic', produces *conditions for the occurrence of changes of state*. When these states are to be executed in practice, they need to be expressed in *operational form* which is the point of 'theory meeting practice'.

F. It is worth mentioning that the application of both, linguistic and mathematical models has been shown at the *same problem* in examples noted in Figure 5.25. [farmer/milk] and Figure 6.17. [life boat].

G. The concept of 'property' is central in the living sphere, it is central in this book. It is the means for expressing beliefs, opinions etc and is described as a *thought* that can be ascribed to any entity once expressed as a symbolic structure. The notion can be cast in a 'nested hierarchy' depending on its degree of abstractness and is arranged so as to make sense. For example, the 'opening sentence' of this paragraph makes *sense* but if 'central' is replaced by 'yellow' it would not or in 'this person is good' if we remove 'good' or 'person' the sense or the belief would be lost or lessened. This topic needs to be explored further considering its importance in communication by living things and in the sciences.

H. The criteria discussed in section 1.3. in constructing symbolic structures are important. However, the 1st criterion is more so and has been a preoccupation to civilisations since ancient times, Greek, ayurvedic [Levene, 2010].

I. Motivation for *recognising the need for 'change'* by living things using their brain/mind is generated in Part A. of the scheme in Figure 3.1. either by perception or as a result of imagination, perhaps spontaneously. We can distinguish two *sources* of motivation potentially residing in the brain/mind or the central nervous system :

1. Emotions The wide range of emotions : In humans but much less in animals, possibly zero in plants,
The will to survive : In humans but much less in animals and plants.

2. Ambitions
The will to achieve : In humans but practically limited to zero in animals and plants.

The presence and extent of emotions and ambitions are the function of evolutionary development. They are *states of mind* which to be executed, require : = =

Desire for change and innovation or *attitude of mind* to the world as well as insight, ingenuity, inspiration, creativity, curiosity etc or *capability of mind.*

Figure A4.3. shows the diagram of *motivational representation* of purposive change as seen to take place in the living sphere.

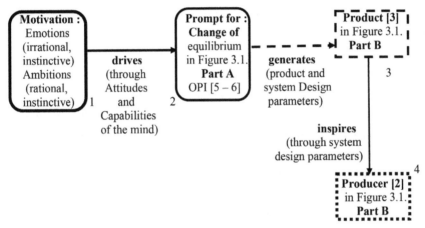

Figure A4.3. Motivational structure of purpose change

At the basic level perhaps all living things operate according to the scheme in Figure A4.3., the details depend on the level of evolutionary development of their brain/mind apparatus. As far as humans are concerned we assume that their state of mind as shown in Motivation contour 1 has not changed appreciably from the time of their fairly early existence to modern times. However, the

Circumstances of their existence, and the

Environment of their existence

have immeasurably changed due to the exercise of the Attitudes and Capabilities of their brain/mind which carry particular instances of Motivation into Part A in contour 2 as shown in detail in Figure 3.1., sections 4.3. and 6.2. Part A then generates Part B in contours 3 and 4 in accordance with the 'second hypothesis' in section 3.1. which realise the 'circumstances' and affect the 'environment'.

The *indiscriminate use* of **Motivation** in particular the **Emotion** part has been the practice over the millennia which is a natural mental process, not requiring much intellectual effort, instinctive and can be irrational. However, through the use of Capabilities this practice has led to : = =

Point 1. From *low level* of technology and population with low level of consumption and exploitation of environment,

Point 2. To *high level* of technology and population with high level of consumption and exploitation of environment.

The *change* has occurred because of the unceasing endeavour to satisfy or improve demand for : Survival, convenience, power, influence, creative activities for expression and explanation [arts and sciences] and so on.

From this brief discussion, we conclude that:

--- Point 2. is regarded as the 'problematic issue' or OPI [5] in Figure 3.1. The *interaction* from Figure A4.3. to bring about OPI [6] is suggested as the '*directed use*' of Motivation through affecting mental state, in particular the reduction of the use of 'emotive states' like desire for power, greatness or greed or anger or blame and increase of the use like spirit of understanding, cooperation and rational 'ambitions'. This kind of approach should lead to the creation of the appropriate 'products' and 'systems or structures' as shown in Part B. in Figures 3.1. and A4.3. The *evaluation* of the desirability and feasibility of this direction of action is not attempted here. ---

Emotions and ambitions and any other object or agent are recognised, identified and designated by the *simultaneous presence of perceivable properties*, they are complex phenomena. For example, 'an angry person' can be recognised by the geometrical features of h/her face or a 'knife' is recognised by a conjunction of material and geometrical properties. A *complex phenomenon*, natural or artificial is created by 'fabrication' and 'assembly' or adopted in case of 'Utilising systems'. According to physics, complex elements in the periodic table of elements have been created inside the stars like the Sun by *fusion* which is a kind of 'assembly'. 'Hydrogen' is the element which must have been 'fabricated'.

The concept of *property* is the fundamental component of 'predicate' as shown in contour 2 in Figure 2.1., it turns context – free sentences to context

– dependent and enables to expose a statement to the test of observation or experiment [Popper, 1972]. The creation of 'complex or emergent properties' is carried out by *deductive organisations* which the User/producer [2] in Figure 3.1. is in relation to the product [3]. To bring into existence a 'property' as stipulated by generalisation 222. in Appendix 2. except in case of 'natural systems' where the same thing happens by 'chance', demands its own purposive *system or structure* which is a 'necessary condition' i.e. without the operation of a system or structure no property appears, a form of *universal causation* [Hospers, 1978]. For example, Figures 6.9. and 6.10. in section 6.1. demonstrate this assertion or the expansion of an organisation to contain departments for 'accounts' or 'quality control' from mere fabrication and assembly is demanded by the need of the product. Similar argument holds for expansion of an organisation itself as dictated by the need of the living such as 'eating and drinking' which leads to an additional facility called 'restaurant'.

J. Natural language is by far the most widely applicable symbolic structure with immense expressive power for putting *thoughts* created by imagination or induced in response to input from sense organs. It is called here the *primary model* which can be the first attempt at expressing thoughts in symbols and into which by and large the vast variety of other models can be transformed. Thus, natural language due to its general applicability, at least in principle, matches the generality of the 'systemic or structural view' of parts of the world and, accordingly, is used as the raw material for 'linguistic modelling' as a 'story' or narrative of a scenario.

Here we intend to show how a 'theory' or a conjecture is rooted in 'natural language'. A 'theory' is *useful* when it can predict or confirm states of affairs accurately according to *expectations*. In addition, it may be seen as *scientific* when the predictions are 'observable and measurable' or testable in practice. Whether a 'theory' or conjecture can be trusted is a different matter and the criteria of *trustworthiness* is not discussed here. The discussion should demonstrate that the proposed 'systems theory' may be described as 'useful, scientific and trustworthy'.

Accordingly, we select three aspects of natural language :
1. Declarative sentences expressed in *general terms*,
2. Declarative sentences expressed in *particular terms*, and
3. Their *relation* and *connection* by 'logical conditional'.

The *following scheme* can be seen to exhibit the 'relation' and 'connection' =
= =

'There is a Hyp : Statement of a *mental* or *physical state* and an *expression of
interest*' followed by
'IF there is an Ori : Original plan, a suggestion, a proposal or a state of affairs
AND an Act : *Action* THEN an Asp : *Aspect of the mental* or *physical state*
may be fulfilled',
'IF a Ppp : *Particular plan, suggestion, a proposal* or a state of affairs is
put in practice AND the Paa : *Particular aspect of the mental* or *physical
state* is seen to be : [X. Fulfilled or Y. Not] THEN the Css : Original plan,
suggestion, proposal or state of affairs may or may not be useful and/or
scientific theory'.

We demonstrate the application of the scheme by examples as follows using
the abbreviations introduced in the scheme.

1st example
Hyp : John feels the need for entertainment
Ori : He remembers there is a cinema nearby
Act : He thinks he might go to the cinema
Asp : He thinks he might be entertained

Ppp : There is a cinema nearby and John goes there
Paa : After seeing the film, he feels disappointed
Css :   The 'particular' does not confirm the 'original' which has been
constructed as an expression of the 'hypothesis' so the 'original' is *not* a useful
and a scientific theory.

2nd example
Hyp : A material body stays at rest or continues at a steady motion along a
straight line until a force acts on it
Ori : There is a force and material body defined
Act : Force acts on the body
Asp : The result is acceleration

Ppp : There is a railway carriage stationary with an engine next

Paa : The engine pushes the carriage resulting in its acceleration

Css : The 'particular' confirms the 'original' which has been constructed as an expression of the 'hypothesis' so the 'original' is useful, scientific theory, it is trustworthy because it is based on using the scientific method of observation, conceptualisation, construction of symbolic structures which can be exposed to the test of observation or experiment.

3rd example

Hyp : Joe is interested to find out how long he will live

Ori : He chooses to consult a graphologist

Act : He visits one

Asp : He thinks consulting the geometrical features of the palm can yield the expected result

Ppp : He actually goes ahead and visits a graphologist

Paa : The graphologist after examining his palm, assures him that he will have a long life

Css : Joe is reassured and answers his expectation, Hyp, so the 'particular' fits into the 'original' so the 'theory' is useful, not scientific and not trustworthy.

4th example

Hyp : This example concerns the proposed 'systems theory'. The second hypothesis in section 3.1. is about the 'change of equilibrium'

Ori : The systems theory fits the pattern of exp 5.2.

Act : Linguistic modelling

Asp : Linguistic modelling shows instances of 'change of equilibrium'

Ppp : Linguistic modelling of a scenario is developed

Paa : A 1 – or 2 – place sentence exhibits an instance of 'change of equilibrium' as an 'acquired property' which can be expressed in numerical terms

Css : Particular cases of 'change of equilibrium' are exhibited, the proposed 'systems theory' is useful and scientific.

CONCLUSIONS

The question in linguistics concerning general ideas implying 'activity' or 'state' AND their 'implementation' in specific or concrete terms, has been raised. For example :

A general idea = = 'The police continue the search for witnesses',

Implementation = = 'Policemen and women are sent out to question people'. A scheme has been constructed which appears to be able to examine if there is a relation between the two notions and if the relation leads to satisfaction of certain criteria. The proposed 'systems theory' as expected exhibits the relation between 'hypotheses' as put forward in section 3.1. AND their instances as shown by symbolic structure of 'linguistic modelling' in CHAPTER 6.

In the course of every day practice of using natural language people put forward general ideas which are accepted, mocked, laughed at, thought if useful or not, true or not and so on but their implementation is rarely questioned. Scientific work is the exception where one instance of *invalidity* falsify the general idea.

K. The proposed 'systems theory' introduces the use of processed natural language in the form of 'linguistic modelling' as the symbolic structure or model. Natural sciences use 'mathematical models' for the same purpose.

Mathematical models use precisely defined properties or variables expressed in terms of numbers with units assigned. For example, the 'property' of the 'table top' is that its 'length is 1.5 m'. There is no ambiguity, uncertainty or indeterminacy in this statement, at least for the purpose of this discussion.

On the other hand, the symbolism of natural language admits *indeterminacy* and uncertainty as introduced in section 5.4., for example, or in terms of 'fuzzy sets' [Zadeh, 1965]. Choice for expressing the same thought is open as in 'fat', 'obese' or 'well rounded' and graduation of qualifiers can be used as introduced in section 5.5. Mistakes can be made when linguistic expressions are misinterpreted. All this allows flexibility of thought in application of modelling to people as opposed to the precision may be required in description of natural and technical description. Possibility and desirability of this kind of treatment appears to be function of prevailing *culture* of the age.

Mathematics because it utilises 'quantifiable properties' only, is restrictive in applications, processed natural language does not discriminate and its terms can carry *influence*. Mathematical and linguistic models are symbolisms which can reach to the *fundamentals* of physical and mental matters. A wide variety of models has been developed by humans in the sense of generalisation **VWX.** in section 2.2., much less so by animals and possibly zero by plants, as a result of people needing various ways to express their *thoughts* prompted by the limitless *imagination*. For example, fine and performing arts, gestures, road signs and so on.

APPENDIX 5

DIVERSITY AND INCONSISTENCY IN INTELLECTUAL PRODUCTS

Introduction

An *intellectual product* is created either by the imagination or in response to input from the sense organs by the brain/mind apparatus. Whether it is a 'fairy tale', an 'instruction manual', a 'book of fiction', a 'scientific theory', a 'painting', 'ballet', a 'gesture', a 'road sign' and so on to the immense variety of such products which have been created to satisfy *human curiosity or use*. They fit into the notion of 'product [3]' in Figure 3.1.

An intellectual product is a *symbolic structure* freely created by imagination to describe aspects of parts of the real or *empirical* or imaginary world for carrying thoughts. People have created a wide *diversity* and variety of such structures and their *consistency* in relation to other structures has never been questioned. However, Figure 2.1. draws attention to the difference between *Conventional Disciplines* such as 'natural sciences', 'fine and performing arts' and *Modern Disciplines* like 'control theory', 'operational research', 'systems thinking', 'the proposed systems theory in this book. The two kinds of Disciplines are fundamentally different in their *purpose, application* and in the *characteristics of the 'properties'* they use as their 'elementary constituents (elcon)'. Trying to inject unsuitable diversity of subject matter into the Modern Disciplines and vice versa may not be a suitable exercise. The intention of this paper is to try to clarify this matter.

Basic ideas of expressing thoughts

Natural language is by far the most widely used symbolic structure invented by the brain/mind of humans. The possibility of its general use and immense expressive power makes it the 'primary model' and its structure is that of the *subject – predicate*. The function of the 'subject' is to locate aspects of a part of the world, real or imaginary which are of interest for further development of *thoughts* and the function of the 'predicate' is to express a view, belief or to make assertions about the 'subject'.

We note :

1. The subject – predicate structure is the only one that can make sense of *thinking* about aspects of parts of the real or imaginary world,

2. It is a *symbolic structure* called a model when a thought is translated into a 'medium', the practice which all other models or ways of expressing thoughts, follow,

3. Any part of the world, concrete, symbolic, abstract or imaginary, is seen as a *structure* or a *system* the concept which is general, universal and unique and is constructed of structural properties,

4. The means of viewing the 'predicate' is the notion of *property* which is applied to the 'subject' in its variety and diversity.

Diversity and inconsistency in human intellectual endeavours

Conventional Disciplines of physics, chemistry, geography, nuclear physics, the arts etc are part of human intellectual endeavour and produce intellectual products to satisfy curiosity in its various forms and to be used by technology and society throughout the ages of history and perhaps before. These Disciplines *contribute* to *problem solving* as indicated in Figure 2.1.

We can say that :

A. Conventional Disciplines elected to use the 'Large *variety and diversity* of *qualitative and quantitative properties* in their narrower sense as 'elcons'. In particular, physics and chemistry selected material and energetic properties.
B. Conventional Disciplines produced an equally large *variety and diversity* of *mathematical and artistic models* which use the 'elcons'. Mathematical models are demanded by the need for satisfying the testability criterion of scientific models, one of the 4 criteria for constructing empirical models suggested in section 1.3.

For example, the material properties of mass, density, elasticity etc and energetic properties of force, momentum, speed etc have produced mechanical models when organised into the symbolic structure of mathematics [mass divided by volume equals density]. Also, the electrical, energetic properties of voltage, current etc have produced electrical models when organised into the symbolic structure of mathematics [voltage divided by current equals resistance (Ohm's law)].

Points A. and B. are *consistent* in the sense that the *diversity* of A. is followed by the *diversity* of B. We are familiar with the problems in engineering education caused by attempt at dealing with *interdisciplinarity* in the 2nd half of the 20th century [Korn, 2009]

Modern Disciplines of control systems theories, operational research, systems thinking are also part of human intellectual endeavour and produce intellectual products which exhibit structures such as *block diagrams* of *transfer functions* in control theory. OR uses mathematical models describing specific topics, systems thinking have produced VSM, SSM, causal mapping etc, each having their deficiencies as far as the notion of a 'comprehensive systems theory' is concerned. All these particular approaches within systems thinking have been invented not to *contribute to* but to *solve problems* which none of them do except SSM explicitly.

We can say that :

C. Modern Disciplines are preoccupied with the *concept of structure or system* which is a general or *universal* concept and their fundamental task is *problem solving*. Any part of the concrete, symbolic, abstract, imaginary world can be seen as a static or dynamic *structure*, there is no other way. Therefore, the structural description of aspects of parts of the world must use a *single structural property* as 'elcon'.
D. Modern Disciplines so far have produced a *variety and diversity* of symbolic structures in the form of *speculative, descriptive and structural models* as referred to above.

Points C. and D. are inconsistent in the sense that the 'notion of single property' in C. is followed by the diversity of 'models' in D. The idea of General Systems Theory makes Points C. and D. *consistent*.

The position of ISSS

It is widely recognised that von Bertalanffy in the 1950's introduced the idea of generality of the notion of system or structure [added by the author] and advocated the construction of a 'General Systems Theory, GST' as some kind of super science. This was followed by the writings of a number of workers such as Boulding in 1956, Kast and Rosenzweig 'GST – basis for unification of science' and the discussion remained at the speculative level. Authors like Klir, Mesarovic, Miller and others used aspects of mathematics to create a GST which was not suitable because the language of mathematics is too restrictive, it takes into account 'quantitative aspects' of parts of the world.

In the later part of the last century, workers seemed to have admitted the impossibility of creating a GST and constructed a number of methods such as VSM, SSM, systems dynamics which were not satisfactory as they do not satisfy the 4 criteria of construction of a symbolic structure covering only aspects of 'systems thinking'. These approaches introduced *diversity* into systems thinking.

The bylaws of ISSS recognise that GST is basic to understand the phenomenon of 'system or structure' and says '2.1. Purposes. The overall purpose of the ISSS is to promote the development of conceptual frameworks based on *general systems theory* as well as their implementation in practice'. However, at the session of a SIG, 10/09/2022, it was said 'Purpose of the session is to appreciate the *diversity* in the community of the systems concept and the concept of systems science.' And 'To embrace *diversity*, to recognise assumptions and to promote shared understanding of ourselves and each other in this tricky space of concepts'. Here is another instance of *inconsistency* if this interpretation constitutes an inconsistency or incompatibility.

CONCLUSIONS

ISSS is a learned institution, a member of the multitude of learned institutions. Institutions usually have a clearly defined subject matter of interest and activity to promote this interest, ISSS is unique in having inconsistency, vagueness and practically non existent *learned element* in its subject matter. The last point is shared with other institutions.

There is nothing unacceptable in pursuing 'diversity' if it is well defined and fits into some objective towards achievement of an equally well defined *change of mental state*. This is not the case in the arts, for example, where unbridled diversity is admitted and appreciated but the ISSS is an *organisation* with purpose of existence and operation. Human activities in general are governed by diversity which appear to have resulted in the currently recognised problems in the world over.

We need to recognise the fundamental difference between :
X. The wide variety of 'properties' used by Conventional Disciplines produced by the limitless *imagination* AND the uniqueness of the 'systemic or structural view' of parts of the world or the Modern Disciplines which allows only a 'single property', and
Y. The role in human thinking and activities of Conventional Disciplines which is to satisfy *curiosity* and *contribute to applications* in technology and society AND of Modern Disciplines which is *problem solving*.

Another issue is that GST and systems thinking are still seen to be related to conventional science which is reflected in the bylaws of ISSS which says 'To foster the investigation of the analogy or isomorphy of concepts, laws and models in various disciplines and professions'.

A new approach is needed based on the concepts of systems or structures with 3 hypotheses and linguistic modelling which leads to recognition of the 4 criteria of construction of intellectual products, in particular the 'elementary constituents 'elcon''. The failure to identify a suitable elcon for the construction of a comprehensive systems theory perhaps is the reason for its absence. However, a suggestion now exists which is available for peer review [Korn, 2022]. This suggestion recognises the required 'single, structural property' of aspects of parts of the world, real and imaginary, and the corresponding 'single, systems theory' which integrates the notion of system or structure and problem solving. This approach if found acceptable, removes the inconsistency between Points C. and D. and allows diversity by admitting the use of mathematical models, knowledge of natural and social sciences and any other like emotive states of mind at the object or agent level. Any other ideas need to be considered as the limitless power of human imagination, creativity and ingenuity cannot be restricted.

A BRIEF CONTRIBUTION TO THE DEBATE
AT ISSS MEETING, 10TH 09/2022

The topic of the debate

'Systems as a concept and the concepts of systems science'

The contribution

This contribution can be useful in appreciating the topic of 'Diversity and inconsistency in intellectual products.

The term 'concept' refers to a thought produced and designated by the brain/mind through the work of *imagination* or in response to an input from the *sense organs*. Empirical concepts arise as a result of considering aspects of parts of the world. The 'concept of system' arises when we see a part of the world in terms of its 'structure', 'systems thinking'. It is a means of description just like 'colour', it is a *property* of concrete, symbolic, abstract or imaginary things, only it is a 'universal means of description' applicable to everything, there is no alternative.

The representation of 'systems concept' as a symbolic *structure* or model is a different matter, it is the CORE OF THE PROBLEM.

'The concepts of systems science' arise as a matter of necessity as part of inventing a 'systems science', they cannot just be conjured up without reference to something. For example, the concepts of SSM like CATWOE and others emerged as a consequence of inventing this method. The concepts of any discipline of conventional science emerged when it was invented, for example, concepts like 'force', 'density' and so on emerged when the science of mechanics was invented or the concepts of 'heat', 'energy', 'work' or 'entropy' emerged when the science of thermodynamics was invented.

Remark $$$

Although we have referred to the question of 'modelling' before, the practically whole mental activity of the brain/mind is about modelling, we need to emphasise a point again in connection with the generalisation **VWX.** in section 2.2.

Reproducing this expanded generalisation: 'We can make an ***infinite number of statements*** about any part of the world which means that perfect knowledge is impossible'. We, therefore, select a few statements with the selection directed by a 'point of view' or interest in an aspect of a selected part of the world which is called the ***symbolic structure*** resulting from implementing a 'thought'. This structure becomes a **model** when it is encoded in a 'medium'. A symbolic structure then becomes a *candidate* for **knowledge**. When such a structure satisfies the 4 criteria in section 1.3. or the demands of being a 'scientific theory' i.e. falsifiable or exposable to observation or experimentation or producing *testable predictions*, then it may be considered *knowledge*.

In general, the features of *knowledge* are,
First feature : Knowledge is subjective and its acceptability is conditional on the **circumstances** surrounding the selected part of the world or the 'rest of the world' remaining *constant*, and
Second feature : Knowledge, when encoded in a medium and transmitted, is interpreted **subjectively** by the receiver or with possible mistakes relative to what is intended.

It then follows that knowledge is 'uncertain', subject to 'prejudices' and serves the furtherance of interests of individuals or groups of people.

In current work we take or 'systems thinking' takes the 'structural view' or 'structural aspect' of a part of the world just like any other means of description or **property**. For example, the 'discipline of mechanics' has a distinct selection of properties and variables or 'elementary constituents' which enables us to :
1. Identify an object as part of the domain of mechanics, and
2. Construct symbolic structures.
For example, the 'elementary constituents' of *mechanics* or the mechanical properties : Density, viscosity, elasticity and the mechanical variables : Force, speed etc. their appropriate combination can be seen as a mathematical model. Thus, we can say 'This jug of water has density = 1000 kg/m^3 and volume = 0.1 m^3 which makes its mass = 1000 times 0.1= 100 kg and which makes it part of the domain of mechanics [Korn, 2009].

We can regard 'systems thinking' as a discipline because the proposed 'systems theory' satisfies the 4 criteria in section 1.3.

The **First feature** limits the *certainty of applicability* of symbolic structures to scenarios with objects or agents in the range of 'inanimate, natural' to purely 'human'. For example,

1. Inanimate natural
'The sun warms the atmosphere and water evaporates from the ocean' which can be expressed as a *conditional* :
'If the sun warms the atmosphere then water evaporates from the ocean."
We can say that if the antecedent is true 'the sun does warm the atmosphere' then the consequent is also true because we have a natural process which always takes place under terrestrial conditions unless the 'earth disappears into outer space.

2. Scenario with inanimate natural or artificial objects and human agents
'There are 3 apples on this table and 9 apples on the other table and a goat eats 2 apples on the second table leads to 10 apples remaining' which can be expressed in terms of a *conditional* :
'If there are 3 apples on this table and 9 apples on the other and a goat eats 2 apples then there are 10 left."
We can then say that if the antecedent is true 'There are 3 apples.....' then the consequent is also true when the 'goat actually does' as stated. However, 'the goat' is an agent who can change its mind due to threatening circumstances or other aspects of the circumstances can change, 'an apple can fall off the table' which means that the model can supply testable prediction with less **certainty** then in case 1.

3. Scenario with human agents
'John feels alone but has a friend living nearby so he decides to see h/her' which can be expressed as a *conditional* :
'If John feels alone but has a friend living nearby and he decides to see and actually has seen h/her then John's loneliness may be alleviated".
We can then say that if the antecedent is true 'John has actually seen his friend' then apart from the *uncertainties* associated with any aspects of the 'surroundings' the mental state of the brain/mind of a human being can remain unsatisfied or can be changed deliberately.

CONCLUSIONS

We have drawn attention to an aspect of modelling which is not often if at all considered in the course of constructing symbolic structures. Perhaps this helps to minimise the uncertainty in a particular application and introduces awareness of this aspect. This is already the case when constructing 'train timetables', for instance, and is taken for granted when dealing with members of the armed forces.

The proposed 'systems theory' helps assessing and making explicit relevant instances of the 'First feature' due to its use of 'linguistic modelling' or processed, natural language which pays attention to the 2nd criterion in section 1.3. More research is needed.

PARADIGM CHANGE IN 'SYSTEMS THINKING'

Introduction

This writing is about 'systems thinking' which is a topic within the subject matter of the 'systemic or structural view' of aspects of chosen parts of the world. We are engaged in 'systems thinking' when we view a part of the world, concrete, symbolic, abstract, imaginary, in terms of its *structural or systemic properties.*

For example,

'A book may be described as : 'It consists of 250 pages *bound by* hard cover' as opposed to 'It is interesting' which is a description by a *qualitative property*'. Or

'The government *raised* the interest by 1% which *annoyed* many people' as opposed to

'The government has the power to raise the interest by 1%' which is a description by a *qualitative/quantitative property*'.

All sentences conform to the 'subject – predicate' structure. We observe that 'systems thinking' refers to static or dynamic aspects of the *empirical world* which may or may not be observable. We aim to construct an 'empirical, systems theory' not a 'view concerning, or not, 'systems thinking''. Here we attempt to introduce the basic notions behind such theory.

A description of parts of the world

Living things cannot exist in static state, they are engaged in incessant activities of *interaction* with their physical and/or mental *environments* in terms of transfer of material as 'physical [matter and energy] and/or sensual [matter as medium carrying influence or information]' realised as far as this discussion is concerned by :

Inputting raw *material*,
Processing the resulting raw *material*, and
Producing output and waste *material*.

These *activities*, individually or together 'necessary' to define the concept of 'living' but not all details are restricted to such. Natural and artificial non-living things like a 'volcano', 'control, computer systems', 'robots' can be active as well.

The objectives of living things in carrying out these activities, are physical *survival* and/or realising *ambitions* details of which are conjured up by *imagination* or created by *thoughts* as a result of input from the *sense organs*. The results of mental activity can be expressed in terms of *symbolic structures* known as 'models' for representation and communication. We can say that :

A. Survival is about maintenance of status quo or **current state**
B. Ambition is about achievement of **future state**.

Accordingly, living things are incessantly engaged in *changes of state* one way or another which is called **problem solving**. The intellectual activity of 'problem solving' involves :

A. The perception or vision of = =
An undesirable in some sense, physical or mental *initial state* followed, or not, by
A consistent, desirable, physical or mental *final state* of ---
An aspect of a selected part of the world which is expected to satisfy a *particular* living thing.
B. The executor of *change of state* called **system** or overall *structure* consisting of a = =
x. 'Physical or intellectual product' the function of which is to generate the *interaction* required to accomplish the change of state, and the
y. 'Structure' the function of which is to create and/or or to prompt the 'product' so that it can exert the *required interaction*.

C. Selection or design of = =

The appropriate 'product' and 'structure' as prompted by Point A. so as to create Point B.

We are considering 'Utilising systems' which are in general use and 'Manufacturing systems' consisting of the *principles* of = 1. Generality of systems, 2. Equilibrium, 3. Purposive activity plus *linguistic modelling* of processed natural language. Point A. involves the exercise of creativity, innovation, ingenuity, Point B. needs *familiarity* with :

Available, existing hard, soft and living ware, Organising manufacture or fabrication and application of design thinking.

Accordingly, we have outlined a scheme of *integrated whole* of a **problem solving functional entity** of Points A. and B. related by Point C. operating in a *purposive configuration*. It involves concepts abstracted from consideration of aspects of the natural world and as such it is close to the disciplines of natural sciences and engineering. The underlying effect may be described as the *principle of change of equilibrium* of physical [or mental] state which allows the idea of problem solving to be extended to inanimate and artificial or non-living things.

Conclusions

'Problem solving' activity is **innate** and **universal** in the living sphere. In addition humans possess a range of *abilities* or 'properties' such as emotions, ingenuity, creativity, innovation etc which have enabled them to evolve social, artistic and technical advances reaching the current level of complexity and of convenience and performance in life.

Humans have also created a range of **intellectual products** to facilitate understanding the nature of the world including own body and to help solving problems. This writing so far has introduced the background ideas to a *proposed 'systems theory'* which is the analytical expression of the 'integrated whole of problem solving'.

The extended version intends to describe these *products* including 'systems thinking'. Their *diversity* produced by the fertile human imagination and the *lack of clarity* in their role in 'problem solving' constitutes the *problematic issue.* The aim of this version is to examine the contribution of the intellectual products to the activity of 'problem solving' concluding with a brief description and comparison of the proposed 'systems theory' which is the *paradigm change.* It is offered as a possible *resolution* of the problematic issue. This 'theory' subject to peer review, addition of software and more extensive application is thought to be in line with the by laws of the ISSS regarding 'purpose, education and implementation' : It is sufficiently general to cope with the generality of the systemic view, teachable at all levels and can be expressed in operational terms unless refuted.

The extended version

The intellectual products or the 'human, intellectual endeavour' is summarised in the diagram in Figure 2.1. We note the three branches which we intend to discuss :

A. *Branch of contour 6*

'Problem solving' is innate and universal in the living sphere which living things exercise without pause *instinctively* organising themselves in a 'purposive structure'. This exercise is also engaged in 'design thinking'.

The discipline of 'systems engineering' had been developed perhaps based on engineering and practical experience called by the need for handling *complex* problems. Systems engineering is about 'conception, design, development, production and operation of *physical systems.* There are a number of structural schemes describing how to apply systems engineering and many modelling formalisms.

Thus, systems engineering is restrictive, not related to basic principles of 'systems thinking' and with a great deal of practical background. As shown in Figure 2.1. by the dotted line, systems engineering made use of the knowledge in the natural sciences. It shares the basic idea of 'systems design' with the scheme in Figure 3.1. but does not have the clarity of function and definition of the concepts and the single modelling technique.

B. <u>Branch beginning with contour 3</u>

The great majority of intellectual products have been produced along this branch ranging from speculative, philosophical such as the Greek to modelling like graphology to the eventual development of *conventional science* which conforms to the 4 criteria in section 1.3.

The particular instances of 'conventional science' or Conventional Disciplines in APPENDIX 5. fit into the scheme in Figure 3.1. as intellectual product [3] as producers of mental interaction to satisfy *curiosity* and understanding natural phenomena for changing the mental state or OPI [5 – 6] or people. It also has provided knowledge of components in engineering and technology.

The fine and performing arts and the means of entertainments have provided the mental interaction to achieve *wellbeing* and as such fit into the idea of people carrying a problem or OPI [5 – 6].

Qualitative and quantitative properties had been chosen for constructing symbolic structures because such properties are close to human perception and interest. Their use has led to great success in providing benefit to society and technology.

C. <u>Branch beginning with contour 4</u>

The subject matter or Modern Disciplines as discussed in APPENDIX 5., has come into existence much later than Conventional Disciplines and with the intention of *resolving problematic issues* as in case of 'servomechanisms', part of 'control theories', which were developed for helping to shoot moving targets in the 2nd WW.

Modern Disciplines encountered a great deal of inadequacies in the theoretical front as discussed in section 2.2., for example. They do not satisfy the 4 criteria in section 1.3. and fall short of the comprehensive, well founded nature of the scheme in Figure 3.1. [Korn, 2009, 2018b].
Parts of Modern Disciplines like control theories and OR selected quantitative properties as the 'elementary constituents' for constructing symbolic structures which were suitable for their application but restricted

it. When in the 1950's the generality of the 'systemic or structural view' was realised researchers failed to find the appropriate 'elementary constituents'. This has resulted in the lack of theoretical framework satisfying the 4 criteria in section 1.3. equivalent to those in Conventional Disciplines. The need for recognition of appropriate structural properties has not been great because of the 'innateness' of problem solving and obvious appearance of 'structure'. This is needed in manufacturing of artifacts.

Conclusions

We have made a few critical remarks about parts of current intellectual endeavour as presented in Figure 2.1. in section 2.1. which highlights their role in problem solving in relation to the scheme in Figure 3.1. but more research is needed. The large variety of this endeavour has been dictated by 'thoughts' of living things especially by humans.

The lack of comprehensive approach to problem solving and design thinking and that of a more general, methodical and empirical systems theory have prompted the development of the proposed 'systems theory' which as yet has to prove itself. Assuming it will have passed evaluation, it should help individuals and organisations in problem solving and eventually may be adopted to be part of teaching programmes at school to university levels.

We summarise the scheme in Figure 3.1. as a generalisation :

1000. --- 'Part A. represents the *change of equilibrium state* arrived at intentionally or by chance and represented by a change of *property*. Each such a change requires an appropriate *interaction* generated by a *complex product* [3] (a nail to be inserted in a piece of wood [change of state] needs a blow [interaction] by a hammer [complex product [3]]) which is fabricated by a *user/producer* [2] in accordance with a *purpose* or *by chance* (lava to burn the surrounding is produced by a volcano). All this is modelled by 'linguistic modelling' in Part B. This modelling enables the creation of *predictive structures*. For example, the so called *emergent property* of the 'hammer' can be predicted from the constituent, related fabricating and delivering structure or system, all other conditions remaining *quiescent* [Nagel, 1968].

Newton's 1st law of motion is an example of this generalisation. ---

EPILOGUE

Janos Korn graduated in 1960 in mechanical engineering at Queen Mary College, University of London with a 2nd Class Honours Degree. After a few years in industry as a development engineer, he became a lecturer, a position he retained until leaving Middlesex University somewhat prematurely in 1996. He was part time tutor at the Open University for 20 years. He obtained an M Phil and Ph D degrees at QMC and was a member of the Institutions of Mechanical and Electrical Engineers. Published six books and about 146 papers in professional journals and conferences. Research interests are :

1. 'Network modelling of engineering systems' which attempts to cover the quantifiable aspects of statics and dynamics of the world of engineering from a single point of view and introduced elements of 'problem solving' and 'design' as part of network modelling into engineering teaching, and

2. The development of a 'system theory' which aims at presenting an integrated approach to 'problem solving' AND the 'systemic or structural view' of parts of the world joined by 'design thinking'.

Perhaps all this interest in generalisation has arisen as a result of the author's exposure to varied educational and employment experience as outlined in section 1.1., to observe the effect of *specialisation* as prompted by the immense success of 'conventional science' or part of Conventional Disciplines, on teaching and thinking in organisations. Contrasting the features of this science with the lack of similar in a 'systems science', has become a driving force.

Previous work by pioneers in the field as in point 1. like R. S. Sanford, F. J. Evans, A. G. J. MacFarlane and others, introduced the idea of 'classification of variables' into *'through'* and *'across'* which covered 'passive networks' construction of mechanical, electrical and fluid phenomena. 'Network modelling of engineering systems' [Korn, 2012] has extended this approach to 'thermal and control networks' resulting in a unified presentation of 'energy conversion' including 'heat transfer' and 'analysis of stability and design of networks'. A more complete 'network view' of aspects of parts of the world became possible. As referred to in section 1.1. and example 5. in section 6.2., sets of 'non-isothermal, nonlinear differential equations' can be derived.

Previous work by pioneers in the field as in point 2. like R. V. L. Hartley, P. M. S. Blackett, H. Nyquist, L. von Bertalanffy, K. E. Boulding, P. Checkland and many others introduced the ground breaking ideas of 'systemic or structural view' with the central issue of 'problem solving' which the Modern Disciplines are about.

Problematic issues had been identified with previous work as discussed in CHAPTER 2. and Appendices 2. and 3. Current work along the lines of the 'Research interests' has been going on since the 1970's and had been mostly concerned with the development of 'linguistic modelling', aspects of design and notions of problem solving. This book which uses some of the previously produced material, presents the idea of an integrated treatment of 'problem solving' and the 'systemic or structural view' parts of the world as shown in Figure 3.1.

Part A. in this figure is an exercise of inspiration, innovation and creativity and is shown to drive human advancement towards creating more and more complex entities or systems or structures for aiding survival and the satisfaction of human needs and desires. Accordingly, this part develops the 'design parameters' for the creation of products and systems to ensure that the needs and desires are satisfied. Part B. introduces a systems theory of 'three principles' as discussed in section 3.1. and 'linguistic modelling of scenarios'. This modelling uses 'processed natural language' to generate the symbolic structures into which mathematical models of uncertainties, algebraic and differential equations and additional knowledge from Conventional and/or Modern Disciplines can be made use of at object or agent level.

Essentially, features of human nature such as desire for power and convenience, ingenuity, love etc, have not changed over the millennia. However, the characteristics of its field of operations have from low population, low consumption, low technology, low effects on the physical environment to the same in the current era but with adjective 'high'. We are, thus, witnessing acute problems attributed to human behaviour which are in urgent need of resolution, the situation designated as OPI [5] in Figure 3.1. and in section

4.3. Human, intellectual endeavour as superficially shown in the diagram of Figure 2.1., so far has proved incapable of providing the 'intellectual product', product [3] in Figure 3.1. to drive a desirable change towards resolution, OPI [6] or change of equilibrium state. The reason is seen as *fragmentation* of this endeavour and the inability to produce intellectual products in the 'structural interest' branch, contour 4 in Figure 2.1., comparable in representation and predictive power to those in the Conventional Disciplines in the contour 3 branch. Perhaps the reason for this is the lack of recognition for the need and/ or interest in the 4 criteria suggested in section 1.3., especially the importance of the 1st, the *elementary constituents* which had been recognised even in ancient times [Levene, 2010]. The aim of the content of this book is to suggest a 'systems theory' subject to peer evaluation, which perhaps can lessen the 'fragmentation' and provide suitable 'elementary constituents'.

A conclusion is that perhaps the method suggested by the diagram of Figure 3.1. may help to drive the features of human nature or the change the characteristics of its field of operation to a desirable state, or both. Perhaps helped by the implementation of the scheme in Figure 3.1., human imagination and ingenuity will find a resolution.

REFERENCES

Ackoff, R. I. Towards a system of systems concepts, Management Science, v17, n11, 1971.

Anon., The Chambers Dictionary, Chambers, Edinburgh, UK, 1994.

Anon., A consensus of the INCOSE fellows, Wikipedia, 2004.

Anon., Solving problems, Chartered Management Institute, Corby, UK, March 2014.

Anon., Wikipedia, Problem solving, 2018.

Anon., J of the Operational Research Soc, Taylor & Francis, London, UK, 2022.

Bar-Hillel, Y. Language and information, Addison-Wesley, London, UK, 1964.

Beer, S. The heart of enterprise, Wiley: Chichester, UK, 1979.

Beishon, J., Peters, G. ed. Systems behaviour, The Open U Press, 1976.

Bertalanffy von, L. An outline of general systems theory, The British J for the Phil of Science, 1950, v1, n2, 134-165.

Bittner, K., Spence, I. Use case modelling, Addison-Wesley, USA, 2001.

Blackett, P. M. S. Operational research, Advanced Science, v5, n17, 1948.

Boulding, K. E. General systems theory, the skeleton of science, Management Science, v2, n3, 1956.

Boylestad, R. L. Introductory circuit analysis, Merrill Pub Co, Columbus, USA, 1987.

Brillouin, L. Science and information theory, Academic Press, NY, 1956.

Brown, G., Campbell, D. P., Principles of servomechanisms, Wiley, NY, 1948.

Burton, S. H. Mastering English grammar, Macmillan, London, 1984.

Checkland, P. Systems thinking, systems practice, Wiley: Chichester, UK, 1982.

Checkland, P. Scholes, J. Soft systems methodology in action, Wiley, NY, 1995.

Chomsky, N. Aspects of the theory of syntax, Cambridge, Mass, USA, 1965.

Copi, I. M. Introduction to logic, Macmillan, NY, 1978.

Cross, N. Engineering design methods, Wiley, Chichester, UK, 1989.

Devlin, K. Logic and information, Cambridge UP, 1991.

Durell, C. U. Advanced algebra, G. Bell & Sons, London, UK, 1959.

Durkin, J. Expert systems, Macmillan, NY, USA, 1994.

Feilden, G. B. R. Engineering design (report), HMSO, London, UK, 1963.

Fillmore, C. The case for case, In Bach and Harms, 'Universals In linguistic theory', University of Texas, Austin, 1968.

Finniston, Lord. Engineering our future, HMSO, London, UK, 1983.

Floridi, L. Information, Oxford UP, 2010.

Flynn, D. Information systems requirements, MacGraw Hill Co, 1998.

Foerster von, H. Ethics and Second-Order Cybernetics, Cybernetics and Human Knowing, v1, n1, 1992.

Forrester, J. W. Industrial dynamics, The MIT Press, USA, 1969.

Gilbert, N. Agent-based modelling, Sage Publication, London, 2007.

Hartley, R. V. L. Transmission of information, Bell System Technical J, 1928.

Hempel, C. G., Oppenheim, P. Studies in the logic of explanations, Philosophy of science, v15, n2.

Hospers, J. Introduction to philosophical analysis, Prentice-Hall, NJ, USA, 1978.

Hubka, V., Eder, W. E. Design science, Springer-Verlag, London, UK, 1996.

Jackson, M. C. Systems approaches to management, Kluwer Academic: NY, 2000.

Jacobson, I., Grady, B., Rumbaugh, J. The unified software development process, Addison-Wesley, Longman, USA, 1998.

Johnson-Laird, P. N. The computer and the mind, Fontana Paperbacks, London, UK, 1988.

Jones, J. C. Design methods, Wiley, NY, USA, 1980.

Jung-Ming Xu, Theory and practice of graphs, Kluwer, London, UK, 2003.

Klir, G. J. An approach to general systems theory, Van Nostrand, NY, USA, 1969.

Koestler, A. The ghost in the machine, Hutchinson, London, UK, 1967.

Korn, J. Alternative derivation of equations of motion, J Franklin Inst, v311, n3, 1981.

Korn, J. Systems and design as the basis of engineering knowledge, IEE Proceedings, v136 Pt A, n2, London, UK, 1989.

Korn, J., Huss, F., Cumbers, J. Analysis and design of socio-economic systems, in 'Systems thinking in Europe' ed M. C. Jackson et al Plenum Press, NY, 1988.

Korn, J., Takats, A. Propagation of uncertainties in socio-economic systems in 'Critical issues in systems theory and practice', ed K. Ellis et al., Plenum

Press, NY, 1995.

Korn, J. Theory of spontaneous processes, Structural Engineering Review, v7, n1, 1995.

Korn, J. Science and design of systems, Troubadour Publishing, Leicester, UK, 2009.

Korn, J. Concept and design of information and IS, UKAIS Conf, 24/25 March, Oxford, 2010.

Korn, J. Network modelling of engineering systems, Troubadour Publishing: Leicester, UK, 2012.

Korn, J. Linguistic modelling of scenarios, Troubadour Publishing, Leicester, UK, 2013.

Korn, J. The purpose of change is problem solving, Troubadour Publishing, Leicester, 2016.

Korn, J. General principles of systems, Kybernetes, v47, n8, 2018.

Korn, J. Crises and systems thinking, Acta Europeana Systematica, v8, n8, 2018a

Korn, J. Crisis in systems thinking, Kybernetes, v49, n7. 2018b.

Korn, J. Application of linguistic modelling to systems and product design, Int J of Markets and Business Systems, v4, n1, 2020a.

Korn, J. Developments in the resolution of systemic problems, Int J of Markets and Business Systems, v2, n2, 2020b.

Kuhn, Th. The structure of scientific revolutions, U of Chicago: Pa, USA, 1996.

Levene, L. I think, therefore, I am, M. O'Mara Books, London, 2010.

Lewin, D. Engineering philosophy-the third culture, Proc of the Royal Soc of Arts, 1981, v129, n5, 653-666.

Lipschutz, S. Essential computer mathematics, Schaum Publications, NY, 1982.

MacFarlane, A. G. J. Dynamical system models, Harrap & Co, London, UK, 1970.

Magee, B. *Popper*, Fontana Press: London, 1985.

Maturana, H. R., Varela, F. J. Autopoiesis and cognition, D. Reidel Pub Co, 1980.

Maxwell, J. C. On engine governors, Proc of the Royal Society, London, UK, v16, 1868.

Miller, J. G. Living systems, McGraw Hill, NY, 1978.

Mingers, J., Rosenhead, J. Problem structuring methods in action, European

J of OR, v152, n3, 2004

Monod, J. Chance and necessity, Fontana Press, UK, 1974.

Murata, T. Properties, analysis and applications, Proc of the IEEE, v77, n4, April 1989.

Nagel, E. The structure of science, Routledge & Kegan Paul, London, UK, 1968.

Nise, N. S. Control systems engineering, Wiley, Chichester, 2008.

Nyquist, H. Certain factors affecting telegraph speed, Bell System Technical J, April 1924.

Ore, O. Theory of graphs, American Mathematical Society, 1962.

Pahl, G., Beitz, W. Engineering design, The Design Council, London, UK, 1984.

Penn, A., Barbrook-Johnson, P. Fuzzy cognitive maps, A participating workshop tool, ERIE Steerplex note, 2016.

Pledge, H. T. Science since the 1500, HMSO, London, UK, 1966.

Popper, K. The logic of scientific discovery, Hutchinson: London, 1972.

Prigogine, I. Introduction to thermodynamics of irreversible processes, Ch C Thomas, Illinois, USA, 1955.

Rittel, H. W., Webber, M. M. Dilemmas in general theory of planning, Policy Sciences, v4, 1955 – 1969, 1973.

Robbins, Lord. Higher education (report), HMSO, London, UK, 1963.

Rogers, G. F. C., Mayhew, Y. R. Engineering thermodynamics, Longmans, NY, 1957.

Rose, J. Nested Revels of Organised Systems, Conf of ISSS, Corvallis, USA, 2018

Rousseau, D. Systems research and the quest for scientific systems principles. *Systems*, n5, 2017, 1-16.

Russell, B. The philosophy of logical atomism, Routledge, NY, 1972.

Saeed, J. I. Semantics, Blackwell Publishers: Oxford, UK, 1998.

Schwaninger, M., Scheef, C. A test of the viable system model, Theoretical claim vs. Empirical evidence, Cybernetics and Systems, DOI: 10.1080/01969722.2016.1209375.

Sanford, R. S. Physical networks, Prentice Hall. NJ, USA, 1965.

Searle, J. Minds, brains and science, BBC Press, London, UK, 1984.

Shannon, C. E., Weaver, W. The mathematical theory of communication, U of Illinois Press, Urbana, USA, 1964.

Senge, P. The fifth discipline, Doubleday, NY, 1990.

Stair, R. et al. Fundamentals of business information systems, Cengage Learning, EMEA, 2008.

Steels, L. The symbol grounding problem has been solved. So what's next ?, Sony Computer Science Laboratory, August 13, 2007.

Szilard, L. Z. Physik, 53, 1929.

Taha, H. A. Operations research, Prentice Hall, NJ, USA, 2003.

Troncale, L. R. Future of general systems research, Systems Research, v2, n1, 1985.

Winder, R. L. et al (ed), Philosophical aspects of information systems, Taylor & Francis, London, UK, 1997.

Wiener, N. Cybernetics, control and communication in animal, man and machine, MIT Press, 1948.

Yolles, M. Implications of Beer's ontological system/metasystem dichotomy, Kybernetes, v33, n3/4, 2004.

Zadeh, L., A. Fuzzy sets, Information & Control, v8, n3, 1965.

Lightning Source UK Ltd.
Milton Keynes UK
UKHW022122080223
416681UK00012B/2874